Language GRADE 6
Fundamentals

Correlated
to State Standards

Visit
www.teaching-standards.com
to view a correlation of
this book's activities
to your state's standards.
This is a free service.

EMC 2756
Evan-Moor ®
EDUCATIONAL PUBLISHERS
Helping Children Learn since 1979

Editorial
Development: Bonnie Brook
Communications
Editors: Marilyn Evans
Leslie Sorg
Copy Editors: Sonny Bennett
Laurie Westrich
Illustrator: Mary Rojas
Desktop: Arynne Elfenbein
Cover: Liliana Potigian

Table of Contents

Language Fundamentals • EMC 2756 • © Evan-Moor Corp.

Capitalization

Abbreviations

Punctuation

What's in *Language Fundamentals*?

Language Fundamentals is your comprehensive resource for grade-level grammar, mechanics, usage, and vocabulary practice. The broad scope of language skills and the range in difficulty of the activity pages enables you to precisely target those skills that each student needs to practice.

Targeted Skill Practice

The core of *Language Fundamentals* is the 160-plus pages of student-friendly skill activities.

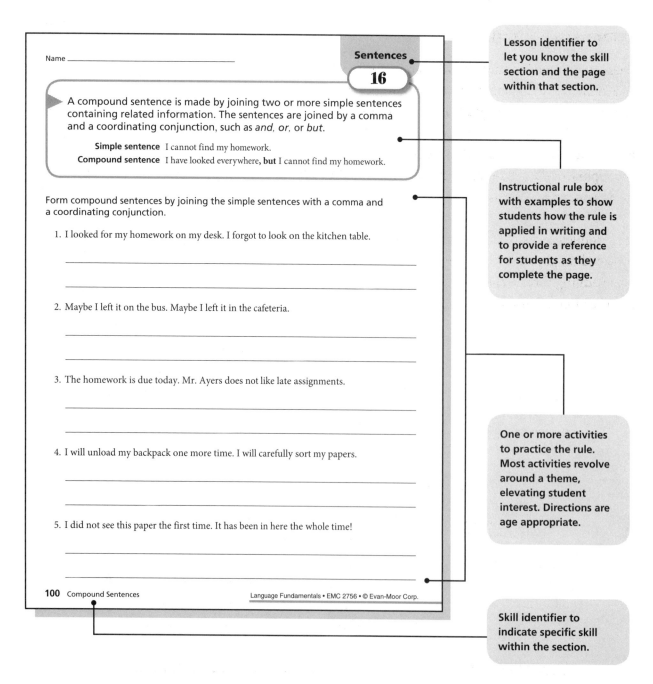

Name _____

Sentences

16

A compound sentence is made by joining two or more simple sentences containing related information. The sentences are joined by a comma and a coordinating conjunction, such as *and, or,* or *but*.

Simple sentence I cannot find my homework.
Compound sentence I have looked everywhere, **but** I cannot find my homework.

Form compound sentences by joining the simple sentences with a comma and a coordinating conjunction.

1. I looked for my homework on my desk. I forgot to look on the kitchen table.

   _____

   _____

2. Maybe I left it on the bus. Maybe I left it in the cafeteria.

   _____

   _____

3. The homework is due today. Mr. Ayers does not like late assignments.

   _____

   _____

4. I will unload my backpack one more time. I will carefully sort my papers.

   _____

   _____

5. I did not see this paper the first time. It has been in here the whole time!

   _____

   _____

100 Compound Sentences

Language Fundamentals • EMC 2756 • © Evan-Moor Corp.

Lesson identifier to let you know the skill section and the page within that section.

Instructional rule box with examples to show students how the rule is applied in writing and to provide a reference for students as they complete the page.

One or more activities to practice the rule. Most activities revolve around a theme, elevating student interest. Directions are age appropriate.

Skill identifier to indicate specific skill within the section.

Review Pages

There are 33 review pages presented in multiple-choice test format to provide test-prep practice. Each review covers a small subset of skills and may be used as an assessment of student skill acquisition.

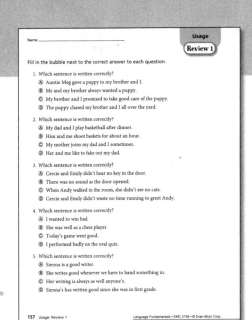

Paragraph Editing

These pages provide students with an opportunity to edit and correct paragraphs containing errors commonly made at this grade level. Each page is tied to specific skills addressed in the Targeted Skill Practice pages. After practicing a skill, students can use the corresponding pages in this section to transfer the skill to the context of writing.

A reproducible chart of proofreading marks is provided on page 185. Students can refer to this chart when editing those pages that direct students to use proofreading marks.

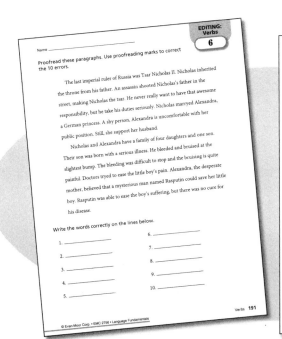

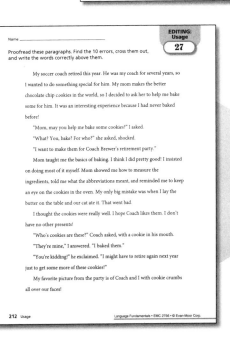

Use *Language Fundamentals* to Reteach and Reinforce

As a supplement to your core language arts program

What if...

- you've finished the material on a particular skill in your core program and your students still don't seem to get it?

- there is an objective in your state standards that is not covered in the core program?

- you need homework materials to reinforce the core program lessons?

- you have a new student who missed a number of vital language lessons?

- you want to provide a resource teacher, after-school program, or tutor with language practice that connects with class work?

- you want to provide ongoing test-prep exercises as you move through your language program?

> *Language Fundamentals* can meet all these needs.

As an at-the-ready resource for those teachable moments

What if...

- you grade student essays and find a wide variety of errors, and you want to ensure that each student's needs are met?

- you grade vocabulary quizzes and realize that some students have little transference of affix meaning from a known word to an unfamiliar word?

- you notice that several students' personal narratives contain errors in subject and object pronoun usage?

> *Language Fundamentals* has practice to address these skill needs.

Language Fundamentals • EMC 2756 • © Evan-Moor Corp.

As the perfect companion for Evan-Moor's *Daily Language Review*

Thousands of grade 1 through 6 classrooms use *Daily Language Review* for focused practice and review. Multiple studies show that this type of distributed, or spaced, practice is a powerful strategy for achieving proficiency and retention of skills.

Student responses on the weekly *Daily Language Review* units will indicate those skills needing further reinforcement. *Language Fundamentals* can then be used to provide the reteaching and additional practice. For example:

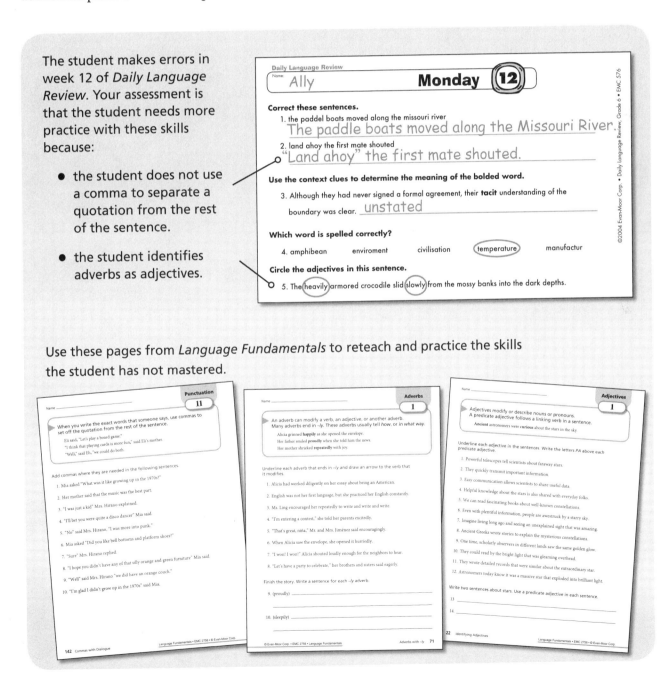

The student makes errors in week 12 of *Daily Language Review*. Your assessment is that the student needs more practice with these skills because:

- the student does not use a comma to separate a quotation from the rest of the sentence.

- the student identifies adverbs as adjectives.

Use these pages from *Language Fundamentals* to reteach and practice the skills the student has not mastered.

> Nouns name people, places, things, or ideas.
>
> **Anna** wants to meet me at the **store** to buy a **gift** for your **birthday**.
>
> | **Person** | **Place** | **Thing** | **Idea** |
> |------------|-----------|-----------|----------|
> | Anna | store | gift | birthday |

Underline all the nouns in the sentences. Identify each noun by writing *person*, *place*, *thing*, or *idea* below it.

1. Planning a surprise party can be a challenge.

   _____

2. There are many worries that come with being the host.

   _____

3. Do you have a good location, such as a house with a big basement?

   _____

4. Should you send invitations, or ask the kids you want to invite at school?

   _____

5. Will the guests keep the party a secret?

   _____

Write a sentence with at least two nouns about a surprise party. Underline each noun.

6. _____

   _____

> **Nouns can be singular or plural.**
>
> - A singular noun names one person, place, thing, or idea.
>
>   There is one **house** with a **dog** on our **street.**
>
> - A plural noun names more than one. Add *s* to most nouns to make them plural.
>
>   Some **streets** have more **dogs** than **houses.**

Circle the correct nouns in each sentence. Cross out the incorrect noun and write it correctly above it.

pets

1. Both the boys and girls in our class have many pet.

2. One individuals brought a surprise to school for her friends.

3. It was a photos of kittens that her family could not keep.

4. There was a yellow basket with two white kitten inside.

5. Several students asked if the class could adopt an animals.

6. The teacher suggested whales and other endangered creature.

7. There was confusions in the classroom that day.

8. The teacher improved the communication with the student.

9. She said "no" to kittens but "yes" to helping a group of cats like tiger.

Describe an animal you would like your class to adopt. Use singular and plural nouns.

10. _____

_____

> Nouns that end in *sh, ch, x, s,* and *z* require *es* to form the plural.
>
> One class is in the auditorium, while other **classes** are waiting to enter.
>
> If I had one wish, I would ask for more **wishes!**

Underline the nouns that have the *es* plural form. Circle the nouns that have the *s* plural ending.

1. All of the houses have porches with bushes around them.

2. All of the beaches have sand and shells.

3. All of the lunches are choices with sandwiches.

4. All of the dances at the ball are waltzes.

5. All of the dishes have matching cups and glasses.

6. All of the dresses have ruffles and patches of lace.

7. All of the foxes are being chased by hunters and hounds.

8. All of the lynxes are related to cougars and mountain lions.

9. All of the football players who missed the passes feel like klutzes.

Complete the sentence with at least one noun with the *es* plural ending.

10. All of the _____

_____

_____

To form the plural of nouns that end in a consonant and *y*, change the *y* to *i* and add *es*.

Singular	Plural
library	libraries
balcony	balconies

If a noun ends in a vowel and *y*, just add *s*.

Singular	Plural
key	keys
joy	joys

Rewrite each sentence with the correct plural form of the underlined words.

1. Many <u>country</u> celebrate different <u>holiday</u>.

   _____

2. They have different <u>story</u> and <u>custom</u>.

   _____

3. The youngest <u>baby</u> through oldest <u>adult</u> celebrate with <u>family</u>.

   _____

4. The <u>alley</u> and <u>avenue</u> are decorated in <u>city</u>.

   _____

5. All the <u>bakery</u> are busy selling <u>box</u> and <u>tray</u> of <u>treat</u>.

   _____

6. There are <u>candy</u> and <u>cake</u> for <u>boy</u> and <u>girl</u> to enjoy.

   _____

Name _____

> Some nouns have irregular plural forms. The plural forms are spelled differently.

	Singular			Irregular Plural	
mouse	tooth	child	mice	teeth	children
goose	foot	woman	geese	feet	women
ox	person	man	oxen	people	men

Complete each sentence with the correct plural form from the rule box.

1. She is six _____ tall.

2. We use our _____ for chewing and smiling.

3. Farmers used animals such as _____ to pull heavy loads.

4. _____ fly south for the winter.

5. Hungry owls eat _____.

6. The excited _____ play in the park.

Choose two irregular plurals from the rule box that are not among your answers above. Write a sentence that uses each word in the plural form.

7. _____

_____

8. _____

_____

Some nouns are the same in the singular and the plural form.
Use the context of a sentence to tell if nouns are singular or plural.

aircraft   bison   buffalo   deer   elk   moose   sheep   trout

Singular One **fish** can feed two people.
Plural We need many **fish** for this crowd.

For each word in bold, circle *Singular* or *Plural.* If it is singular, write a sentence using the plural form. If it is plural, write a sentence using the singular form.

1. I can see a **trout** swimming below the boat.   Singular   Plural

_____

2. I see several **deer** in that open field.   Singular   Plural

_____

3. **Elk** are not usually found in this area.   Singular   Plural

_____

4. There are more **moose** around than people think.   Singular   Plural

_____

5. **Buffalo** are also known as bison.   Singular   Plural

_____

6. Those baby **sheep** are all white lambs.   Singular   Plural

_____

Fill in the bubble next to the correct answer.

1. Which word in the sentence is a noun that names an idea?
   People throughout the world can make progress through inventions.
   Ⓐ inventions
   Ⓑ progress
   Ⓒ world
   Ⓓ people

2. Which sentence has plural nouns correctly formed with *es*?
   Ⓐ Tools like axes should be stored in boxes.
   Ⓑ Sawes are required to cut the thick branchs of trees.
   Ⓒ The ranchs we visited had cactuses growing everywhere.
   Ⓓ We saw birds called thrushes and finchs in the bushes.

3. Which sentence has the correct plural form of the word that ends in *y*?
   Ⓐ A large city needs several librarys.
   Ⓑ There are balconis on all of the apartment buildings.
   Ⓒ Some people were having parties to watch the fireworks.
   Ⓓ The skys were clear and sunny every day of our trip.

4. How many plural words are found in this sentence?
   I need the oxen and horses more than a sheep and geese.
   Ⓐ one
   Ⓑ two
   Ⓒ three
   Ⓓ four

5. Which sentence has all nouns in the plural form?
   Ⓐ The children love to catch trout with worms.
   Ⓑ The deer saw the people and ran from the field.
   Ⓒ That aircraft is landing on the water.
   Ⓓ Look out the window and you will see elk and moose.

> Possessive nouns are used to show ownership or possession. For singular nouns, add an apostrophe and s ('s) to form the possessive.
>
> an **actor's** lines
> a **theater's** stage
> a **costume's** sleeve
> a **mystery's** solution

Underline the noun that should be possessive in each sentence.
Write the noun correctly on the line.

1. My friend brother is moving to Hollywood. _____

2. He got a job as a chef assistant on a movie. _____

3. Many of the movie scenes are in a restaurant. _____

4. He will help make the food for each scene characters to eat. _____

5. Each day schedule starts very early in the morning. _____

6. He says that an assistant life involves a lot of hard work. _____

7. He hopes his years of experience will catch the director eye. _____

8. He hopes a scene in the restaurant kitchen will need an extra. _____

9. Perhaps the director will give him the extra role in the movie. _____

10. He wants to be discovered as an actor and have a star life! _____

Write two sentences about being an actor. Use a possessive noun in each sentence.

11. _____

12. _____

> Possessive nouns can be singular or plural. For plural nouns that end in *s*, add an apostrophe after the *s* (*s'*).
>
> **explorers'** ships
> **countries'** borders
> **flags'** colors
> **problems'** hurdles
>
> Form the possessive of irregular plurals by adding an apostrophe and *s* (*'s*).
>
> **women's** songs
> **deer's** fawns

Write the correct plural possessive form of each underlined word.

1. Some <u>mountain</u> peaks are very tall.   _____

2. Some <u>river</u> currents are very fast.   _____

3. Some <u>city</u> ports are on the ocean.   _____

4. Some <u>island</u> climates are tropical.   _____

5. Some <u>people</u> trips are to faraway places.   _____

6. Some <u>family</u> vacations are always at the beach.   _____

7. Some <u>beach</u> sand is pink in color.   _____

8. Some <u>fish</u> colors are beautiful.   _____

9. Some <u>story</u> endings are amazing.   _____

10. Some <u>children</u> imaginations are endless.   _____

A proper noun names a specific person, place, thing, or idea.
A proper noun begins with a capital letter.

A common noun names any person, place, thing, or idea.
It does not begin with a capital letter.

Common Noun	Proper Noun
neighbor	Mrs. Boyd
continent	Africa
statue	Statue of Liberty
gratitude	Thanksgiving

Underline the common nouns. For each proper noun, circle the letter or letters that should be capitalized.

1. Every state has a capital, but washington, d.c., is the federal capital.

2. The city is on the potomac river and borders the states of virginia and maryland.

3. The capitol is where congress meets to make laws.

4. The white house is where every president since john adams has lived.

5. Nine justices make up the supreme court.

6. The courthouse is on first street.

7. The national archives holds documents that are important to our history.

8. The declaration of independence and the constitution are there.

9. The creation of a new country was an amazing achievement.

10. That's why americans celebrate each year on the fourth of july.

Language Fundamentals • EMC 2756 • © Evan-Moor Corp.

Name _____

Fill in the bubble next to the correct answer.

1. Choose the correct possessive noun to complete the sentence.
   A _____ outcome is always better with teamwork.

   Ⓐ game's

   Ⓑ players'

   Ⓒ teams'

   Ⓓ assignment's

2. Choose the correct plural possessive for *fish*.

   Ⓐ fishies

   Ⓑ fishe's

   Ⓒ fish's

   Ⓓ fish

3. Which sentence has singular and plural possessive nouns?

   Ⓐ The knight's armor was heavy and the horses were big.

   Ⓑ The lord's robes and ladies' dresses were made of rich fabric.

   Ⓒ The castle's moat was a form of protection.

   Ⓓ Castles' windows were small and the rooms' light was dim.

4. Choose the correct proper noun to complete the sentence.
   My _____ is Dad's brother.

   Ⓐ best friend

   Ⓑ Coach

   Ⓒ uncle

   Ⓓ Uncle Dan

5. How many proper nouns are in this sentence?
   Grandma said she will take our family to a play or a musical.

   Ⓐ none

   Ⓑ one

   Ⓒ three

   Ⓓ four

> Adjectives modify or describe nouns or pronouns.
> A predicate adjective follows a linking verb in a sentence.
>
> **Ancient** astronomers were **curious** about the stars in the sky.

Underline each adjective in the sentences. Write the letters *PA* above each predicate adjective.

1. Powerful telescopes tell scientists about faraway stars.

2. They quickly transmit important information.

3. Easy communication allows scientists to share useful data.

4. Helpful knowledge about the stars is also shared with everyday folks.

5. We can read fascinating books about well-known constellations.

6. Even with plentiful information, people are awestruck by a starry sky.

7. Imagine living long ago and seeing an unexplained sight that was amazing.

8. Ancient Greeks wrote stories to explain the mysterious constellations.

9. One time, scholarly observers in different lands saw the same golden glow.

10. They could read by the bright light that was gleaming overhead.

11. They wrote detailed records that were similar about the extraordinary star.

12. Astronomers today know it was a massive star that exploded into brilliant light.

Write two sentences about stars. Use a predicate adjective in each sentence.

13. _____

14. _____

Language Fundamentals • EMC 2756 • © Evan-Moor Corp.

Sensory adjectives describe the sight, sound, smell, touch, or taste of a noun.

A **buzzing** sound is coming from the **pink** flowers.

Yellow bees are attracted to the **flowery** smell of the blossoms.

They land on the **soft** petals and enjoy a **sweet** snack.

Read the sentence and the type of adjective identified in parentheses ( ).
Circle the correct adjective to complete the sentence.

1. The amusement park is _____.
   (sound)

   wet   quiet   bright

2. The weather is rainy and the air is _____.
   (touch)

   cool   clear   sweet

3. A few kids are munching _____ popcorn.
   (taste)

   sticky   white   buttered

4. On a _____ day, the park is jammed with people.
   (sight)

   sunny   stinky   warm

5. _____ popcorn scents the air.
   (smell)

   Crunchy   Buttery   Hot

6. Children in _____ play clothes run everywhere
   (sight)

   soft   crackling   colorful

Write two more sentences about an amusement park. Include at least two sensory adjectives in each sentence.

7. _____

   _____

8. _____

   _____

Some adjectives describe the quantity or quality of nouns or pronouns.

- *Quantity* tells how many.

   The team has **nine** members. There are **fewer** students who want to join.

- *Quality* tells what kind.

   The team has **new** members. There are **older** students in the group, too.

Underline all the adjectives in the sentences. Identify each adjective by writing *quantity* or *quality* below it.

1. Some kids have many buddies, but I have four good friends.

2. One friend is tall and funny.

3. I am short and serious, so we are two opposites.

4. My second friend is a trivia expert who knows a thousand facts.

5. The third friend is a math whiz who can figure several problems at once.

6. The fourth friend is kind and listens to every worry and goofy fear.

7. I don't need a dozen pals, but I need a few friends who are loyal and fun!

Describe a friend with at least one quantity adjective and one quality adjective.

8. _____

   _____

   _____

Fill in the bubble next to the correct answer.

1. Which sentence has the most adjectives?
   - Ⓐ The red boots are perfect for me.
   - Ⓑ The suede hat is old and stained.
   - Ⓒ The gold necklace is broken.
   - Ⓓ The dark shirt has a tear.

2. Which is the predicate adjective in this sentence?
   The teachers were confident in their decision.
   - Ⓐ teachers
   - Ⓑ were
   - Ⓒ confident
   - Ⓓ decision

3. Complete the sentence with a sensory adjective.
   The band leader was frustrated because many instruments were _____.
   - Ⓐ expensive
   - Ⓑ old
   - Ⓒ missing
   - Ⓓ squeaky

4. Complete the sentence with the adjective that describes quantity.
   Some students are involved in _____ activities.
   - Ⓐ imaginative
   - Ⓑ numerous
   - Ⓒ patriotic
   - Ⓓ exciting

5. Complete the sentence with the adjective that describes quality.
   There are _____ reasons to look for the treasure here.
   - Ⓐ convincing
   - Ⓑ abundant
   - Ⓒ some
   - Ⓓ countless

> Adjectives are used to make comparisons.
>
> • Comparative adjectives use *er* to compare two people, places, things, or ideas.
>
>   loud + **er** = louder
>
>   The siren is **louder** today than yesterday.
>
> • Superlative adjectives use *est* to compare three or more people, places, things, or ideas.
>
>   old + **est** = oldest
>
>   This is the **oldest** tree in the yard.

Circle the correct form of the adjective to complete each sentence. On the line, write C for *comparative* or S for *superlative* to identify the type of adjective.

1. The Rocky Mountains are _____ than the Appalachians.   taller   tallest

2. The Mississippi is the _____ river and the most famous.   mightier   mightiest

3. Chicago is the _____ city, according to its nickname.   windier   windiest

4. I visited New York City, and it was _____ than where I live.   noisier   noisiest

5. Florida, the "Sunshine State," must be _____ than Illinois.   sunnier   sunniest

6. Alaska must be the _____ state, being so far north.   colder   coldest

7. Many places could claim to be the _____ in America.   prettier   prettiest

8. I would like to live in the place that is the _____.   friendlier   friendliest

Write two sentences about the place where you live. Include a comparative adjective in one sentence and a superlative adjective in the other.

9. _____

_____

10. _____

_____

> Comparative adjectives use *–er* to compare two nouns.
> Some adjectives with two or more syllables use *more* or *less.*
>
> Russia is **larger** than Italy.
>
> Italy is **more** popular with tourists than Russia.
>
> Superlative adjectives use *–est* to compare three or more nouns.
> Some adjectives with two or more syllables use *most* or *least.*
>
> Australia is the **smallest** continent.
>
> The continent of Antarctica is the **least** populated.

Complete each sentence with the correct comparative or superlative form of the adjective in parentheses. Then write *C* or *S* above the word(s) to identify the type of adjective.

1. Rome was once the _____ city in the world. (powerful)

2. The Roman Empire spread _____ than the empire of the Greeks. (far)

3. Roman law was _____ than other civilizations' because it established order. (advanced)

4. Roman roads were carefully constructed and _____ to travel on than older roads. (dangerous)

5. The emperor's palaces were the _____ homes in Rome. (grand)

6. Even today they are the _____ of all the ruins. (fascinating)

7. The Roman Circus is the _____ site of all because it is only a grassy park now. (impressive)

8. Stand inside the Colosseum and you can hear the _____ echoes of the past. (loud)

Some comparative and superlative adjectives have irregular forms.

Adjective	Comparative	Superlative
little	less	least
good	better	best
bad	worse	worst
many	more	most

There was **little** argument about the verdict.

The jury spent **less** time deliberating than anyone imagined.

The defendant got the **least** amount of time possible for the offense.

Circle the correct adjective to complete the sentence. Then rewrite the sentence using a different comparative or superlative adjective to give the sentence the opposite meaning.

1. This museum is the _____ I've ever visited.   least   better   best

_____

2. There is _____ to see than in any other museum in the city.   more   most   least

_____

3. I spent the _____ amount of time in the modern art section.   less   least   worst

_____

4. That collection was the _____ in the entire building.   better   worse   worst

_____

5. The paintings by Renoir were the _____ impressive of all.   less   more   most

_____

Name _____

Fill in the bubble next to the correct answer.

1. Complete the sentence with the correct form of the adjective.
   This camera is the _____ we can afford to buy.
   - Ⓐ most expensive
   - Ⓑ less expensive
   - Ⓒ more expensive
   - Ⓓ expensivest

2. Which sentence has a comparative adjective and a superlative adjective?
   - Ⓐ They have the newest house but the oldest car in the neighborhood.
   - Ⓑ There are more trees in their yard and more flowers in ours.
   - Ⓒ The person with cleanest bedroom in our family wins a prize each week.
   - Ⓓ The best solution for my messy bedroom may be a bigger closet.

3. Which adjective could be used to compare three friends?
   - Ⓐ blonder
   - Ⓑ funniest
   - Ⓒ more athletic
   - Ⓓ less patient

4. Choose the correct adjective to complete the sentence.
   The winning team is always _____ than its opponent.
   - Ⓐ most strategic
   - Ⓑ less competitive
   - Ⓒ more successful
   - Ⓓ best focused

5. Which statement about adjectives is correct?
   - Ⓐ Adjectives usually follow a noun.
   - Ⓑ Most adjectives have three syllables.
   - Ⓒ Adjectives that make comparisons may end in *er*.
   - Ⓓ Irregular comparative adjectives compare irregular nouns.

Some proper adjectives are made from proper nouns.
Proper adjectives are capitalized.

Proper Noun	Proper Adjective	Proper Noun	Proper Adjective
Canada	**Canadian**	Bolivia	**Bolivian**
Mexico	**Mexican**	Chile	**Chilean**
United States of America	**American**	Cuba	**Cuban**
Colombia	**Colombian**	Peru	**Peruvian**
Venezuela	**Venezuelan**	Uruguay	**Uruguayan**
Brazil	**Brazilian**	Argentina	**Argentinian**

Write the proper adjective for the proper noun.

1. Cuba   _____

2. Bolivia   _____

3. Uruguay   _____

4. Chile   _____

5. Peru   _____

6. Argentina   _____

7. Mexico   _____

8. Canada   _____

Write two sentences. Use two more proper adjectives from the rule box.

9. _____

_____

10. _____

_____

The adjectives *a*, *an*, and *the* are called articles.

- Use *a* before singular nouns or other adjectives that start with a consonant.

    I love **a book** with **a surprise** ending!

- Use *an* before singular nouns or other adjectives that start with a vowel.

    An essay takes **an enormous** amount of time to write.

This, *that*, *these*, and *those* are called demonstrative adjectives. They point out specific nouns.

- Use *this* and *that* before singular nouns.

    This movie is too scary, and **that one** is too silly.

- Use *these* and *those* before plural nouns.

    We need to find **those tickets** in order to see **these films**.

Underline each article once and each demonstrative adjective twice.
For each article, circle the noun or adjective that determines the choice of article.
For each demonstrative adjective, circle the specific noun being pointed out.

1. I think I will have the best vacation ever this summer.

2. I am taking an airplane alone for the first time.

3. That part is very exciting because it makes me feel like a young adult.

4. Then I am meeting an adventure group and going to a wilderness camp.

5. This group advertises that it provides the experiences to help kids mature.

6. Those benefits appealed to my mother, but it was the activities that sold me.

7. We will ride a raft down a raging river to get to the camp.

8. We learn to read those clues that signal if an animal is nearby.

9. We learn all the rules for camping and how to follow those rules.

10. I think these experiences will provide the best lessons I will learn this year!

Fill in the bubble next to the correct answer.

1. Which word is the correct proper adjective for Canada?
   Ⓐ Canadese
   Ⓑ Canadish
   Ⓒ Canadian
   Ⓓ Canadan

2. Which pair is <u>not</u> correct?
   Ⓐ Peru: Peruvian
   Ⓑ America: American
   Ⓒ Colombia: Colombian
   Ⓓ Brazil: Brazilish

3. Which sentence has the most articles?
   Ⓐ An elevator is stuck in the store with a crowd inside.
   Ⓑ A technician has gone to the ninth floor to fix it.
   Ⓒ An older woman got off just in the nick of time.
   Ⓓ An episode like this reminds me to always take the stairs.

4. Which sentence correctly uses demonstrative adjectives?
   Ⓐ These shoe are too old to wear again this year.
   Ⓑ Those sandals were put in that box for donations.
   Ⓒ This coat is made of those itchy wool I can't wear.
   Ⓓ The shopping trip will take more time than we expected.

5. How many adjectives are in this sentence?
   These Hawaiian flowers are the kind you see on a tropical island.
   Ⓐ three
   Ⓑ four
   Ⓒ five
   Ⓓ six

> Pronouns are used in place of nouns. Pronouns can be singular or plural.
>
> I   you   he   she   it   they   we   me   him   her   them   us
>
> **Isaac** is in the band.   **Jessica** is in the band, too.
> **He** is in the band.   **She** is in the band, too.
>
> **Connor and Brooke** like to sing.   **Lily and I** like to dance.
> **They** like to sing.   **We** like to dance.

Underline the pronoun in each pair of sentences. On the line, write the noun that the pronoun replaced.

1. Mr. Kenzo is the band leader. He would like more band members.   _____

2. Paige wants to learn the trumpet. She will join the band.   _____

3. Kevin plays the drums at home. Mr. Kenzo would like him to join.   _____

4. Jordan and Luke used to be in band. Perhaps they will rejoin.   _____

5. The band needs ten new members. It needs more instruments, too.   _____

6. Rachel just got a guitar. Mr. Kenzo asked her to play in the concert.   _____

7. Ty and I were surprised. We thought the band was a marching band.   _____

8. The band knows rock tunes. The members play them well!   _____

Write two sentences about a band. In one sentence, include the pronoun *us*. In the other sentence, include the pronoun *you* or *me.*

9. _____

_____

10. _____

_____

> Pronouns are used in place of nouns. Use pronouns to avoid repeating the same names, words in a sentence, or words in a group of sentences.
>
> **I   me   you   he   she   him   her   it   they   them   we   us**
>
> **Evan** is reading **a new book,** and **Evan** likes **the book.**
>
> **Evan** is reading **a new book,** and **he** likes **it.**

Read the paragraphs. Replace the underlined words with the correct pronouns. Write the pronouns above the words.

Nicole and Aaron are at the library. <u>Nicole and Aaron</u> both have reports to finish. Nicole is writing about ancient Egypt for social studies. <u>Nicole</u> read books about <u>ancient Egypt</u>. <u>Nicole</u> watched a video about <u>ancient Egypt</u>. Aaron told <u>Nicole</u> that <u>Nicole</u> must be an expert. She told <u>Aaron</u> that <u>Nicole</u> would like to visit Egypt.

Aaron is writing about cats for science. Mrs. Armstrong, the librarian, brought <u>Aaron and Nicole</u> books that <u>Aaron and Nicole</u> requested. <u>Mrs. Armstrong</u> explained that cats were important to the Egyptians. Aaron decided that <u>Aaron</u> would like to go to Egypt. Nicole told Aaron that <u>Aaron and Nicole</u> could go together. When I saw <u>Aaron and Nicole</u>, Nicole suggested that <u>Nicole, Aaron, and I</u> go to Egypt. I said <u>Egypt</u> is too far to go this afternoon! Mrs. Armstrong told <u>Aaron, Nicole, and me</u> that <u>Aaron, Nicole, and me</u> could be armchair travelers to Egypt by getting our reports done.

The antecedent of a pronoun is the noun or nouns the pronoun refers to or replaces.

- The antecedent can be in the same sentence.

  Mackenzie has a speech to give, and **she** would like to practice.
  Antecedent   Pronoun

- The antecedent can be in a different sentence.

  Jason wants to make a video. **He** is looking for good scenes to include in it.
  Antecedent   Pronoun

- Be sure the pronoun agrees with the antecedent in gender (male or female) and number (singular or plural).

  Mrs. Taylor wants to see original **presentations**. **They** need to be creative.
                                       Antecedent   Pronoun

The antecedent is underlined in each sentence or pair of sentences. Fill in each blank line with the correct pronoun to match the antecedent.

1. <u>Students</u> are excited about the class business. _____ are making greeting cards.

2. <u>Amanda</u> got the idea for the cards. _____ has a card-making program at home.

3. Here is how the <u>business</u> will work, and _____ should be simple to run.

4. Amanda will make some sample <u>cards</u>, and _____ will be shown to customers.

5. <u>Sid</u> will be in charge of taking orders for cards. _____ will collect all the orders.

6. Then students working with <u>Trisha</u> will make the cards. _____ is a good artist.

7. The cards are delivered to the <u>customers</u>, and money is collected from _____.

8. <u>I</u> would like to be part of a class enterprise. It sounds exciting to _____.

9. <u>Destiny and I</u> have a plan. _____ want to advertise on the school Web site.

10. Our idea is a healthy <u>snack</u> to sell. _____ will be nutritious and delicious!

The antecedent is the noun or nouns the pronoun refers to or replaces. If a pronoun can refer to more than one noun, the antecedent may be unclear. When this happens, rewrite the sentence to fix the unclear antecedent.

Unclear Antecedent   The girls are looking for flowers. **They** are everywhere.

Explanation   It is unclear whether *they* refers to *the girls* or *flowers*.

Rewrite the sentence to clarify the antecedent.

Clear Antecedent   There are flowers everywhere. The girls are looking for them.

Explain why each sentence is unclear. Rewrite each sentence correctly.

1. Diego and Ashton have new skateboards, and they want to race.

   Explanation: _____

   _____

   Rewrite: _____

   _____

2. Other kids have skateboards to race, and they are fast.

   Explanation: _____

   _____

   Rewrite: _____

   _____

3. Diego has brought Cory, his dog. He jumps on the board and is ready to go!

   Explanation: _____

   Rewrite: _____

   _____

   Language Fundamentals • EMC 2756 • © Evan-Moor Corp.

A singular personal pronoun takes the place of one person, place, thing, or idea.

I   you   he   she   it   me   him   her

The woman is a customer.   **The man** is a server.
She is a customer.   **He** is a server.

The restaurant is busy.   **The menu** is large.
It is busy.   **It** is large.

Hunger brought **the woman** here.   **The woman** called to the **server**.
It brought **her** here.   **She** called to **him**.

Write the correct singular pronoun on a line to replace each underlined noun.

1. The store is having a big sale.   _____

2. The computer sale ends tomorrow.   _____

3. Matt is looking at a computer.   _____

4. Megan sees Matt in the store.   _____

5. Matt asks Megan, "Which computer do you like?"   _____

6. Megan tells Matt, "I like the laptop."   _____

7. Megan adds, "But the computer is not for Megan." _____

8. Matt smiles at Megan.   _____

9. Megan thinks Matt is getting a computer.   _____

10. Actually, the laptop will be a birthday surprise for Megan!   _____

A plural personal pronoun takes the place of more than one person, place, thing, or idea.

they   we   them   us   you

The cats and dogs are pets.   I own **the cats and dogs.**
They are pets.   I own **them.**

Angel and I have fish, too.   Pets are fun for **Angel and me.**
We have fish, too.   Pets are fun for **us.**

Replace each underlined noun with the correct plural pronoun. Write the pronoun on the line.

1. <u>Kyle and I</u> are always coming up with <u>ideas</u>.

   _____ are always coming up with _____ .

2. <u>Our parents</u> are usually not in favor of <u>our plans</u>.

   _____ are usually not in favor of _____ .

3. Our latest plan is for <u>Kyle and me</u> to share a pet.

   Our latest plan is for _____ to share a pet.

4. After all, <u>you and Jasmine</u> share a cat with <u>Victoria and Noah</u>.

   After all, _____ share a cat with _____ .

5. <u>My parents</u> reminded <u>Kyle and me</u> that <u>you, Jasmine, Victoria, and Noah</u> are neighbors.

   _____ reminded _____ that _____ are neighbors.

6. <u>Kyle and I</u> do live miles apart, but <u>Kyle and I</u> can exchange a snake in a cage easily!

   _____ do live miles apart, but _____ can exchange a snake in a cage easily!

          Language Fundamentals • EMC 2756 • © Evan-Moor Corp.

Fill in the bubble next to the correct answer.

1. Which sentence gives a correct rule for using pronouns?

   Ⓐ Pronouns always replace nouns and articles.

   Ⓑ Use pronouns to write shorter sentences.

   Ⓒ Call someone by a pronoun if you don't know the person's name.

   Ⓓ Use pronouns to avoid repeating names or words in a sentence.

2. Choose the correct pronoun to complete this sentence:
   There is a skunk under the porch, and _____ will cause a stink!

   Ⓐ they

   Ⓑ we

   Ⓒ it

   Ⓓ you

3. Choose the correct pronoun to complete this sentence:
   Our friends are having a party and need _____ to help.

   Ⓐ him

   Ⓑ us

   Ⓒ we

   Ⓓ her

4. Which word is the antecedent of *they?*
   Isabella waved to the neighbors. They think she is polite.

   Ⓐ Isabella

   Ⓑ neighbors

   Ⓒ Isabella and the neighbors

   Ⓓ unclear

5. Which is the best revision of these sentences?
   Kelly wants to visit the Smiths' kittens. She thinks they are sweet.

   Ⓐ Kelly wants to visit the Smiths' kittens. She thinks the kittens are sweet.

   Ⓑ Kelly wants to visit the Smiths' kittens because they are sweet.

   Ⓒ Kelly wants to visit the Smiths' kittens. Kelly thinks they are sweet.

   Ⓓ She wants to visit their kittens. She think they are sweet.

A subject pronoun replaces a noun that is the subject of a sentence.

I   you   he   she   it   we   they

Zach has a camera.   **Zach and I** have a plan.
He has a camera.   **We** have a plan.

The camera will come in handy.   **Mrs. Lu** asked us to photograph **the class play.**
It will come in handy.   **She** asked us to photograph **it.**

Read the words in parentheses ( ). Write the correct subject pronoun for each sentence.

1. _____ is sponsoring a contest. (The camera shop)

2. _____ is to submit the best photo of the first signs of spring. (The idea)

3. _____ are all shots of outdoor scenes. (My pictures)

4. _____ always say I have a good eye for color. (My art teachers)

5. _____ says my imagination is strong. (My mother)

6. _____ volunteered to get my film developed. (My father)

7. _____ got a surprise when the pictures came back! (My parents and I)

8. _____ asked where my father took the photos. (Mom and I)

9. _____ answered with the name of the camera shop having the contest! (Dad)

Write a sentence with *I* to finish the story.

10. _____

_____

_____

> An object pronoun follows an action verb or a preposition (words such as *about, at, for, of, to,* and *with*).
>
> **me   you   him   her   it   us   them**
>
> That family is coming to see **us.** The desert is too hot for **me.**

Read the words in parentheses ( ). Write the correct object pronoun in each sentence.

Our family took a trip to the Arizona-Sonoran Desert Museum near

Tucson. As we were about to head out on the trail, a guide said she wanted to

share some tips with _____ (our family). She said the desert can be

dangerous and we should respect _____ (the desert). I noticed the guide

was looking right at _____ (myself). I wondered if she thought I would

not believe _____ (the guide). She should have been looking at _____

(my brother). He is not afraid of anything, including _____ (dangerous

desert animals). My parents were watching _____ very closely (their son).

Mom thanked _____ (the guide) and said they would keep a close eye on

_____ (my brother and me).

Use the context of these sentences to fill in the object pronouns.

The guide told _____, "I wish more people were like _____. The

desert is interesting to _____, but they don't want to be careful in

_____."

A possessive pronoun shows ownership. A possessive pronoun does <u>not</u> need an apostrophe.

- Some possessive pronouns are used before a noun and serve as adjectives.

  her   his   its   my   our   their   your

  The students have **their** assignments. Alexis has **her** report ready.

- Some possessive pronouns can stand alone.

  his   hers   mine   ours   yours   theirs

  Luis says this book is **his.** Zoe and I think that book is **ours.**

Complete each sentence with one or more possessive pronouns.

1. Our sixth-grade class is taking _____ yearly field trip.

2. Each student has brought _____ or _____ sandwich to eat on the bus.

3. I like _____ sandwich, but some students want to trade _____.

4. Makayla has a turkey sandwich, but she wants _____.

5. I took half of _____ sandwich and kept half of _____.

6. Jack likes turkey, so he asked Makayla if she wanted half of _____ sandwich.

7. Jack said to Makayla and me, "Now half of each of _____ sandwiches is turkey."

8. Jack says each type of sandwich has _____ appeal.

Language Fundamentals • EMC 2756 • © Evan-Moor Corp.

Fill in the bubble next to the correct answer.

1. Which subject pronoun replaces the underlined words?
   The forest path is filled with large and small rocks.

   Ⓐ They

   Ⓑ Its

   Ⓒ It

   Ⓓ They

2. Which object pronoun replaces the underlined words?
   Give the ball back to my brother!

   Ⓐ him

   Ⓑ it

   Ⓒ its

   Ⓓ them

3. Which object pronoun replaces the underlined words?
   Is Kari going to the fair with Keenan and Jilon?

   Ⓐ they

   Ⓑ us

   Ⓒ them

   Ⓓ you

4. Choose the correct possessive pronoun to complete the sentence.
   Thalia has to go to _____ dance class.

   Ⓐ the

   Ⓑ their

   Ⓒ your

   Ⓓ her

5. Choose the possessive pronoun that can stand alone in the sentence.
   Brianna and I think that bag is ours, but it actually belongs to him.

   Ⓐ I

   Ⓑ ours

   Ⓒ it

   Ⓓ him

Some pronouns do not name the word they replace.
These are called indefinite pronouns.

all	another	anybody	anyone	anything
both	each	everybody	everyone	everything
few	many	most	none	no one
nothing	one	other	several	some
somebody	something	such		

Most are coming to graduation.
Nothing was done correctly.
Somebody needs to do **something**.

Circle the correct indefinite pronoun to complete the sentence.

1. We need _____ to help out this weekend for the class cleanup.
   (one, everybody, all)

2. _____ have signed up for litter patrol in the park.
   (Each, Several, Other)

3. Surprisingly, _____ has volunteered yet to work at the beach.
   (few, another, no one)

4. _____ needs to pick up the trash there.
   (Somebody, Both, Most)

5. _____ leave behind bottles and cans.
   (Both, None, Many)

6. Can _____ explain why caring for the environment is so important?
   (some, anyone, something)

7. Actually, _____ have through their actions and attitudes.
   (none, such, many)

8. For example, just about _____ recycles today.
   (everyone, everything, most)

Name _____

> Some pronouns are used to ask a question.
> These are called interrogative pronouns.
>
> **what who which whose whom**
>
> **What** happened to our luggage?
>
> **Who** is going to find our suitcase?
>
> **Which** color suitcase is yours?
>
> **Whose** bag is missing?
>
> With **whom** should we discuss the lost bag?

Complete each sentence with the correct interrogative pronoun from the box above. Write the word on the line.

1. _____ is organizing the surprise party?

2. _____ can I do to help?

3. _____ idea was it to go ice-skating?

4. _____ if they don't like to ice-skate?

5. _____ place did you tell them?

6. _____ said that park had an ice-skating rink?

7. To _____ did you give that information?

8. _____ kids should we call first?

9. _____ will we do if everyone shows up at the wrong place?

10. _____ surprise is likely to be greater, theirs or ours, if the plan works?

Some pronouns refer back to the subject.
These are called reflexive pronouns.

himself   herself   yourself   myself   itself   ourselves   yourselves   themselves

I did the project by **myself**.

Felicia has the computer to **herself** today.

Those students found **themselves** without enough time to finish.

Read each sentence. Underline the subject, then circle the correct reflexive pronoun to complete the sentence.

1. You need the kitchen to _____ because you are a messy cook.
   (itself, yourself)

2. Dad and Mom want the porch to _____ while they discuss our family vacation.
   (themselves, ourselves)

3. Hunter has planned a great trip for us all by _____.
   (himself, ourselves)

4. Emily says she will help you in the kitchen or clean up by _____.
   (yourself, herself)

5. Too bad that pan cannot clean _____!
   (itself, myself)

6. We are bringing a lot of great food for _____ to the beach house.
   (ourselves, yourselves)

Fill in the bubble next to the correct answer.

1. Identify the correct interrogative pronoun to complete the sentence.
   With _____ will you attend the dance?
   Ⓐ what
   Ⓑ whom
   Ⓒ whose
   Ⓓ which

2. Choose the correct reflexive pronoun to complete the sentence.
   Jenny and Dan want to see the project for _____.
   Ⓐ theirselves
   Ⓑ ourselves
   Ⓒ themselves
   Ⓓ themself

3. Complete the sentence with the correct indefinite pronoun.
   _____ is needed in that play to make it more fun to watch.
   Ⓐ Few
   Ⓑ None
   Ⓒ Both
   Ⓓ Something

4. Identify the correct interrogative pronoun to complete the sentence.
   _____ has to come the farthest to camp?
   Ⓐ Who
   Ⓑ Whom
   Ⓒ Which
   Ⓓ Whose

5. Choose the correct reflexive pronoun to complete the sentence.
   Gavin and Michael want to put the team together _____.
   Ⓐ himself
   Ⓑ themselves
   Ⓒ theirselves
   Ⓓ itself

A verb is a word that expresses action or a state of being. It tells what a subject does or is. A verb is the main word in the predicate of a sentence.

Action Verb	Being Verb
leap	is
saw	are
sing	was

Underline the verb in each sentence. Write *action* or *being* on the line.

1. Blue jays are noisy birds. _____

2. They bully the other birds at the bird feeder. _____

3. A blue jay chases the other birds. _____

4. It wants the food to itself. _____

5. My cat stares through the window at the birds. _____

6. Her whiskers are cute. _____

7. I open a can of food for her. _____

8. She runs to the kitchen for her breakfast. _____

9. She gobbles her food quickly. _____

10. She was definitely hungry! _____

11. Every day she washes her face after breakfast. _____

12. She is very sweet! _____

Name _____

An action verb tells what the subject does.

- Some action verbs tell about actions that can be seen or heard.

    We **trod** along the wooded path. We **sang** a lively hiking song.

- Some action verbs tell about actions that cannot be seen or heard.

    Mr. Krebs **thinks** about resting. He **wants** a snack.

Write the action verb in each sentence.

1. The Nature Club hikes in the woods.   _____

2. Our leaders teach us about plants and animals.   _____

3. Ms. Curtis points to some poison ivy.   _____

4. Avoid those shiny green leaves!   _____

5. Ms. Curtis leads us away from the dangerous plant.   _____

Choose an action verb from the word box below to complete each sentence.
Circle *yes* if the action can be seen or heard or *no* if it cannot be seen or heard.

flowed   hope   will explore   waded   are planning

6. Yesterday we _____ in a creek in the woods.   yes   no

7. The water _____ over our toes and ankles.   yes   no

8. We _____ another hike.   yes   no

9. The club _____ another trail with Mr. Krebs and Ms. Curtis.   yes   no

10. We all _____ for a sunny day.   yes   no

A linking verb links the subject to a predicate noun or a predicate adjective.

am   are   is   was   were   been   being   will be

Rebecca is my cousin.

Subject   Linking   Predicate
           Verb   Noun

Our family reunion was fun.

Subject   Linking   Predicate
               Verb   Adjective

Circle the linking verb in each sentence. Write the predicate noun on the line.

1. Franklin is our hometown.   _____

2. My mother's sisters are my aunts.   _____

3. This family reunion is an important event.   _____

4. Our great-grandparents were farmers.   _____

5. This land was once their farm.   _____

Circle the linking verb in each sentence. Write the predicate adjective on the line.

6. This potato salad is quite delicious.   _____

7. That spinach salad is bright green!   _____

8. Some family stories are funny.   _____

9. Some stories are inspirational.   _____

10. Our great-grandparents were strong.   _____

Language Fundamentals • EMC 2756 • © Evan-Moor Corp.

A linking verb connects the subject of a sentence to a predicate noun or a predicate adjective. The most common linking verb is *to be*. Other linking verbs include *appear, become, feel, look, seem, smell, sound,* and *taste.*

The blooming violets **smell** sweet.   The bird's song **sounds** lovely.

Circle the linking verb and underline the predicate adjective.

1. The buds on the trees look swollen.

2. The trees seem ready for spring.

3. That patch of skunk cabbage smells bad!

4. The violet's petals feel soft.

5. Some special violets dipped in sugar taste good.

Write sentences about plants with linking verbs. Use a different linking verb in each sentence.

6. _____

_____

7. _____

_____

8. _____

_____

9. _____

_____

10. _____

_____

Fill in the bubble next to the correct answer.

1. In which sentence is the verb underlined?
   Ⓐ Miners dig <u>coal</u> from deep holes in the Earth.
   Ⓑ Mining is a dangerous <u>job</u>.
   Ⓒ The coal <u>dust</u> gets in the miners' lungs.
   Ⓓ The miners <u>arrive</u> for work.

2. Which sentence below contains an action verb?
   Ⓐ The miners wear lights on their hard hats.
   Ⓑ The right equipment is important.
   Ⓒ Miners are serious about safety.
   Ⓓ The crew seems ready to go.

3. Which sentence contains a linking verb?
   Ⓐ Old furnaces burned coal.
   Ⓑ The buildings were black with coal dust.
   Ⓒ Trucks delivered coal to homes.
   Ⓓ Furnaces glowed with fire.

4. Which sentence contains a linking verb?
   Ⓐ Coal smoke rose over a town.
   Ⓑ Sometimes the days looked as dark as night.
   Ⓒ Look at these old photographs.
   Ⓓ I can see the mine entrance in the distance.

5. Which of the verbs below can be a linking verb?
   Ⓐ dance
   Ⓑ jump
   Ⓒ hurry
   Ⓓ taste

Language Fundamentals • EMC 2756 • © Evan-Moor Corp.

Name _____

> A verb's tense tells when the action takes place. It tells whether the action is happening in the present, happened in the past, or will happen in the future.

Present Tense	The kids **ride** their bikes after school.
Past Tense	Yesterday Gavin **rode** down that hill at top speed.
Future Tense	He **will ride** in a race tomorrow.

Decide whether the action is happening in the present, has happened in the past, or will happen in the future. Underline the verb and circle *present, past,* or *future.*

1. Hannah washes her bike with the garden hose.   present   past   future

2. Her friends will meet her on the corner.   present   past   future

3. Taylor received a new bike last week.   present   past   future

4. Hannah's clean bike gleams like new.   present   past   future

5. The friends will coast down the hill.   present   past   future

6. Jenny waited for the others at the bottom.   present   past   future

7. Her bike was the fastest.   present   past   future

Write a present tense sentence, a past tense sentence, and a future tense sentence. Underline the verb.

8. _____

_____

9. _____

_____

10. _____

_____

The present tense tells that the action or state of being is happening now or happens regularly.

Is Happening Now My favorite television show **is** on.
Happens Regularly The main character **gets** into trouble each week.

Read each sentence. Underline the present tense verb. Write *now* or *regularly*.

1. I watch my favorite show on Wednesday evenings. _____

2. On those nights, my family sits on the couch together. _____

3. We pause for a commercial. _____

4. During the commercial, my dad gets a snack in the kitchen. _____

5. Sometimes, we eat ice cream during the show. _____

6. I enjoy the jokes and funny situations on the show. _____

7. In every episode, the dad in the show gets the last word. _____

Write three sentences in the present tense to show action that is happening now and regularly.

8. _____

_____

9. _____

_____

10. _____

_____

> A past tense verb tells that an action or state of being took place in the past and is over.
>
> My family **traveled** to Germany last summer.
>
> We **went** on a boat down a river.
>
> The guide **pointed** to old castles on the shore.

Circle the past tense verb in each pair of sentences.

1. Here are the pictures of our trip to Europe. We boarded this enormous plane.

2. My parents gave me this camera before the trip. I like taking pictures.

3. This picture shows a town square in Germany. We ate lunch in that town.

4. I tried a dish of sauerkraut. You are wrinkling your nose.

5. I liked the sauerkraut! I want to have it again soon.

6. In this picture, we are in Berlin. We saw many monuments there.

7. This bomb-damaged church is a war monument now. People were quiet there.

8. We brought these spicy cookies back with us. I'll share them with you.

Write sentences in the past tense about something that happened and is over.

9. _____

_____

10. _____

_____

The past tense of most verbs is formed by adding *ed* to the verb. Verbs that follow this rule are called regular verbs. For some regular verbs, you must make spelling changes before adding the *ed* ending.

- When a regular verb ends with one vowel and one consonant, double the final consonant before adding **ed.**

Present	stop	rub	plan
Past	stopped	rubbed	planned

- When a regular verb ends in a silent **e**, drop that **e** before adding **ed.**

Present	snore	type	save
Past	snored	typed	saved

- When a regular verb ends in a consonant followed by a **y**, change the **y** to **i** and add **ed.**

Present	hurry	marry	study
Past	hurried	married	studied

Write the past tense of each regular verb.

1. carry _____
2. play _____
3. push _____
4. help _____
5. stay _____
6. hope _____
7. wave _____
8. joke _____
9. slip _____
10. fry _____

11. sigh _____
12. bake _____
13. turn _____
14. argue _____
15. hope _____
16. map _____
17. refuse _____
18. flip _____
19. knit _____
20. vibrate _____

> Irregular verbs have special past tense forms.
>
> **Present Tense**   I **ride** horses. Ginny **has** horses in her stable.
> **Past Tense**   I **rode** a horse at camp. The camp **had** three horses for the campers.

Fill in the blank with the past tense of the irregular verb in parentheses ( ).
Use the word box to help you.

ate	brought	built	chose	fed	had
sang	sat	saw	slid	swam	told

1. We _____ a cookout at summer camp. (have)

2. The camp counselors _____ a fire. (build)

3. They _____ small dry sticks to start the fire. (choose)

4. Everyone _____ around the fire. (sit)

5. Counselor Adam _____ us to start cooking our hot dogs. (tell)

6. We _____ our favorite camp songs. (sing)

7. I _____ my hot dog fall into the fire! (see)

8. It _____ right off the stick. (slide)

9. Counselor Ginny _____ me another hot dog. (bring)

10. We _____ watermelon for dessert. (eat)

11. The cookout _____ twenty kids and four counselors. (feed)

12. Later, we _____ in the lake. (swim)

Irregular verbs have special past tense forms. There are no rules for forming the past tense of those irregular verbs.

Present Tense	Past Tense
I usually **wake** in the morning at 7 o'clock.	On Sunday, I **woke** at 9 o'clock.
Sunday **is** a quiet day at our house.	Last Sunday **was** an exception.
I **go** downstairs for breakfast in the morning.	We **went** to the pancake house.

Fill in the blank with the past tense of the irregular verb in parentheses ( ).

1. The waiter _____ a pitcher of orange juice to our table. (bring)

2. I _____ my order with a bowl of oatmeal. (begin)

3. Dad _____ into a slice of cantaloupe. (bite)

4. Mom _____ a spoon into her grapefruit. (stick)

5. The juice _____ my brother in the eye. (hit)

6. His glass of milk _____ to the floor. (fall)

7. The glass _____ into a thousand pieces. (break)

8. Our server _____ into action! (spring)

9. He _____ through the kitchen doors with a mop. (burst)

10. Another server _____ on the spilled milk. (slide)

11. She _____ a tray that crashed to the floor. (hold)

12. The restaurant manager _____ her head in dismay. (shake)

Fill in the bubble next to the correct answer.

1. Which sentence is in the present tense?

Ⓐ Ms. Reed strode into the room.

Ⓑ She was on a mission.

Ⓒ She cleared her throat.

Ⓓ Her voice rings strong and clear now.

2. Which sentence is in the past tense?

Ⓐ Ms. Reed is the chemistry teacher at the high school.

Ⓑ She shows our class a big chart.

Ⓒ She calls it the periodic table of elements.

Ⓓ My older sister studied this chart last year.

3. Which sentence contains a regular verb in the past tense?

Ⓐ The table looked complicated to me.

Ⓑ There was a symbol in every square.

Ⓒ Ms. Reed tells us about the elements.

Ⓓ She brought some test tubes to our classroom, too.

4. What is the past tense of *stay*?

Ⓐ stayyed

Ⓑ staied

Ⓒ stayed

Ⓓ staied

5. Which sentence contains the correct past tense form of its verb?

Ⓐ My brother forgetted his chemistry book.

Ⓑ My mother became a chemist.

Ⓒ I finded the subject interesting.

Ⓓ I will read more about it.

A verb phrase is made up of a helping verb and a main verb.

am	is	are	was
were	have	has	can
should	could	must	will

Sentence	Helping Verb	Main Verb
Shannon **will make** the team.	will	make
Our team **should practice** more often.	should	practice

Write the helping verb and the main verb in the correct column. If there is no helping verb in a sentence, put an **X** in that column.

	Helping Verb	Main Verb
1. Our town has built a new playing field.	_____	_____
2. The field has lights for night games.	_____	_____
3. The football team can play on Friday nights now.	_____	_____
4. You can walk to the field from our house.	_____	_____
5. My softball team has played on the new field.	_____	_____
6. You must come to our next game.	_____	_____
7. We are improving every week.	_____	_____
8. By the next game, we should be great!	_____	_____
9. I know we will win our next game.	_____	_____
10. I am excited to be on the team!	_____	_____

> A verb in the future tense tells what is going to happen.
> To form the future tense of a main verb, use the helping verb *will*.
>
> We **will go** on vacation to Cape Cod.

Rewrite each sentence in the future tense and underline the future tense verb.

1. We drive to Cape Cod, Massachusetts.

   _____

2. My family stays at an old cottage.

   _____

3. I sleep in a tiny room in an old-fashioned bed.

   _____

4. Mom runs on the beach in the morning.

   _____

5. She brings pretty seashells back to the cottage.

   _____

Write one sentence about something you are planning to do. Use the future tense.

6. _____

   _____

   _____

> The present progressive tense of a verb shows that an action
> is in progress. The action is happening now and will continue
> for a period of time.

Subject	Helping Verb	Main Verb + *ing*
Lee	is	**shopping** for a new coat.
I	am	**shopping** for new shoes.

Underline the present progressive verb in each sentence.

1. Shoppers are waiting for the store to open.

2. The manager is unlocking the door.

3. Everyone is hoping for a bargain!

4. I am searching for shoes for the party.

5. Chris is unfolding a green sweater.

6. I am paying for these shoes.

7. These new shoes are pinching my feet!

8. You are stepping on my toe!

Write two sentences with verbs in the present progressive tense.

9. _____

_____

10. _____

_____

The tense of the verb indicates when the action happens.

- **Present Tense:** is happening now or happens regularly

  I **call** my friend Jenny almost every day.

- **Present Progressive Tense:** is happening now and continuing for a period of time

  The phone **is ringing.**

- **Past Tense:** has happened before now and is over

  Jenny **left** a message for me yesterday.

- **Future Tense:** will happen sometime after now

  I **will call** her back later.

Fill in the blank with the verb in the correct tense for the sentence.
Write the name of the tense.

1. Jenny always _____ me after school. (call)   _____

2. Yesterday we _____ about a school assignment. (talk)   _____

3. We _____ together on an ongoing project. (work)   _____

4. Our class _____ in the science fair. (participate)   _____

5. Next month, Dr. Tilton _____ prizes to the best
   projects. (award)   _____

6. She _____ science. (teach)   _____

7. Last week, Dr. Tilton _____ us about viruses
   and bacteria. (teach)   _____

8. My friend Jenny _____ a career as a doctor. (want)   _____

9. Dr. Tilton always _____ Jenny to study hard. (encourage) _____

10. Someday, Jenny _____ surgery. (perform)   _____

It is important to stay with the same verb tense unless there is a good reason to change tenses.

Incorrect Brad **writes** for the school newspaper. He **will write** a story every month.

Correct Brad **writes** for the school newspaper. He **writes** a story every month.

Incorrect Last month, Brad **reported** on cafeteria food. Next month, he **reported** on the computer lab.

Correct Last month, Brad **reported** on cafeteria food. Next month, he **will report** on the computer lab.

Underline the verb in the first sentence. Fill in the blank in the second sentence with the correct tense of the verb in parentheses ( ).

1. Brad reports on school events. Mia _____ photographs for the paper. (take)

2. The story on the cafeteria was entertaining. It _____ all the menus. (cover)

3. Brad named "crumble burger" the worst dish. He _____ it "icky." (call)

4. I like the turkey burgers. The cafeteria _____ them once a month. (serve)

5. The school paper will run a story on the library next. I _____ it. (write)

6. I am writing about library fines. Next year, the library _____ fines. (raise)

7. That is a good idea. The fines _____ too low now. (be)

8. People often return books late. Higher fines _____ late returns. (discourage)

Fill in the bubble next to the correct answer.

1. Which sentence is in the future tense?
   - Ⓐ George is playing soccer.
   - Ⓑ He will walk the dog later.
   - Ⓒ Charlie waits for George by the back door.
   - Ⓓ He wags his tail when he sees George.

2. In which sentence is the main verb underlined?
   - Ⓐ Charlie <u>will</u> chase squirrels in the yard.
   - Ⓑ That one <u>has</u> scampered up a tree.
   - Ⓒ The squirrel is <u>chattering</u> at Charlie from a branch.
   - Ⓓ George <u>is</u> tugging at the leash.

3. In which sentence is the helping verb underlined?
   - Ⓐ George and Charlie will <u>follow</u> a path through the woods.
   - Ⓑ They have <u>walked</u> this path many times.
   - Ⓒ Charlie <u>is</u> nervous.
   - Ⓓ He <u>is</u> sniffing at the air.

4. Which sentence is in the present progressive tense?
   - Ⓐ Charlie has spotted a rabbit in the underbrush.
   - Ⓑ Charlie is very still.
   - Ⓒ George is holding tight to the leash.
   - Ⓓ The rabbit escapes into the woods.

5. In which sentence is the verb in the correct tense?
   - Ⓐ Yesterday, Charlie almost caught the rabbit.
   - Ⓑ Before, George will chase him through the woods.
   - Ⓒ Yesterday, George is remembering Charlie's leash.
   - Ⓓ Yesterday, Charlie takes off after a rabbit.

Verbs may be in the active or passive voice.

- A verb is in the active voice if the subject does the action.

  Keli **writes** in her notebook.

  Jade **pitied** the sick dog.

- A verb is in the passive voice if the subject does not do the action. A verb in the passive voice uses a form of the verb *to be (am, is, are, was, were, be, being, been).*

  The notebook **was written** in by Keli.

  The sick dog **was pitied** by Jade.

Underline the verb in the sentence. Circle whether the sentence is active or passive.

1. Last Saturday, the attic was cleaned by us.   active   passive

2. In a large trunk, we found old-fashioned clothes.   active   passive

3. Grace lifted a leather jacket from the trunk.   active   passive

4. Rob snapped some red suspenders.   active   passive

5. The findings are examined by everyone today.   active   passive

6. The yellowed pages of a cookbook are turned by Alice.   active   passive

7. A typewriter is examined by Dorothy.   active   passive

8. She taps lightly on the keys.   active   passive

Choose two sentences written in the passive voice. Rewrite them in the active voice.

9. _____

_____

10. _____

_____

Verbs may be in the active or passive voice. Using the active voice in your writing makes it more interesting.

- A verb is in the active voice if the subject does the action.

  The team **wears** red uniforms for home games.

  Delia **wrote** a letter to me about her decision.

- A verb is in the passive voice if the subject does not do the action. A verb in the passive voice uses a form of the verb *to be (am, is, are, was, were, be, being, been).*

  Red shirts **are worn** by the team for home games.

  A letter **was written** to me by Delia about her decision.

Write a paragraph of at least four sentences about your family. Use the active voice.

_____

_____

_____

_____

_____

_____

_____

_____

_____

_____

_____

> A subject and a verb must agree in number. A singular subject requires a singular verb, and a plural subject requires a plural verb.
>
> **Incorrect** A cat show judge **hold** a squirming kitten.
> The girls **holds** ribbons in their hands.
>
> **Correct** A cat show judge **holds** a squirming kitten.
> The girls **hold** ribbons in their hands.

Circle the correct form of the verb. Write *singular* or *plural* after the sentence.

1. Cat shows attracts/attract many pet owners. _____

2. I enters/enter my cat in the house pet category. _____

3. Special breeds competes/compete in a different category. _____

4. A judge gently displays/display a cat's bushy tail. _____

5. My cat yawns/yawn as she waits her turn. _____

Write the correct present tense form of the verb in parentheses ( ).

6. The Siamese cat _____ in her cage. (stretch)

7. The judge _____ the cat with a feather toy. (tempt)

8. The toy _____ the cat's alertness. (test)

9. Long-haired cats _____ lots of fur. (shed)

10. Judges _____ ribbons to the cats' cages. (attach)

Every verb must agree in number with its subject.

- A subject with two parts joined by *and* is called a compound subject. A compound subject takes a plural verb.

  Amy and Aaron **study** together.

- When the verb includes a main verb and a helping verb, the helping verb must agree in number with the subject.

  Aaron **is studying** history. Amy and Aaron **are studying** history.

Rewrite each sentence, correcting the mistake in subject-verb agreement.

1. Nicholas and Alexandra was rulers of Russia.

   _____

2. Aaron are writing a report on Russia.

   _____

3. He and Amy looks for books at the library.

   _____

4. Amy are looking for a book about Tibet.

   _____

5. Tibet and China is two countries Amy would like to visit.

   _____

   _____

Use what you know about verb tenses to answer to each question.

1. Which sentence is in the passive voice?

   Ⓐ The store clerk returns change to a customer.

   Ⓑ The shelves are full.

   Ⓒ The shopping is being done by Dylan today.

   Ⓓ The fresh bread smells good.

2. Which sentence is in the active voice?

   Ⓐ A box of cereal was taken from the shelf by Dylan.

   Ⓑ The information on nutrition was checked.

   Ⓒ The box of Sugar Shock was placed back on the shelf.

   Ⓓ He chose a box of Whole Wheat Wonder instead.

3. Which one is the best revision from passive to active voice?
   A cart is being pushed by Dylan with a squeaky wheel.

   Ⓐ The cart with a squeaky wheel is being pushed by Dylan.

   Ⓑ Dylan pushes a cart with a squeaky wheel.

   Ⓒ The cart pushed by Dylan has a squeaky wheel.

   Ⓓ Squeaky wheels on the cart are pushed by Dylan.

4. In which sentence does the verb agree with its subject?

   Ⓐ Dylan choose a large purple eggplant.

   Ⓑ He are planning an Italian meal.

   Ⓒ Dylan and his dad cook together.

   Ⓓ They makes great tomato sauce.

5. In which sentence does the verb agree with its subject?

   Ⓐ In the kitchen, Dylan consult a cookbook.

   Ⓑ He take a large pan from the cupboard.

   Ⓒ This recipe have a long list of ingredients.

   Ⓓ The instructions are complicated.

> An adverb can modify a verb, an adjective, or another adverb.
> Many adverbs end in *–ly*. These adverbs usually tell *how*, or *in what way*.
>
> Alicia grinned **happily** as she opened the envelope.
>
> Her father smiled **proudly** when she told him the news.
>
> Her mother shrieked **repeatedly** with joy.

Underline each adverb that ends in *–ly* and draw an arrow to the verb that it modifies.

1. Alicia had worked diligently on her essay about being an American.

2. English was not her first language, but she practiced her English constantly.

3. Ms. Ling encouraged her repeatedly to write and write and write.

4. "I'm entering a contest," she told her parents excitedly.

5. "That's great, niña," Mr. and Mrs. Jiménez said encouragingly.

6. When Alicia saw the envelope, she opened it hurriedly.

7. "I won! I won!" Alicia shouted loudly enough for the neighbors to hear.

8. "Let's have a party to celebrate," her brothers and sisters said eagerly.

Finish the story. Write a sentence for each *–ly* adverb.

9. (proudly) _____

_____

10. (sleepily) _____

_____

Many adverbs don't end in *–ly*. These adverbs often tell *where*, *when*, and *to what extent*. The words *tomorrow*, *there*, *soon*, *here*, *very*, and *too* are all adverbs.

> **Where** Gina was tired once she got **there.**
> **When** **Yesterday** she had finished her drawing.
> **To What Extent** She was **very** pleased with her final version.

Find the adverb in each sentence and circle it. Then write *where*, *when*, or *to what extent* on the line.

1. Gina drew daily, trying to finish her self-portrait for the state fair. _____

2. First prize was something she wanted very much. _____

3. If she won, she and her family would be so happy. _____

4. First prize was a trip to New York, and she and her family would fly there. _____

5. Gina was going to learn tomorrow who won the contest. _____

Complete each sentence with the type of adverb in parentheses.

6. Gina looked _____ (where) to see if she could find the judges.

7. She knew they would be on stage _____ (when).

8. _____ (when) one of the judges spoke.

9. Gina's family was _____ (to what extent) proud to hear her name announced.

10. Gina was _____ (to what extent) stunned to move!

An adverb can modify a verb, an adjective, or another adverb.
Adverbs can tell *where, how, when,* and *to what extent.*

Modifying a Verb   Alexander walked **here** from school.

Modifying an Adjective   He was **too** quiet.

Modifying an Adverb   He opened the door **very** quickly.

The words *tomorrow, there, soon, here, very,* and *too* are all adverbs.

Underline the adverb and draw an arrow to the word it modifies.

1. "There you are!" cried Alex's mother.

2. His mother anxiously asked him where he'd been.

3. "I missed the bus and had to walk here," Alex replied.

4. "You have an orthodontist appointment tomorrow," Alex's mother said.

5. "That means you have to leave school early," she continued.

6. "I'll be very happy when my braces are removed," Alex said.

7. "Me, too," his mother replied tiredly.

Write an adverb to complete each sentence. Use the hint in parentheses ( )
to know which type of adverb to use.

8. After the movie, Alex ran _____ (how) for the bus.

9. The movie ended _____ (to what extent) late, so Alex missed the bus.

10. Alex got _____ (where) just after 8:30.

> Use *more* or *less* with an adverb when comparing two things.
>
> My brother Donnie exercises **more often** than I do.
> I exercise **less often** than Donnie does.
>
> Use *the most* or *the least* with an adverb when comparing three or more things.
>
> My sister Cecilia exercises **the most often** of anyone in the family.
> My father exercises **the least often** of us all!

Write the correct form of the adverb to complete the sentence.

1. I need to exercise _____ than my little sister.
   (frequently)

2. She runs up and down the stairs _____ than I do.
   (frequently)

3. My big sister exercises _____ of us all.
   (frequently)

4. The _____ she exercises, the stronger her muscles will be!
   (frequently)

Write the correct form of the adverb to complete the sentence. Add *less* or *the least*.

5. Angela, my oldest sister, speaks Italian _____ than I do.
   (frequently)

6. My baby brother speaks Italian _____ of the three of us.
   (fluently)

Write two sentences about exercising. Use *more* or *less* and *the most* or *the least*.

7. _____

   _____

8. _____

   _____

Language Fundamentals • EMC 2756 • © Evan-Moor Corp.

Name _____

> Some adverbs have irregular forms for comparisons.
>
> Daniele danced **well** at her recital.
> She danced **better** than she did last year.
> She hopes to dance **the best** she's ever danced next year.
>
> Caleb threw **badly** this morning as he got ready for the game.
> He threw **worse** than he did last night.
> This was **the worst** he had thrown in months.

Write the correct form of the adverb under each line to complete the sentence.

1. The team played _____ than they did last week.
   (well)

2. They played _____ last week than this week.
   (badly)

3. They have played _____ this year than last year.
   (well)

4. Once, they played _____ of any team in the league.
   (badly)

5. With more practice, they can play _____ of any team in the county.
   (well)

Write a sentence, using the words in parentheses.

6. (dance the best) _____

   _____

7. (sing the worst) _____

   _____

8. (pitch better) _____

   _____

> Negatives are words that mean "no" or "not."
>
> Celinda asked her teacher **not** to call on her today.
> She had **never** been unprepared before.
> She had looked for her homework, and it was **nowhere** to be found.

Complete each sentence with a negative.

1. Celinda _____ forgot her homework.

2. She was _____ the kind of person who came to class unprepared.

3. This morning, she could _____ find her homework.

4. She had _____ forgotten her homework before, so her teacher was understanding.

5. She had looked high and low, but her homework was _____ to be found.

6. From now on, Celinda was going _____ without her homework.

7. This was _____ going to happen again.

Write a sentence for each negative.

8. (not) _____

_____

9. (never) _____

_____

10. (nowhere) _____

_____

Fill in the bubble next to the correct answer.

1. Which underlined adverb tells *where?*

   Ⓐ We left <u>quickly</u> after the show was over.

   Ⓑ It was <u>decidedly</u> the worst show ever!

   Ⓒ Mom is going to see it <u>tomorrow</u>.

   Ⓓ It's playing <u>there</u> until Saturday.

2. Which underlined adverb tells *how?*

   Ⓐ Eric shouted <u>loudly</u> when he won first place.

   Ⓑ Steffi called <u>home</u> when she heard the news.

   Ⓒ Brian said he'd be there <u>tomorrow</u>.

   Ⓓ Cara sang <u>yesterday</u> at the spring concert.

3. Which underlined adverb tells *to what extent?*

   Ⓐ Zoe tiptoed <u>quietly</u> into the room.

   Ⓑ Her little brother, Liam, was sleeping <u>soundly</u>.

   Ⓒ She was <u>so</u> happy to have a little brother.

   Ⓓ <u>Tomorrow</u> they were going to the park together.

4. Which sentence is written correctly?

   Ⓐ Zachary snores more loud than all of us.

   Ⓑ When we camp, no one cooks more oftener than Luis.

   Ⓒ Robert digs the most quicker of anyone setting up the trenches.

   Ⓓ Wang pitches his tent the most rapidly of anyone.

5. Which word is a negative in this sentence?
   Nonah never knotted knots before.

   Ⓐ never

   Ⓑ knotted

   Ⓒ knots

   Ⓓ Nonah

A preposition is used to show the relationship of a noun or pronoun to another word. Prepositions can show position, direction, or other relationships.

above	across	after	around	at	before	behind
below	beside	between	during	for	from	inside
off	on	through	to	toward	under	with

The team is playing **in** the championship game.

The fans **inside** the gym are very excited.

The player **with** the ball dribbled **across** the court.

Underline the prepositions in the sentences.

1. Our basketball coach had a surprise for us during practice today.

2. We met with a professional player named Verry Tawl.

3. Verry arrived after our main workout and before our practice game.

4. Coach wanted Verry to watch us shoot from the foul line.

5. We are good shots and usually get the ball through the hoop.

6. Many players bounced the ball off the rim or hit it on the backboard before making the basket.

7. Verry watched us run around the court and pass the ball between players.

8. We dribbled down the court, moving the ball toward our basket to score.

9. Team members at practice were photographed standing beside Verry.

10. There was space above my head for Verry Tawl to sign the picture!

Language Fundamentals • EMC 2756 • © Evan-Moor Corp.

Name _____

A prepositional phrase is made up of a preposition, its object, and any words in between. The object of the preposition is the noun or pronoun that follows the preposition.

above	across	around	at	before	behind	below
beside	between	during	for	from	inside	off
on	onto	through	to	toward	under	with

Prepositional
Phrase

Our class is planning a dinner **before** the concert.

Preposition   Object of the Preposition

Choose the prepositional phrase from the word box to complete each sentence. Circle the preposition. Draw a line under the object of the preposition.

around the room	for our class trip	onto warm plates
after messy diners	to the dumpster	at school
during the meal	inside the cafeteria	

1. The sixth grade had a spaghetti dinner _____.

2. We wanted to raise money _____.

3. The dinner was held _____.

4. We put up twinkling lights _____ so it would look special.

5. We played music _____ to be festive.

6. Some students dished up the spaghetti and sauce _____.

7. Other students cleared the tables and cleaned up _____.

8. Others took the trash _____.

A prepositional phrase is made up of a preposition, the noun or pronoun that is the object of the preposition, and any words in between.

Some prepositional phrases serve as adjectives to describe nouns.

Prepositional Phrase

The family **inside that car** looks familiar.
Noun

Prepositional Phrase

These pants **with big pockets** are comfortable.
Noun

Complete each sentence with a prepositional phrase from the word box. Then circle the object of each preposition.

below the surface	above the prairie	behind the house
under our feet	toward the west	from the Arctic

1. The snow _____ is melting.

2. The wind _____ is freezing.

3. The water _____ is colder.

4. The ice _____ is dangerous.

5. The moon _____ is full tonight.

6. The clouds _____ are purple.

Complete each sentence using a prepositional phrase to describe each noun.

7. The sun _____

_____

8. The mud _____

_____

Name _____

> A prepositional phrase is made up of a preposition, the noun or pronoun that is the object of the preposition, and any words in between.
>
> Some prepositional phrases act like adverbs. They tell *where*, *when*, and *how*.
>
> **Where** The planet is **behind the sun.**
> **When** The light glows **after the flash.**
> **How** The hero appears **in a spacesuit.**

Underline the prepositional phrase in each sentence. Circle the object of the preposition. Then write *how*, *when*, or *where* on the line to explain what the phrase tells.

1. The movie ended with a loud explosion. _____

2. The main characters escaped before the big blast. _____

3. They were transported off the doomed planet. _____

4. It looked like they were headed toward Earth. _____

5. Their old planet was scattered across the galaxy. _____

6. Never leave your seat during the final moments. _____

7. I thought the movie was longer, and that I would be back in time. _____

8. I knew from my friends' reactions that I missed the best part! _____

Complete each sentence using a prepositional phrase that acts as an adverb.

9. My friends said the villain jumped _____.

10. The star of the movie went _____.

Fill in the bubble next to the correct answer.

1. Which word is the preposition in the sentence?
   The skiers raced down the slope and went a long way before they fell.
   Ⓐ down
   Ⓑ and
   Ⓒ went
   Ⓓ before

2. Identify the prepositional phrase in this sentence:
   The rain in the morning will cause the fog to be heavy.
   Ⓐ cause the fog
   Ⓑ to be heavy
   Ⓒ The rain in
   Ⓓ in the morning

3. Find the object of the preposition in this sentence:
   Someone left a bicycle under the old bridge.
   Ⓐ someone
   Ⓑ bicycle
   Ⓒ bridge
   Ⓓ old

4. Which sentence has a prepositional phrase that serves as an adjective?
   Ⓐ The oranges were picked after the frost.
   Ⓑ The apples in the barn are drying.
   Ⓒ The grapes are purple and green in color.
   Ⓓ The lemons are a sunny yellow.

5. Which sentence has a prepositional phrase that serves as an adverb?
   Ⓐ The ducks have nested on the seawall.
   Ⓑ The eggs in the nest should be hatching soon.
   Ⓒ The water is rising quickly every day.
   Ⓓ The quacking sound from the nest means new ducklings.

Language Fundamentals • EMC 2756 • © Evan-Moor Corp.

A sentence is a group of words that expresses a complete thought or statement. A declarative sentence tells something and ends with a period. Declarative sentences are the most common kind of sentences.

The clash of warm air with cold air causes thunder.

Thunder and lightning make me nervous.

I think we should go inside.

Write a declarative sentence about each topic. Be sure to begin your statement with a capital letter and end it with a period.

1. (a game) _____

2. (a holiday) _____

3. (a historic event) _____

4. (a friend) _____

5. (a movie) _____

6. (a hero) _____

7. (a personal goal) _____

8. (a memory) _____

9. (your school) _____

10. (a book) _____

An interrogative sentence asks a question and ends with a question mark (?).

- Many interrogative sentences begin with a helping verb. The subject is between the helping verb and the main verb.

  Do you **play** a musical instrument?

  Are you **going** to the concert?

- Many interrogative sentences begin with one of these common question words: *who, what, when, where, why,* or *how.*

  Who is playing? **What** kind of music will we hear? **When** does the concert begin?

  Where is the concert hall? **Why** aren't we going in the car? **How** will we get there?

Write an interrogative sentence to go with each answer. Place a question mark at the end of each one.

1. Question: _____

   Answer: That is Ravi Shankar, a famous musician.

2. Question: _____

   Answer: He plays an instrument called the sitar.

3. Question: _____

   Answer: A sitar is a stringed instrument.

4. Question: _____

   Answer: Mr. Shankar is from India.

5. Question: _____

   Answer: No, I can't play the sitar.

6. Question: _____

   Answer: Yes, I'd love to learn how to play the sitar!

An exclamatory sentence expresses excitement or other strong feeling.

- An exclamatory sentence ends with an exclamation point (*!*).

    Our team is going to win**!**

    Stand up and cheer**!**

- Some exclamations begin with *what* or *how*. Do not mistake these exclamations for questions.

    What a great kick!

    How amazing!

Label each sentence as either *exclamatory* or *interrogative.* Add the correct punctuation mark to the end of each sentence.

1. How many touchdowns do we need to win___   _____

2. What an amazing athlete he is___   _____

3. That was a great play___   _____

4. What is the score___   _____

5. Look how upset the other coach is___   _____

6. How can I get the pitcher's autograph___   _____

7. This is the best game ever___   _____

8. The roar of the crowd is amazing___   _____

9. Our team is going to the Super Bowl___   _____

10. How can we get tickets___   _____

An imperative sentence gives a command. It ends with a period (.).

Pay attention to the directions.

Use a pencil for the test.

Do not skip questions.

An imperative sentence may include the courtesy word *please*. An imperative sentence might also include the name of the person or animal being addressed.

Take out a piece of paper, please.

Students, please fill in the circles carefully.

Work quietly, Pam.

Label the sentence as *declarative* or *imperative*.

1. The test will take one hour to complete.   _____

2. Close your books, please.   _____

3. Do not talk during the test.   _____

4. This test is important.   _____

5. Concentrate, please.   _____

Write an imperative sentence that someone might say in each setting.

6. (a restaurant) _____

7. (a movie theater) _____

8. (a school bus) _____

9. (a store) _____

10. (a swimming pool) _____

Language Fundamentals • EMC 2756 • © Evan-Moor Corp.

A sentence is a group of words that expresses a complete thought. There are four kinds of sentences.

- A declarative sentence states something and ends with a period.

- An interrogative sentence asks a question and ends with a question mark.

- An imperative sentence gives a command and ends with a period.

- An exclamatory sentence expresses strong feeling and ends with an exclamation point.

Add the correct end mark to each sentence. Then label the sentence *declarative, interrogative, imperative,* or *exclamatory.*

1. I carry my artwork in a large case called a portfolio___   _____

2. Help me with my easel___   _____

3. Have you ever drawn a self-portrait___   _____

4. Does this look like me___   _____

5. This kind of drawing is called a still life___   _____

6. What an amazing painting___   _____

Write one of each kind of sentence. Be sure to use correct punctuation.

7. Declarative: _____

8. Interrogative: _____

9. Imperative: _____

10. Exclamatory: _____

A sentence must express a complete thought. A group of words that does not express a complete thought is called a sentence fragment.

Fragment A slow-moving mass of ice.
Sentence A glacier is a slow-moving mass of ice.

Read each group of words and decide whether it expresses a complete thought or not. Circle *sentence* if the group of words expresses a complete thought. Circle *fragment* if it does not.

1. Glaciers cover approximately 10% of the Earth's land.   sentence   fragment

2. Icebergs break away from glaciers.   sentence   fragment

3. The largest masses of ice on Earth.   sentence   fragment

4. A moving glacier drags earth and gravel with it.   sentence   fragment

5. Very destructive.   sentence   fragment

6. Formed valleys and lakes in many places on Earth.   sentence   fragment

7. Scientists study glaciers.   sentence   fragment

8. Record of changes in the climate.   sentence   fragment

9. In some areas, the ice never melts.   sentence   fragment

10. Scientists measure the ice.   sentence   fragment

11. Are melting in some places.   sentence   fragment

12. Causing sea levels to rise.   sentence   fragment

> A complete sentence must have a subject and a predicate.
> A sentence fragment is missing a subject, a predicate, or both.

Sentence Fragment	Pete Seeger a folk singer.
Complete Sentence	Pete Seeger is a folk singer.
Sentence Fragment	Plays his songs.
Complete Sentence	Pete Seeger plays his songs.
Sentence Fragment	On an instrument called the banjo.
Complete Sentence	Pete Seeger plays his songs on an instrument called the banjo.

Write *Sentence* or *Fragment* after each group of words.

1. Pete Seeger's banjo has five strings. _____

2. Has written some famous songs. _____

3. He sang with a group called the Almanac Singers. _____

4. And another group called the Weavers. _____

5. Pete Seeger has helped to clean up the environment, too. _____

6. He and other dedicated people. _____

7. Took a boat on the Hudson River to draw attention to pollution. _____

8. Sang folk songs as they sailed. _____

Choose two fragments from the above exercise and turn them into complete sentences.

9. _____

10. _____

Fill in the bubble next to the correct answer.

1. Which group of words is a declarative sentence?
   Ⓐ Have you seen my autograph book?
   Ⓑ I want to collect the signatures of famous people.
   Ⓒ How exciting it would be to meet a movie star!
   Ⓓ Be polite when you ask for an autograph.

2. Which group of words is an interrogative sentence?
   Ⓐ I will start with famous people in our town.
   Ⓑ What a great person our mayor is!
   Ⓒ Do you think she will give me her autograph?
   Ⓓ The town meeting will be a good place to meet her.

3. Which group of words is an exclamatory sentence punctuated correctly?
   Ⓐ What should I say to her?
   Ⓑ She should sign my book.
   Ⓒ Will you sign my autograph book!
   Ⓓ How kind she was!

4. Which group of words is an imperative sentence?
   Ⓐ I should send her a thank-you note.
   Ⓑ Choose a nice piece of stationery.
   Ⓒ Should I write with red ink?
   Ⓓ I think blue ink would be better.

5. Which group of words is a complete sentence?
   Ⓐ There are no movie stars living in our town.
   Ⓑ Ms. Guzzo, the director of the community theater.
   Ⓒ Kindly gave me her autograph.
   Ⓓ The actors in this production.

Name _____

> Every sentence has two parts, a subject and a predicate.
>
> • The subject tells who or what the sentence is about.
> • The predicate tells what the subject is or does.
>
> | Subject | Predicate |
> | --- | --- |
> | Everyone in our school | rode the bus to Rainbow Park. |
> | Even the teachers | were excited about the school picnic. |

Divide each sentence into its two parts and write them on the lines.

1. Rainbow Park is a popular place for school picnics.

   Subject: _____

   Predicate: _____

2. The park has roller coasters and other rides.

   Subject: _____

   Predicate: _____

3. Dennis and Jimmy took Ms. White on the merry-go-round.

   Subject: _____

   Predicate: _____

4. Some kids from my class rowed a boat on the lake.

   Subject: _____

   Predicate: _____

5. I won a stuffed bear at the game tent.

   Subject: _____

   Predicate: _____

Name _____

A complete sentence has two parts, a subject and a predicate.

- The complete subject includes the main noun or pronoun and all the words related to it.

- The complete predicate contains the verb and all the words related to it.

Complete Subject	Complete Predicate
My world studies class	is planning an international dinner.
Our teacher	will make an exotic dish.

Underline the complete subject and circle the complete predicate.

1. Mr. Crosby made chicken curry with rice.

2. Curry is a mixture of spices popular in India.

3. My friend Rachel is bringing a Hungarian dish with noodles.

4. My mother helped me to make fried okra.

5. Fried okra is a popular vegetable dish in the southern United States.

Complete each sentence with its missing part.

6. _____ is my favorite food.

7. Raw oysters on the half-shell _____.

8. My family _____.

9. _____ will eat anything.

10. I _____.

> In an imperative sentence, *you* is always the subject, even though
> it is not stated. We understand that the subject is *you*, so we say that
> the subject is "you, understood."
>
> **(You)** Joan, bring a clean towel to the gym.
> **(You)** Wear athletic shoes on the gym floor.
> **(You)** Please follow my instructions.

Write the subject of each sentence.

1. Change into your gym clothes in the locker room.   _____

2. The floor may be wet.   _____

3. Be careful.   _____

4. Take your place on the mat.   _____

5. We will try yoga poses today.   _____

6. Stretch slowly.   _____

Write an imperative sentence for each setting.

7. (a school hallway) _____

   _____

8. (a dance class) _____

   _____

9. (a doctor's office) _____

   _____

10. (a restaurant) _____

   _____

Name _____

The complete subject of a sentence contains all the words that tell about the subject.

- The simple subject is the main noun or pronoun in the complete subject.

Simple
Subject

The atmosphere of this planet contains oxygen.

Complete Subject

- Sometimes the simple subject and the complete subject are the same.

Galileo Galilei was an astronomer.

Complete Subject
and
Simple Subject

Underline the complete subject and write the simple subject.

1. Astronomers study objects outside the Earth's atmosphere.   _____

2. Powerful telescopes are important for their work.   _____

3. Too much light in the sky can be a problem.   _____

4. The stars can be difficult to see in a bright night sky.   _____

5. The four satellites of Jupiter were discovered by Galileo.   _____

6. He discovered the satellites in the 17th century.   _____

7. European scientists sent a probe to Saturn in the 21st century.   _____

8. The probe landed on Titan, a moon of Saturn.   _____

9. The atmosphere of Titan contains a gas called methane.   _____

10. Astronomers will continue to study Titan.   _____

Language Fundamentals • EMC 2756 • © Evan-Moor Corp.

The simple subject is the main noun or pronoun in the complete subject.

- Sometimes the simple subject and the complete subject are the same.

He stepped onto the old red scooter.
|
Simple Subject

It belonged to my grandmother.
|
Simple Subject

- To find the simple subject of an interrogative sentence, rearrange the words of the sentence to make it a declarative sentence. Ask *who* or *what* does the action.

Interrogative Sentence May I ride the scooter?
Declarative Sentence I may ride the scooter.
Simple Subject I

Circle the simple subject in each sentence.

1. Some interesting old toys are stored in the garage.

2. This scooter is big and heavy.

3. Timmy placed one foot on my grandmother's scooter.

4. The wheels of the rusty old toy squeaked loudly.

5. Will your grandmother show us how to ride?

6. My best friend found an oil can for the wheels.

7. Do I see a pogo stick?

8. The dark corners of this garage hold some great treasures.

Write one interrogative and one declarative sentence. Circle the simple subjects.

9. _____

10. _____

The complete predicate includes all the words in the predicate. The simple predicate is the verb in the complete predicate.

- The simple predicate may be only one word.

Simple
Predicate

Joanne **makes sandwiches for lunch.**

Complete Predicate

- The simple predicate may be the helping verb and the main verb.

Simple
Predicate

She **is making tuna fish and egg salad sandwiches.**

Complete Predicate

Underline the complete predicate and write the simple predicate.

1. Joanne scoops mayonnaise from a jar.   _____

2. This china bowl will hold a tangy mustard.   _____

3. You may use this knife for the cheese.   _____

4. I have placed slices of whole wheat bread in a basket. _____

5. Slice these vegetables for the salad.   _____

6. Joanne irons a fresh tablecloth.   _____

7. The doorbell rings twice.   _____

8. Aunt Inez and Uncle Frank have arrived for lunch.   _____

9. The family enjoyed the sandwiches and salad.   _____

10. We will eat this beautiful cake for dessert!   _____

Language Fundamentals • EMC 2756 • © Evan-Moor Corp.

> The complete predicate includes all the words in the predicate.
>
> - The simple predicate is the verb.
>
>   My whole family **listens** to books on tape.
> |
>   **Simple Predicate**
>
> - The complete predicate and the simple predicate can be the same.
>
>   Today, even the dog **is listening!**
> |
>   **Simple Predicate**

The complete predicate in each sentence is underlined. Circle the simple predicate in each sentence.

1. Emily Dickinson <u>lived in Amherst, Massachusetts</u>.

2. We <u>studied her poetry in English class</u>.

3. Most of her poems <u>are very short</u>.

4. She <u>communicates an idea with very few words</u>.

5. Emily Dickinson <u>attended a school for girls</u>.

6. I <u>have read some of her letters to her school friends</u>.

7. You <u>can visit Emily Dickinson's house in Amherst</u>.

8. Emily Dickinson <u>is my favorite poet</u>.

Write four sentences about your favorite author. Circle the simple predicate.

9. _____

10. _____

11. _____

12. _____

Fill in the bubble next to the correct answer.

1. In which sentence is the subject "you, understood"?
   Ⓐ Don't you know about the concert?
   Ⓑ You should give those comics to Michael.
   Ⓒ Please wait for me.
   Ⓓ You will arrive early.

2. In which sentence is the complete subject underlined?
   Ⓐ <u>I met Megan</u> in grammar school.
   Ⓑ <u>Megan's family</u> moved last year.
   Ⓒ They <u>now live</u> in a small town.
   Ⓓ Our <u>friendship</u> is important to me.

3. In which sentence is the complete predicate underlined?
   Ⓐ We stay in touch <u>by e-mail and telephone</u>.
   Ⓑ <u>I will write</u> a short e-mail tonight.
   Ⓒ I <u>will tell her about my homework</u>.
   Ⓓ Mr. Amata <u>gave</u> us a big assignment.

4. In which sentence is the simple subject underlined?
   Ⓐ Megan sometimes helps <u>me</u> with my math homework.
   Ⓑ <u>She is</u> a whiz at math!
   Ⓒ My favorite <u>subject</u> is history.
   Ⓓ I can help <u>Megan</u> with her history project.

5. In which sentence is the simple predicate underlined?
   Ⓐ <u>Good friends help</u> each other.
   Ⓑ I <u>have missed</u> Megan this year.
   Ⓒ Our e-mails <u>are important</u>.
   Ⓓ I will <u>press</u> "send" now.

> A compound sentence is made by joining two or more simple sentences containing related information. The sentences are joined by a comma and a coordinating conjunction, such as *and, or,* or *but.*
>
> Will is the best bowler, **and** Andy is the worst bowler.
>
> The bowling alley is empty, **but** it will be busy soon.
>
> Other coordinating conjunctions: **nor   for   so   yet**

Underline the coordinating conjunction in each compound sentence. Add a comma where it belongs.

1. I like to bowl but I am not a good bowler.

2. I like wearing a bowling shirt but I hate those ugly bowling shoes!

3. I like throwing the ball but I'm not very good.

4. I would like to knock down all the pins yet I am happy if any pins fall.

5. I want the ball to go straight so I aim carefully.

6. Most of the time the ball goes off to the side or it will drop into the gutter.

7. You don't score when that happens so it's not good to throw a gutter ball.

Write a compound sentence about how it would feel to knock down all the pins in bowling.

8. _____

_____

_____

A compound sentence is made by joining two or more simple sentences containing related information. The sentences are joined by a comma and a coordinating conjunction, such as *and, or,* or *but.*

Simple Sentence   I cannot find my homework.

Compound Sentence   I have looked everywhere, **but** I cannot find my homework.

Form compound sentences by joining the simple sentences with a comma and a coordinating conjunction.

1. I looked for my homework on my desk. I forgot to look on the kitchen table.

   _____

   _____

2. Maybe I left it on the bus. Maybe I left it in the cafeteria.

   _____

   _____

3. The homework is due today. Mr. Ayers does not like late assignments.

   _____

   _____

4. I will unload my backpack one more time. I will carefully sort my papers.

   _____

   _____

5. I did not see this paper the first time. It has been in here the whole time!

   _____

   _____

Name _____

A clause is a group of related words that has its own subject and predicate.

- An independent clause can stand alone as a complete sentence.

  The parrot speaks when he wants a treat.

- A dependent clause cannot stand alone as a complete sentence.

  He speaks **when he wants a treat**.

Identify the underlined group of words as an independent clause or a dependent clause.

1. <u>Birds are popular pets</u> because 15 million are pets. _____

2. They are popular <u>because they are colorful and smart</u>. _____

3. <u>I have a canary</u> because I love their yellow feathers. _____

4. <u>When I uncover the cage in the morning</u>, he sings. _____

5. <u>I bought my bird</u> at the pet store in the mall. _____

6. When he needs to eat, <u>I fill his cup with seeds</u>. _____

7. I know <u>that I must keep him warm</u>. _____

8. <u>While the canary sings</u>, Pete the parrot asks for a cracker. _____

9. My mom bought Pete <u>because she thinks he is funny</u>. _____

10. Whenever he speaks, <u>she laughs</u>. _____

Fill in the bubble next to the correct answer.

1. In which sentence is an independent clause underlined?

   Ⓐ The loons <u>on the lake</u> are calling.

   Ⓑ Before you leave the cabin, <u>close the windows</u>.

   Ⓒ It might rain <u>after the sun goes down</u>.

   Ⓓ Take a bottle <u>of water with you on your hike</u>.

2. Which sentence includes a coordinating conjunction?

   Ⓐ While we sleep, our dogs like to play.

   Ⓑ As long as I finish my homework, I am allowed to be outside until dark.

   Ⓒ I want to go to the movie rental store.

   Ⓓ I always want to play with my dog, but sometimes she wants to sleep.

3. Which sentence is a compound sentence?

   Ⓐ My mom drives a jeep on the country roads.

   Ⓑ Sometimes the jeep bounces, and my head hits the roof.

   Ⓒ I laugh because the roof is soft.

   Ⓓ The road ends at our cabin.

4. What is the best way to combine this pair of sentences into a compound sentence?
   I want a new dirt bike. My mom says I have to wait until my birthday.

   Ⓐ I want a new dirt bike, but my mom says I have to wait until my birthday.

   Ⓑ I want a new dirt bike, my mom says I have to wait until my birthday.

   Ⓒ My mom says I have to wait until my birthday, I want a new dirt bike.

   Ⓓ I want a new dirt bike but my mom says I have to wait until my birthday.

5. In which complex sentence is a dependent clause underlined?

   Ⓐ When we walk Ralphie on his leash, <u>we never see wild animals</u>.

   Ⓑ <u>The deer and the rabbits know</u> that they should stay away.

   Ⓒ The birds perch high in the trees <u>and call to each other</u>.

   Ⓓ Ralphie barks at them <u>because he wants to chase them</u>.

> A complex sentence is a sentence that includes one independent clause and at least one dependent clause. Both clauses have a subject and a predicate, but a dependent clause needs the independent clause to form a complete thought.

Independent Clause	The football game has been canceled
Dependent Clause	because a storm is coming.
Complex Sentence	The football game has been canceled because a storm is coming.
Complex Sentence	Because a storm is coming, the football game has been canceled.

Circle the independent clause and underline the dependent clause in these complex sentences.

1. The coach called all of the players after he heard the weather forecast.

2. The visiting team could not come because they were already snowed in.

3. After our game was canceled, I checked the television listings.

4. Since I like to watch the state university team play, I turned on the television.

5. My sister became a big fan after she decided to attend the university.

Match each clause on the left to a clause on the right to make the best complex sentence.

6. The college players take the field _____   a. the players concentrate on every play.

7. While the fans are excited, _____   b. because this is a big game.

8. They are nervous _____   c. this will be their last game this year.

9. Unless they win, _____   d. the players look serious.

10. When the stakes are this high, _____   e. after the announcer introduces them.

> A subordinating conjunction begins a dependent clause and connects it to an independent clause to form a complex sentence.
>
> | after | although | as if | as long as | because | before | if | since |
> |-------|----------|-------|------------|---------|--------|-----|-------|
> | so | that | though | unless | until | when | where | while |
>
> **Dependent Clause** **before** our health fair opens.
> **Independent Clause** We have a lot of work to do
> **Complex Sentence** We have a lot of work to do **before** our health fair opens.

Complete each complex sentence with a subordinating conjunction from the box below. Use each word or phrase only once. Write the word or phrase on the line.

> | as long as | so that | after | if |
> |------------|---------|-------|-----|
> | because | when | since | until |

1. Our sixth-grade class is having a health fair _____ this unit ends.

2. We will set up exhibits with information _____ other kids learn how to stay healthy.

3. We want to have healthful snacks for visitors to try _____ our teacher agrees.

4. We can demonstrate simple exercises _____ we have the room.

5. We would prefer to hold the fair in the gym _____ there is more space.

6. We will be limited in what we can do _____ our classroom is small.

Circle the subordinating conjunctions in the box that you did not use. Write a sentence with each one.

7. _____

8. _____

A subordinating conjunction connects an independent clause to a dependent clause to form a complex sentence.

- The subordinating conjunction begins the dependent clause.

- When a subordinating conjunction starts the sentence, place a comma after the dependent clause.

    Since we have the time, let's visit the museum.

- When the subordinating conjunction is in the middle of the sentence, a comma is usually not used.

    Let's visit the museum **since** we have the time.

Circle the subordinating conjunction and underline the dependent clause in each complex sentence. Place a comma in the sentence if it needs one.

1. If the planetarium is open I would like to see the star show.

2. I have been fascinated by stars since I was very young.

3. When the stars are out you can be sure that I am searching the sky.

4. The constellation I know best is the Big Dipper because it's easy to recognize.

5. As long as I see the North Star I can always find the rest of the Dipper.

6. I would like to visit the Southern Hemisphere because the constellations are different.

7. Until that trip happens I will continue enjoying the night sky I know.

Write a complex sentence about stars that begins with a subordinating conjunction.

8. _____

_____

_____

A dependent clause in a complex sentence may begin with a subordinating conjunction or a signal word.

after	although	as	as if	as long as	because	before	if
once	since	so	that	though	unless	until	what
when	whenever	where	wherever	which	while	who	whoever

Complex Sentence **Before** European settlers arrived, native people tapped maples for syrup.
Dependent Clause **Before** European settlers arrived
Independent Clause native people tapped maples for syrup.

Complex Sentence I don't know **which** house is theirs.
Dependent Clause **which** house is theirs.
Independent Clause I don't know

Complete each complex sentence with a subordinating conjunction or signal word.

1. Teachers reward students _____ do their homework.

2. _____ spring is fully underway, the sap in the maple trees begins to flow.

3. We won't find the trail _____ we use the map.

4. _____ we learn the steps, the dance will be easy.

Choose a subordinating conjunction and a signal word from the rule box. Write two sentences that contain dependent clauses.

5. _____

_____

6. _____

_____

Fill in the bubble next to the correct answer.

1. Which complex sentence is written correctly?

Ⓐ Before you leave the cabin close the windows.

Ⓑ Before you leave the cabin, close the windows.

Ⓒ Close the windows, before you leave the cabin.

Ⓓ Close the windows before, you leave the cabin.

2. In which sentence is a clause underlined?

Ⓐ Our cabin <u>on the lake</u> is made of logs.

Ⓑ We sleep <u>in bunk beds</u>.

Ⓒ <u>In the living room</u>, there is a big fireplace.

Ⓓ <u>Since the weather is chilly today</u>, we will build a fire.

3. Where does the comma belong in the following sentence?
Because the jeep bounces my head hits the roof.

Ⓐ a comma is not needed

Ⓑ after *because*

Ⓒ after *bounces*

Ⓓ after *head*

4. Which sentence is a complex sentence?

Ⓐ We like to hike through the woods.

Ⓑ My dad knows every tree and flower in the woods.

Ⓒ My mom studies the insects, and I study animal tracks.

Ⓓ If we see an animal, we stand very still.

5. Choose the correct subordinating conjunction for the sentence.
Mom feels better, we won't be able to go on vacation.

Ⓐ Unless

Ⓑ After

Ⓒ Since

Ⓓ As if

Combine two short sentences to make your writing more interesting. One way to do this is to move key words and phrases from one sentence to another.

Two Sentences	The Pilgrims fed lobsters to their pigs. They fed them on the beach.
Combined Sentence	The Pilgrims fed lobsters to their pigs on the beach.
Two Sentences	Lobsters were washed ashore. They were washed ashore by the surf.
Combined Sentences	Lobsters were washed ashore by the surf.

Combine the sentences by making a phrase in the second sentence part of the first.

1. The Pilgrims sailed from England. They sailed on the *Mayflower*.

   Combined: _____

2. The Pilgrims had a kind of corn. This corn was called flint corn.

   Combined: _____

3. They probably cooked the flint corn. They probably cooked it by boiling it.

   Combined: _____

4. The Wampanoag Indians helped the Pilgrims. They helped them with their crops.

   Combined: _____

5. The Wampanoag built round houses. They built them with tree bark and reeds.

   Combined: _____

6. Men and women built the houses together. They built them in the spring.

   Combined: _____

Language Fundamentals • EMC 2756 • © Evan-Moor Corp.

Combine simple sentences with related ideas to form compound and complex sentences.

- You can use a comma and coordinating conjunction to form a compound sentence.

Simple Sentences	The drama club is presenting a play. Tara is the director.
Compound Sentence	The drama club is presenting a play, **and** Tara is the director.

- Use a subordinating conjunction to build a complex sentence.

Simple Sentences	I will be the star. I am the best actor in school.
Complex Sentence	**Because** I am the best actor in school, I will be the star.

Build a compound sentence or a complex sentence by connecting the simple sentences with the conjunction in parentheses.

1. Our class had a contest. Everyone wrote a play. (and)

   _____

2. Our director chose my play. It was the best one. (because)

   _____

3. I wrote the play. I don't need to practice. (since)

   _____

4. I took the stage at rehearsal with confidence. I couldn't remember anything! (but)

   _____

   _____

5. I could let someone else star in the play. I could study my lines. (or)

   _____

   _____

A run-on sentence is made up of two or more sentences that run together without punctuation or a connecting word.

We can see the lighthouse we can't see the keeper.

- You can correct a run-on sentence by forming two sentences.

    We can see the lighthouse. We can't see the keeper.

- You can also correct the run-on by making it a compound sentence. Add a comma and a coordinating conjunction.

    We can see the lighthouse, **but** we can't see the keeper.

Correct the run-on sentences.

1. Run-on: Long ago, bonfires were built to guide ships people built fires on hillsides.

    Correction: _____

    _____

2. Run-on: Boston Light was the first in North America there is still a lighthouse there.

    Correction: _____

    _____

3. Run-on: Long ago, every lighthouse needed a keeper the keeper lived there.

    Correction: _____

    _____

4. Run-on: The Great Lakes are busy waterways lighthouses guide ships there, too.

    Correction: _____

    _____

A run-on sentence is two sentences run together as if they were one.

- In a "fused" run-on, two sentences are fused together without any punctuation.

    We spent the day at the mall we went to every store.

- In a "comma splice" run-on, a comma alone is used to separate two sentences.

    We spent the day at the mall, we went to every store.

You can correct both kinds of run-ons by turning them into two sentences or by forming a compound or a complex sentence.

Simple Sentences   We spent the day at the mall. We went to every store.
Compound Sentence   We spent the day at the mall, and we went to every store.
Complex Sentence   Since we spent the day at the mall, we went to every store.

Correct and rewrite each run-on sentence in the suggested way.

1. Patty and I went to the shoe store we tried on lots of shoes.

    Simple sentences: _____

2. We went to the card store, I needed a birthday card.

    Complex sentence: _____

3. Patty likes to try on clothes, I would rather try on shoes.

    Compound sentence: _____

4. The candle store is my favorite store it smells so good.

    Complex sentence: _____

5. The food court has great food we ate tuna sandwiches.

    Simple sentences: _____

Fill in the bubble next to the correct answer.

1. Which one combines the short sentences by moving a phrase?
   Aunt Sara opened an antique shop. She opened it on Liberty Street.

   Ⓐ Aunt Sara opened an antique shop on Liberty Street.

   Ⓑ Aunt Sara opened an antique shop, and she opened it on Liberty Street.

   Ⓒ Aunt Sara opened an antique shop she opened it on Liberty Street.

   Ⓓ Aunt Sara opened an antique shop, she opened it on Liberty Street.

2. Which one combines the sentences by forming a compound sentence?
   She specializes in old jewelry. She carries many other antiques, too.

   Ⓐ She specializes in old jewelry she carries other antiques, too.

   Ⓑ She specializes in old jewelry, but she carries other antiques, too.

   Ⓒ She specializes in old jewelry and other antiques, too.

   Ⓓ While she carries many other antiques, she specializes in old jewelry.

3. Which one combines the sentences by forming a complex sentence?

   Ⓐ I like the antique radio, and it doesn't work.

   Ⓑ I like the antique radio it doesn't work.

   Ⓒ I like the antique radio, but it doesn't work.

   Ⓓ Although it doesn't work, I like the antique radio.

4. Which one is a run-on sentence?

   Ⓐ Dad bought a set of fancy cuff links, and I saw him looking at the radio.

   Ⓑ He had a radio just like this one when he was a kid.

   Ⓒ He decided to buy the radio to fix up for me.

   Ⓓ It might be hard to get parts Aunt Sara has just a few old radio tubes.

5. Which one corrects this run-on?
   Mom is excited to see the old radio she remembers one just like it.

   Ⓐ Mom is excited to see the old radio because she remembers one just like it.

   Ⓑ Mom is excited to see the old radio, she remembers one just like it.

   Ⓒ Mom is excited to see the old radio she remembers. One just like it.

   Ⓓ Mom is excited to see the old radio she remembers one just like it.

Name _____

When writing someone's exact words, capitalize the first word in the quotation.

"The king was just and wise," the storyteller said. "He lived a long and happy life."

If there is a break in the sentence in a quotation, do <u>not</u> capitalize the word that starts the next part of the quotation.

"Yes, get some sleep," said Mrs. Gomez, "and you will feel better in no time."

Read the sentences below. Write each word that needs to be capitalized.

1. the teacher gave an unusually hard assignment.   _____

2. she said, "please do your best."   _____

3. once Becca got started, she had no problem.   _____

4. "you know," Oscar said, "this is just too hard."   _____

5. "don't worry," said Becca. "you'll get it."   _____

6. "what if I come over to help?" said Becca.   _____

7. "that would be great," said Oscar. "I could use the help."   _____

Write a dialogue between two characters. Be sure to capitalize the words at the beginning of a sentence.

8. _____

_____

_____

_____

Capitalize the days of the week and the months of the year.

On **Monday,** there was a full moon.

During **December,** we have a snow festival.

Read the letter below. Draw three lines under the first letter of each word that needs to be capitalized.

september 1, 2007

Dear Margo,

So much has changed since I moved to Austin in may. I spent the first monday I was here in the district office, trying to figure out which school I should attend. By tuesday, I was sitting in Fifth Street Elementary School.

By june, I'd made a few friends, but no one like you. One saturday, a few of us had a great hiking adventure. We got so lost, I wasn't sure we'd be home by sunday.

July and august were okay, but mainly I traveled with my parents. I missed our friday movie nights.

Now that it's september again, I'll have to get back to school. We start on the tuesday after Labor Day. How about you? Write back soon!

Love,

Rachel

> Capitalize the names of holidays.
>
> | | | |
> |---|---|---|
> | **Independence Day** | **Presidents' Day** | **Hanukkah** |
> | **Kwanzaa** | **Christmas Day** | **Memorial Day** |
> | **Labor Day** | **New Year's Day** | **Juneteenth** |

Read the paragraph carefully. Draw three lines under the first letter of a word that needs to be capitalized.

Many important things have happened in U.S. history on holidays. Take independence day, for example. On July 4, 1776, we know that the Declaration of Independence was signed. On July 4, 1827, slavery was outlawed in New York State. Other historic events have also happened on holidays. On new year's day in 1808, the Congress of the United States banned the practice of importing people to be sold as slaves. Enslaved people in Texas found out that they had been freed on June 19, 1864, and this day has since been celebrated as juneteenth. On christmas day 1868, President Andrew Johnson pardoned all Southerners who took part in the Civil War. The memorial day holiday was first celebrated after the Civil War to honor the fallen soldiers.

Write the names of the holidays. Use the correct capitalization.

1. thanksgiving day _____

2. new year's eve _____

3. st. patrick's day _____

4. arbor day _____

5. talk like a pirate day _____

Fill in the bubble next to the correct answer.

1. Which sentence has the correct capitalization?
   Ⓐ Ari said, "the new principal is strict."
   Ⓑ Naomi said, "I hear that she's fair, though."
   Ⓒ "she wants to make a lot of changes," said Ari.
   Ⓓ "maybe it's time for changes," Said Naomi.

2. Which sentence has the correct punctuation?
   Ⓐ "The school is really warm," Hayden said, "Because the air conditioning is broken."
   Ⓑ "It's too hot in the spring," said Madison, "it's too cold in winter."
   Ⓒ "it's not so bad," said Hayden, "since it doesn't even get that hot here."
   Ⓓ "I guess you're right," said Madison. "I'm just sensitive to the heat."

Fill in the bubble next to the word or words that should begin with capital letters.

3. Ⓐ week
   Ⓑ morning
   Ⓒ tuesday
   Ⓓ month

4. Ⓐ autumn
   Ⓑ november
   Ⓒ fall
   Ⓓ week

5. Ⓐ holiday
   Ⓑ occasion
   Ⓒ christmas
   Ⓓ day

> **Proper nouns begin with capital letters.**
>
> - Names of people and pets are proper nouns and should be capitalized.
>
>   **Opal   Rex**
>
> - The title before a person's name should also be capitalized.
>
>   **Doctor Galindez   Uncle William**
>
> - Names of specific places are also proper nouns and should be capitalized.
>
>   **Kansas City   Niagara Falls   Rensselaer   New York**

For each sentence, choose the word or words that should be capitalized. Rewrite it correctly.

1. David, there is josephine.   _____

2. Did you tell aunt jean that she was here?   _____

3. No, she's busy walking her dog, inky.   _____

4. Josephine brought her friend, carmen.   _____

5. Carmen brought missy, her dog.   _____

6. I hope that she will get along with our bird, tiny.   _____

7. Did you know that Carmen's aunt is doctor Olivares?   _____

8. I'd like to ask her about grandpa's illness.   _____

9. Maybe if he moved to arizona, he would feel better.   _____

10. I don't think moving to phoenix would help him.   _____

> A proper noun begins with a capital letter.
>
> • The names of businesses, organizations, historic events, and movements are all proper nouns. Do not capitalize minor words in the name, such as *the* and *of*.
>
>   **Ridley Company**   **Big Brothers and Big Sisters**
>   **Revolutionary War**   **Civil Rights Movement**
>
> • The names of buildings, monuments, and schools are also proper nouns and should be capitalized.
>
>   **Chrysler Building**   **Soldier's Memorial**   **Emily Dickinson School**

Read the story. Circle the words that need to be capitalized.

    I'm studying the civil war in school this year. Last year, my family and I visited Gettysburg, Pennsylvania. We stayed near gettysburg college. My father was excited to find a store called civil war memories there. Dad is a member of the wallingford historical society, and he enjoys looking at books and photographs from other eras. He bought a copy of a book by Frederick Douglass, a driving force in the abolitionist movement. We walked all over the battlefields of Gettysburg, where we saw the pennsylvania memorial, the gettysburg hospital, and many other sites dedicated to the memory of those who fought there. We took a tour with a park ranger in which we walked in formation like the soldiers along the path known as railroad cut. One interesting place we visited was the jennie wade house. jennie wade was the only civilian killed during the battle of gettysburg. She was killed while baking bread for the union soldiers.

Capitalize the first and last words and any other important words in the titles of books, songs, and poems.

- Unless they are the first or last words, do not capitalize prepositions, such as *for* or *in;* articles, such as *a* or *the;* or coordinating conjunctions, such as *and* or *but.*

  Ben and Me   "On the Good Ship Lollipop"   "The Bells"

- Follow the same rules for capitalizing the titles of short stories, magazines, and newspapers.

  "The Dream"   Time for Kids   Chicago Tribune

Write the titles. Use the correct capitalization.

1. the wind in the willows

   _____

2. "zlateh the goat"

   _____

3. "you're a grand old flag"

   _____

4. island of the blue dolphins

   _____

5. national geographic

   _____

6. a child's christmas in wales

   _____

Name _____

Fill in the bubble next to the sentence with incorrect capitalization.

1. Ⓐ Jubal is my great-great-grandfather's name.

   Ⓑ The Boy was standing by the door when a loud knock was heard.

   Ⓒ Uncle Jacob came to stay with us when he retired from his job.

   Ⓓ My cousin Ashley and I have so much in common.

2. Ⓐ Officer Adams gave a presentation at our school.

   Ⓑ Gracie is my mother's name.

   Ⓒ That's the Woman who founded the Mathematicians of the Future Club.

   Ⓓ He started at the Smithfield Police Academy last year.

3. Ⓐ The Conflict was not resolved easily.

   Ⓑ We studied the Revolutionary War in Mr. Jamieson's class this year.

   Ⓒ We also learned about the Korean War.

   Ⓓ We saw a movie on the Great Depression.

4. Ⓐ My grandparents live in New Haven, Connecticut.

   Ⓑ My oldest brother is going to school in Princeton, New Jersey.

   Ⓒ My family lives in Palo Alto.

   Ⓓ Palo Alto is a City south of San Francisco.

5. Ⓐ Wind in the Willows is my favorite book.

   Ⓑ My brother's favorite book is Where the Wild Things Are.

   Ⓒ My mother used to read us all kinds of Good Books.

   Ⓓ Her favorite book is Bridge to Terabithia.

 Language Fundamentals • EMC 2756 • © Evan-Moor Corp.

Name _____

An abbreviation is a short way of writing a word or group of words. Many abbreviations end with a period. Some abbreviations, such as those for states and some measurements, do not end with a period.

quart	**qt.**
Senator	**Sen.**
Maine	**ME**
American Medical Association	**AMA**
centimeter	**cm**
President	**Pres.**
ounce	**oz.**
North Carolina	**NC**
Animal Rescue League	**ARL**

Write the abbreviation for each group of words.
Hint: The abbreviations for these words are not usually written with periods.

1. North Atlantic Treaty Organization _____

2. United Nations _____

3. Central Intelligence Agency _____

4. as soon as possible _____

5. miles per hour _____

6. New York _____

Write out the word that each underlined abbreviation stands for.

7. p. 199 _____

8. 179 West Road, Apt. 24 _____

9. 1 oz. milk _____

10. Washington Ave. _____

Name _____

> ### The days of the week have abbreviations.
>
> | | | | |
> |---|---|---|---|
> | Sunday | **Sun.** | Thursday | **Thurs.** |
> | Monday | **Mon.** | Friday | **Fri.** |
> | Tuesday | **Tues.** | Saturday | **Sat.** |
> | Wednesday | **Wed.** | | |

Write a sentence about one thing you do on each day of the week.
Use the abbreviation for each day.

1. _____

2. _____

3. _____

4. _____

5. _____

6. _____

7. _____

Fill in the abbreviations for the rest of the days of the week in the planner below.

Sun.	_____	_____	_____	_____	_____	_____
Go to picnic	History report due	Soccer practice	Remember gym clothes	Piano lesson	Soccer practice	Soccer game

Language Fundamentals • EMC 2756 • © Evan-Moor Corp.

There are abbreviations for most months of the year. These abbreviations use the first three letters of the name of the month. The months *May*, *June*, and *July* are not usually abbreviated because their names are already so short.

Month of the Year	Abbreviation
January	**Jan.**
February	**Feb.**
March	**Mar.**

Gracie's Planner	Things to Do
September	Plan fundraiser for club.
October	Take trip with family to see foliage.
November	Make pies for Thanksgiving.
December	Buy presents for family.
January	Sign up for piano lessons.
February	Annual checkup.
March	Start working on garden.
April	Plan neighborhood block party.
May	Buy Mom a present for Mother's Day.

Use the planner to answer the questions. Write the correct abbreviation for each month.

1. In what month will Gracie sign up for piano lessons? _____

2. In what month will Gracie plan her club's fundraiser? _____

3. In what month does Gracie need to buy presents for her family? _____

4. In what month will Gracie start working in her garden? _____

5. In what month will Gracie buy Mom a present for Mother's Day? _____

There are abbreviations for the titles that come before or after people's names. These abbreviations are usually written with a period.

Doctor	**Dr.**
married woman, missus	**Mrs.**
married or unmarried woman	**Ms.**
married or unmarried man, mister	**Mr.**
Junior	**Jr.**
Senior	**Sr.**

Rewrite each sentence. Use the abbreviation for the underlined word.

1. <u>Doctor</u> Assad plans reforms for the school district.

_____

2. Her husband, <u>Mister</u> Mahjoud Assad, is a lawyer.

_____

3. Dr. Assad's assistant is Henry Carhart, <u>Junior</u>.

_____

4. Henry Carhart, <u>Senior</u>, lives near the school.

_____

5. His wife is <u>Missus</u> Carhart, who works at the local college.

_____

Language Fundamentals • EMC 2756 • © Evan-Moor Corp.

Fill in the bubble to indicate the sentence with the correct abbreviation.

1. Ⓐ I learned that the United States of America is a member of Nato.

   Ⓑ I also learned that the UN is headquartered in New York City.

   Ⓒ New York City is in New Y.

   Ⓓ I'm writing a paper about the UN, and it's due a.sap.

2. Ⓐ On Sat., I went to the library to do research.

   Ⓑ On Sund., I worked on my social studies paper.

   Ⓒ On Mo., I was exhausted.

   Ⓓ On T., I handed in my work.

3. Ⓐ On Apl. 30, my cousin is getting married.

   Ⓑ We had her engagement party on Fbr. 27.

   Ⓒ They will go on their honeymoon on Ma. 1.

   Ⓓ They're moving to our town in Aug.

4. Ⓐ My favorite teacher is Mist. Ferrara.

   Ⓑ Bob Jones is the presid. of the Teachers Association.

   Ⓒ Our principal is Ms. Iyo.

   Ⓓ Mrs Ferrara is nice, too.

5. Ⓐ My father's friend, Mr. Tenaka, is in charge of the English Department.

   Ⓑ Mr Tenaka also organizes the faculty softball games.

   Ⓒ Mrss. McKay is the main pitcher.

   Ⓓ Docr. Alphonse is the catcher.

> The names of most roads, streets, and highways can be abbreviated.
> These abbreviations are usually written with a period.
>
> Ballard **Blvd.** (Boulevard)   Houston **Ave.** (Avenue)
>
> Pacific Coast **Hwy.** (Highway)   Wilmer **Dr.** (Drive)
>
> Johnson **Ln.** (Lane)   State **St.** (Street)
>
> Ransome **Pl.** (Place)   Maryland **Pkwy.** (Parkway)

Write the abbreviation for each underlined word.

1. One of the many landmarks in Washington, D.C., is the
   White House, at 1600 Pennsylvania <u>Avenue</u>.   _____

2. Visitors enjoy seeing the United States Capitol on
   East Capitol <u>Street</u>.   _____

3. The impressive Washington Monument is on 900 Ohio <u>Drive</u>.   _____

4. You can take the George Washington <u>Parkway</u> to get
   around the Washington area.   _____

5. Many people visit the U.S. Holocaust Museum at
   100 Raoul Wallenberg <u>Place</u>.   _____

6. You can get to Washington, D.C., on <u>Highway</u> 95.   _____

The names of states have two-letter abbreviations that are used in addresses. These abbreviations are written with two capital letters and no period.

Alabama AL	Alaska AK	Arizona AZ	Arkansas AR	California CA
Colorado CO	Connecticut CT	Delaware DE	Florida FL	Georgia GA
Hawaii HI	Idaho ID	Illinois IL	Indiana IN	Iowa IA
Kansas KS	Kentucky KY	Louisiana LA	Maine ME	Maryland MD
Massachusetts MA	Michigan MI	Minnesota MN	Mississippi MS	Missouri MO
Montana MT	Nebraska NE	Nevada NV	New Hampshire NH	New Jersey NJ
New Mexico NM	New York NY	North Carolina NC	North Dakota ND	Ohio OH
Oklahoma OK	Oregon OR	Pennsylvania PA	Rhode Island RI	South Carolina SC
South Dakota SD	Tennessee TN	Texas TX	Utah UT	Vermont VT
Virginia VA	Washington WA	West Virginia WV	Wisconsin WI	Wyoming WY

Write the answer to each of the following questions. Use state abbreviations.

1. In which state do you live? _____

2. Which state would you most like to visit? _____

3. Write the names of any states where relatives live. _____

4. Write the name of the state in which you were born. _____

5. In which state was your teacher born? _____

Many measurements have abbreviations.

inch = **in.**   yard = **yd.**

foot = **ft.**   mile = **mi.**

Abbreviations for metric measurements are not written with periods.

centimeter = **cm**   kilometer = **km**

meter   = **m**   millimeter = **mm**

Rewrite each equivalency using the correct abbreviation for each underlined word.

1. 1 <u>meter</u> = 3.28 <u>feet</u>   _____

2. 1 <u>mile</u> = 1.61 <u>kilometers</u>   _____

3. 1 <u>inch</u> = 2.54 <u>centimeters</u>   _____

4. 1 <u>meter</u> = 100 <u>centimeters</u>   _____

5. 1 <u>meter</u> = 1,000 <u>millimeters</u>   _____

6. 1 <u>foot</u> = 12 <u>inches</u>   _____

7. 1 <u>yard</u> = 3 <u>feet</u>   _____

8. 1 <u>centimeter</u> = 10 <u>millimeters</u>   _____

9. 1 <u>mile</u> = 1,760 <u>yards</u>   _____

10. 1 <u>mile</u> = 5,280 <u>feet</u>   _____

> Words that measure weight have abbreviations. Abbreviations for metric measurements are written without periods.
>
> | | | | |
> |---|---|---|---|
> | ounce | **oz.** | liter | **L** |
> | pound | **lb.** | kilogram | **kg** |
>
> Words that measure time have abbreviations.
>
> | | | | |
> |---|---|---|---|
> | year | **yr.** | second | **sec.** |
> | minute | **min.** | before noon | **a.m.** |
> | week | **wk.** | after noon | **p.m.** |

Write the letter of the correct abbreviation next to each of the following words.

1. pound   _____   a. wk.

2. year   _____   b. min.

3. week   _____   c. lb.

4. second   _____   d. kg

5. minute   _____   e. L

6. ounce   _____   f. yr.

7. kilogram   _____   g. sec.

8. liter   _____   h. oz.

Answer the following questions, using abbreviations for the measurement words.

9. What time do you wake up in the morning?   _____

10. What time do you go to sleep at night?   _____

Fill in the bubble next to the correct abbreviation.

1. Parkway
   - Ⓐ Pakwy.
   - Ⓑ Pkwy.
   - Ⓒ Pa.
   - Ⓓ Pak.

2. Place
   - Ⓐ Pl.
   - Ⓑ Pc.
   - Ⓒ Pa
   - Ⓓ Plc.

3. European Union
   - Ⓐ Europe U.
   - Ⓑ Eu. Un.
   - Ⓒ EU
   - Ⓓ E. Union

4. meter
   - Ⓐ mm
   - Ⓑ m
   - Ⓒ mm.
   - Ⓓ mr

5. pound
   - Ⓐ lb.
   - Ⓑ po.
   - Ⓒ ld
   - Ⓓ pd

6. Arkansas
   - Ⓐ AR
   - Ⓑ AZ
   - Ⓒ AK
   - Ⓓ AL

7. Arizona
   - Ⓐ AR
   - Ⓑ AZ
   - Ⓒ AK
   - Ⓓ AL

8. Minnesota
   - Ⓐ ME
   - Ⓑ MI
   - Ⓒ MS
   - Ⓓ MN

9. Iowa
   - Ⓐ ID
   - Ⓑ IA
   - Ⓒ IN
   - Ⓓ IL

10. New Mexico
   - Ⓐ NJ
   - Ⓑ NV
   - Ⓒ NM
   - Ⓓ NE

Name _____

> ▶ Declarative sentences end with a period (.).
>
>   An ape is a large primate.
>
> Most imperative sentences end with a period (.). Use an exclamation point (!) for urgent or emphatic commands.
>
>   Please take me to the Natural History Museum.
>
>   Watch out for that car!
>
> Interrogative sentences end with a question mark (?).
>
>   Which exhibit did you like best?
>
> Exclamatory sentences end with an exclamation point (!).
>
>   The snake pit was amazing!

Add the correct punctuation to each sentence. Then, write *declarative*, *interrogative*, *imperative*, or *exclamatory* to identify what type of sentence it is.

1. Did you know that the names of the constellations come from myths

   _____

2. Please tell me about the constellation named for Orion

   _____

3. That's my absolute favorite

   _____

4. Orion was the son of Poseidon and was a hunter

   _____

5. What a great hunter he was

   _____

> Use commas to separate three or more items in a series.
>
> Do you like **mystery novels, realistic fiction, or biographies?**
>
> The children's bookstore carries **picture books for young children, chapter books for beginning readers, and novels for young adults.**

Correct the sentences by adding commas where they are needed.

1. A human being's five senses are sight hearing touch taste and smell.

2. The cornea the pupil and the lens are three parts of the eye.

3. The muscle known as the iris the jelly-like substance called vitreous fluid and the thumbnail-sized retina are other important eye parts.

4. Ear parts include the canal the ear drum and the cochlea.

5. Hearing can be damaged by loud sounds, such as those made by jet planes jackhammers and live rock concerts.

6. A bacterial infection a viral infection or even an allergy can cause earaches.

7. Taste buds saliva and nerves all work together in your sense of taste.

8. Taste buds recognize salty sweet bitter and sour tastes.

9. The sense of smell helps us identify what food is edible what food is inedible and what food could be harmful if eaten.

10. Receptors for pressure cold heat and pain are all part of our sense of touch.

11. The sense of touch allows you to tell the difference between rough and smooth soft and hard and wet and dry.

12. Your sense of smell involves your nose nasal cavity and brain.

Remember to use commas to separate items in a series of three or more.

We **got on the bus, went to the store, and bought new clothes.**

We **grabbed our bags, found the food court, and sat down to have lunch.**

Proofread and correct this paragraph by adding commas where they are needed.

Ms. Washington teaches language arts, but she also is our school's drama teacher. This spring, Ms. Washington needed to choose a play cast the parts and then start rehearsals, all by the end of the April. She decided on the musical *You're a Good Man, Charlie Brown.* I was cast as Lucy DeyShaun was cast as Charlie Brown and Pedro was cast as Snoopy. We did warm-up exercises read the script together and then tried to act it out. Ms. Washington frowned grimaced and laughed as we struggled to bring the play to life. A piano player came played the score and directed our singing. Some parents took our measurements brought in some sewing machines and made costumes. The technical crew met with the director drew up some plans and made our set. As the weeks went by, we rehearsed our lines practiced our singing and learned some new dances. On opening night, we went onstage performed like pros and took our bows. The director the pianist and the stage crew took bows, too.

> Use a comma between the day and the year in a date.
>
> January 31, 1999
>
> Use a comma to set off the year from the rest of the sentence.
>
> On January 10, 1960, there was a huge blizzard.

Insert commas where they are needed.

1. Rosa McCauley was born on February 14 1913.

2. On December 18 1932 she married Raymond Parks.

3. She became famous because on December 1 1955 she was arrested for refusing to give up her bus seat to a white passenger.

4. On Sunday December 4 word was spread among the African-American community that Rosa Parks had been arrested.

5. On December 5 1955 African Americans in Montgomery, Alabama, began boycotting the bus system.

6. On November 13 1956 the U.S. Supreme Court declared segregation on buses to be unconstitutional.

7. On August 28 1963 Rosa Parks joined the March on Washington, where Dr. Martin Luther King, Jr., delivered his "I Have a Dream" speech.

8. On September 9 1996 President Bill Clinton awarded her the Presidential Medal of Freedom.

9. Rosa Parks died on October 24 2005.

10. City officials in Montgomery announced on October 27 2005 that the front seats of their city buses would display black ribbons in honor of Parks.

> Use a comma between the name of the city and the name of the state, country, or province.
>
> Dallas, Texas
>
> Rome, Italy
>
> Toronto, Ontario
>
> Use a comma to set off the state, country, or province name from the rest of the sentence.
>
> We flew from Boston, Massachusetts, to London, England, last June.
>
> We visited my aunt and uncle in Winnipeg, Manitoba, the year before.

Proofread the paragraph and correct any errors by adding commas where they are needed.

My father and I are big fans of museums. In New York New York there are many world-class museums, such as the Museum of Modern Art, the Metropolitan Museum of Art, and the Guggenheim Museum. The Walters Art Gallery in Baltimore Maryland is another fine museum. The Art Institute of Chicago is on South Michigan Avenue, in Chicago Illinois and it's my dad's favorite. One year, my family went to Paris France on a trip to see my mother's relatives. We went to the Louvre Museum and saw the *Mona Lisa*. My oldest brother is attending college in Houston Texas where they have the fantastic Rice University Art Gallery. Next year, my father is going to take us to the Montreal Museum of Fine Arts, which is in Montreal Quebec. We're driving there from our home in Hampton New Hampshire. I can't wait!

> Use a comma in a compound sentence. Place the comma before the coordinating conjunction, such as *and*, *but*, or *or*, that joins the two independent clauses of the sentence.
>
> I like to go to bookstores, **and** I always find a book to buy.
>
> I was tired from practice, **but** I still had homework to do before I went to bed.

Add a comma before the conjunction that joins the two main parts of each compound sentence.

1. Lacie is a good swimmer and she can also run very fast.

2. Her brother Emilio plays soccer after school or he goes to swim practice.

3. Lacie's sister Rosa would rather read at home but sometimes Lacie and Emilio convince her to play outdoors with them.

4. Rosa can do all of her homework fairly quickly but Lacie has to work much longer.

5. Lacie often sets the table for dinner or she helps her mother with the cooking.

6. Emilio goes to many soccer practices but he would still like to practice more.

7. Rosa is learning to cook and she can make a delicious omelet.

8. It's hard for their mother to keep up with all of their interests but she seems to manage.

9. Lacie will soon go out for track or she will join the swim team.

10. Lacie is really athletic but Rosa and Emilio are not at all jealous.

A complex sentence is made up of two related clauses joined by a subordinating conjunction.

after	although	as if	as long as	because	before	if	since
so	that	though	unless	until	when	where	while

If the conjunction comes at the beginning of the complex sentence, use a comma to separate the two main parts of the sentence.

While Leon and I play instruments, we are not members of the school band.

Although he is a good drummer, Leon would rather play in his garage.

Circle the commas that separate the two clauses of each complex sentence.

1. Because my friend Leon is quite musical, his mother, his father, and his sister want him to perform all the time.

2. While Leon, my mother, and my teacher all encourage me to practice, no one would mistake me for being musical.

3. Although Leon loves the drums most, he also plays guitar, piano, and violin.

4. Whereas I don't always practice, Leon sings, plays, and composes almost every day.

5. Even though I love to play, I don't ever expect to play at a club, church, or concert hall.

Place commas between the two clauses of each of the following complex sentences.

6. Because I enjoy playing popular music from different decades I wish I knew how to play basic rhythm and blues.

7. Although some people don't like classical music I have a collection of classical MP3s.

8. Even though I listen to pop music on the radio I want to know more about world music.

Fill in the bubble next to the sentence that uses the correct punctuation.

1. Ⓐ My favorite writer is J. K. Rowling?

    Ⓑ She was born in Great Britain in 1965,

    Ⓒ She wrote some of the best books I've ever read!

    Ⓓ Do you think she will write another series.

2. Ⓐ Rowling worked as a secretary as a waiter and as a teacher.

    Ⓑ She has lived in London in Scotland, and in Portugal.

    Ⓒ Chris Columbus Alfonso Cuarán, and Mike Newell directed movies based on her books.

    Ⓓ Rowling's children are named Jessica, David, and Mackenzie.

3. Ⓐ First I read the book next I see the movie then I reread the book.

    Ⓑ I like to get a snack, find a comfortable chair, and read all afternoon.

    Ⓒ My friend Matthew tries to read the books gives up, and waits for the movies.

    Ⓓ At the movies we buy our tickets buy popcorn and watch the screen.

4. Ⓐ I like Ron best but my brother likes Hermione the most.

    Ⓑ I think that Professor Snape is scary, and I always get nervous when he shows up.

    Ⓒ I like the actor who plays Harry but the character is different in the books.

    Ⓓ I wish that I could ride the Hogwarts Express and then I could see Hogwarts!

5. Ⓐ Although I love the *Harry Potter* series I have many other favorite books.

    Ⓑ Whereas my brother loves Tolkien I am more of a C. S. Lewis fan.

    Ⓒ While *The Lord of the Rings* books are exciting, I really enjoy the *Narnia* books.

    Ⓓ Even though I've mentioned fantasy authors I also like many authors of realistic fiction.

Name _____

> Use a comma to set off a person's name if he or she is being addressed directly.
>
> Ryan, have you been to the new amusement park?
>
> I think it's great, Emma.
>
> I can tell, Ryan, that you'd like to go again.

Rewrite these sentences correctly, adding commas where they are needed.

1. Kaya have you finished your chores?

   _____

2. I think I have Ben.

   _____

3. Kaya let's get Dad to drive us to the mall.

   _____

4. Dad can you take us to the mall?

   _____

5. I would Kaya but you haven't vacuumed yet.

   _____

6. I will vacuum right now Dad.

   _____

Use commas to set off introductory phrases of four or more words.

> **At the beginning of the year,** I'll open a savings account.

With a short introductory phrase, no comma is needed.

> **After lunch** we will go to the mall.

With single introductory words such as *yes*, *no*, and *well*, use a comma at the beginning of a sentence.

> **Well,** I'm mowing my neighbor's lawn.

Add commas where they are needed.

1. By the end of the month I want to find a new hobby.

2. At home I often waste too much time.

3. However I want that hobby to be fun.

4. By the time he was my age my grandfather had learned how to cook.

5. At times I think I'd like to cook, too.

6. No I don't think I want to make a scrapbook.

7. No I do not like making things.

8. However I do like to make things I can wear.

9. By the end of this week I'll narrow it down to two choices.

10. Well I'll narrow it down to four.

> In a friendly letter, use a comma after the greeting and after the closing.
>
> Dear Alexandra,
>
> Sincerely,

Add commas where they belong in the greetings and the closings.

Dear Patty   Dear Auntie Reni

Your friend   Much love

Dear Mary   Your niece Anja

Dearest Lou   Dear Grandpa

Your sister   Fondly

Read the letter from Daniel to his parents. Write the greeting and the closing.
Use commas.

June 26, 2007

_____

  I'm having a great time at Grandma's. There is a pond where all the neighbors meet to go swimming. We have cookouts every weekend. I've made many new friends.

  I do miss you, of course. It will be great to come back home.

_____

Daniel

> When you write the exact words that someone says, use commas to set off the quotation from the rest of the sentence.
>
> Eli said, "Let's play a board game."
>
> "I think that playing cards is more fun," said Eli's mother.
>
> "Well," said Eli, "we could do both."

Add commas where they are needed in the following sentences.

1. Mia asked "What was it like growing up in the 1970s?"

2. Her mother said that the music was the best part.

3. "I was just a kid" Mrs. Hirano explained.

4. "I'll bet you were quite a disco dancer" Mia said.

5. "No" said Mrs. Hirano, "I was more into punk."

6. Mia asked "Did you like bell bottoms and platform shoes?"

7. "Sure" Mrs. Hirano replied.

8. "I hope you didn't have any of that silly orange and green furniture" Mia said.

9. "Well" said Mrs. Hirano "we did have an orange couch."

10. "I'm glad I didn't grow up in the 1970s" said Mia.

Name _____

Fill in the bubble next to the sentence or phrase that uses the correct punctuation.

1. Ⓐ Henry, do you like poetry?

   Ⓑ I love it Tanya.

   Ⓒ Do you like song lyrics Henry?

   Ⓓ Tanya I like them if they are poetic.

2. Ⓐ Well Tanya didn't think that she could write well.

   Ⓑ As the years went by writing was always a struggle for Tanya.

   Ⓒ Yes, Tanya did like to sing.

   Ⓓ No her parents thought she should focus on school.

3. Ⓐ "Maybe we should go to a poetry reading" said Henry.

   Ⓑ "I don't think so," said, Tanya.

   Ⓒ "They'll have musicians playing along with the poetry" said, Henry.

   Ⓓ Tanya said, "That sounds interesting."

4. Ⓐ Henry said, "You should have seen Tanya at the reading!"

   Ⓑ His mother asked "Why is that?"

   Ⓒ "They asked for volunteers" said Henry.

   Ⓓ Henry explained "She read fantastic poems that I didn't even know she had written!"

5. Which greeting for a friendly letter is written correctly?

   Ⓐ Dear Dad

   Ⓑ Dear, Mom

   Ⓒ Dear Grandma:

   Ⓓ Dear Grandpa,

> If you write the exact words that someone says, use quotation marks before and after the quotation.
>
> "My favorite subject is social studies," said Aisha.
>
> Ali said, "I like math best."

Rewrite each sentence correctly. Remember to use quotation marks around the quotations.

1. What historical figure do you admire most? asked Jack.

   _____

   _____

2. That's an interesting question, said Liz.

   _____

3. Jack said, I have to write about a historical figure.

   _____

   _____

4. Mr. Brown said, Write about Franklin Delano Roosevelt's leadership during the Great Depression.

   _____

   _____

5. Mrs. Brown said, I think Eleanor Roosevelt is fascinating.

   _____

   _____

Name _____

> If a quotation is interrupted by words telling who is speaking, use quotation marks to set off the speaker's words.
>
> "It's a close call," said Emma, "but I think he was out."

Add quotation marks to the sentences where needed.

1. I'm not sure, said Leah, but I think I'm doing this book report wrong.

2. Chen said that he would read it to see if it was okay.

3. I'm sure you'll think it's silly, Leah said, since I didn't know what to include.

4. This is okay, said Chen, but I'm not sure what you think of the book.

5. I liked it, said Leah, but I didn't love it.

6. Chen asked Leah what she liked about the book and what its weaknesses were.

7. If that's what you think, said Chen, then that's what you need to include.

8. Okay, I'll rewrite the report, said Leah. Is there anything here that I should keep in my revision?

9. Of course! said Chen. Your summary of the book is really good and so are the character descriptions.

10. Thanks, said Leah, I think I know how to fix this now.

11. Would you read it again, asked Leah, once I make the revisions?

12. Sure, said Chen, I'd be happy to.

Use quotation marks around the titles of short stories, poems, and songs.

"The Lottery"   "Ballad of the Morning Streets"   "Red River Valley"

Write each of the following sentences correctly. Remember to use quotation marks.

1. I read a story called The Selfish Giant.

   _____

2. My favorite poem is Dream Variations.

   _____

3. My mom likes to sing You've Got a Friend.

   _____

Write the titles of two songs, poems, and short stories that you know.
Use quotation marks.

4. (songs) _____

   _____

5. (poems) _____

   _____

6. (short stories) _____

   _____

Language Fundamentals • EMC 2756 • © Evan-Moor Corp.

Underline the titles of books, movies, television shows, newspapers, and magazines.

<u>Maniac Magee</u>   <u>Hoodwinked</u>   <u>Zoom</u>   <u>Atlanta Journal</u>   <u>Time for Kids</u>

If you are using a computer, you can use *italics* instead of underlining.

Maniac Magee   *Zoom*

Correct the following paragraph. Remember to underline the titles of movies, books, newspapers, magazines, and television shows.

My class read Tuck Everlasting, and most of us loved it! When we looked in the library to find out more about the book, we found a New York Times review about a movie based on the book. My friends and I decided we had to see it. One Friday night, we rented Tuck Everlasting, and we cried our eyes out. Alexis Bleidel, from the television show Gilmore Girls, plays Winnie, who has to make a difficult choice. She's older than the character in the book, but that seemed right in the movie. Now I really want to read Natalie Babbitt's other books, such as The Eyes of the Amaryllis and Herbert Rowbarge.

Answer the questions. Remember to underline each title.

1. What is your favorite movie? _____

2. What is your favorite television show? _____

3. What is your favorite book? _____

4. What is your favorite magazine? _____

Fill in the bubble next to the correct answer to each question.

1. Which sentence is punctuated correctly?
   - Ⓐ Carlos said "I want to take a trip.
   - Ⓑ Mrs. Carales asked, "Where do you want to go?"
   - Ⓒ Carlos said, I'd really like to see the ocean."
   - Ⓓ "Start saving your allowance said Mrs. Carales.

2. Which sentence is punctuated correctly?
   - Ⓐ I'd like to go to the forest," said Dora, "where we could camp.
   - Ⓑ "Aside from the fact that we don't have a tent, said Mrs. Carales, that sounds great.
   - Ⓒ "If Carlos and I save our allowance," said Dora, "we could buy a tent before long."
   - Ⓓ "Don't count me in, said Carlos, since I'm saving to go to the beach.

3. Which poem title is written correctly?
   - Ⓐ The Barefoot Boy
   - Ⓑ *The Barefoot Boy*
   - Ⓒ The Barefoot Boy
   - Ⓓ "The Barefoot Boy"

4. Which book title is written correctly?
   - Ⓐ Alice in Wonderland
   - Ⓑ "Alice in Wonderland"
   - Ⓒ Alice in Wonderland
   - Ⓓ Alice in Wonderland

5. Which movie title is written correctly?
   - Ⓐ Over the Hedge.
   - Ⓑ "Over the Hedge
   - Ⓒ Over the Hedge
   - Ⓓ "Over the Hedge"

An apostrophe takes the place of the missing letters in a contraction. Some commonly contracted words are *not, is, are, will, would,* and *have.*

am = **'m**	will = **'ll**
not = **n't**	would = **'d**
is = **'s**	have = **'ve**
are = **'re**	

Complete each sentence with a contraction.

1. I want to see the newly released animated movie, but _____ not playing in our town until Saturday.

2. It's rated PG, so _____ sure my dad will let me go.

3. Our friends in Salinas said that _____ seen it twice already.

4. If _____ like to come along, we can meet outside the theater.

5. _____ be late or _____ miss the exciting beginning.

Write a sentence using the contraction formed from each two-word pair in the box.

> they would   she is   you will

6. _____

_____

7. _____

_____

8. _____

_____

Possessive nouns show ownership. Here's how to make nouns possessive.

Singular Nouns = add 's

Pete's bike

the cat's dish

Plural Nouns Ending in s = add '

the bridges' designers

the hamsters' cages

Plural Nouns Not Ending in s = add 's

the deer's feeding area

the men's division

Circle the possessive nouns in the sentences below and write them correctly on the lines.

1. In the 1870s, a New England mans business started importing and manufacturing

   bicycles in the United States. _____

2. Americans interest in bicycles began to increase in the late nineteenth century.

   _____

3. In the twentieth century, American adults attention had shifted toward the automobile.

   _____

4. Bicycles were sold chiefly to be used as childrens toys. _____

5. Europeans love for bicycles only grew. _____

6. Engineers designs made the bicycle lightweight and easy to use. _____

7. In the last twenty years, peoples interest in cycling for exercise increased. _____

8. Lance Armstrongs popularity has raised interest in bicycling. _____

> When writing the time, use a colon between the numbers that show the hour and the minutes.
>
> My alarm went off at **4:30** this morning.
>
> I was out of the house by **5:15**.
>
> I had a special swim practice at **6:00** to get ready for Saturday's swim meet.

Write a time in each sentence.

1. Mom and I are going to the store at _____ this morning.

2. She's dropping me off at a birthday party at _____.

3. If the party's over by _____, we'll have time to go to a movie.

4. If the party is not over until after _____, we'll just go home.

5. We're meeting Dad for dinner at _____.

6. I hope that we're home by _____ so I can watch my favorite show.

7. The show is over at _____, and then I'll do some reading.

8. I am usually asleep by _____.

Write a sentence that tells what time you go to bed at night and a sentence about when you get up in the morning. Remember to use a colon between the hour and the minutes.

9. _____

_____

10. _____

_____

> When writing a business letter, use a colon after the greeting.
>
> Dear Ms. Stasio:
>
> To Whom It May Concern:
>
> Dear Sir or Madam:

Add a colon to each greeting that would be for a business letter.

1. Dear Aunt Elaine

2. Dear Dr. Kirk

3. Dear President Marquez

4. Dear Grandma

5. Dear Sir or Madam

6. My dear friend

7. Dear Customer Service Manager

8. Dear Principal Collins

9. Dear Mom

10. To Whom It May Concern

Write a greeting for each business letter described.

11. You ordered a jacket. The wrong one was sent.

   _____

12. You want to convince the mayor of your city to vote for a new park.

   _____

13. You want to write an opinion letter to the local newspaper.

   _____

14. You found a grammatical error in a magazine. You want to alert the editor of the error.

   _____

Language Fundamentals • EMC 2756 • © Evan-Moor Corp.

Fill in the bubble next to the correct answer.

1. Which contraction is written correctly?

   Ⓐ wer'e

   Ⓑ didnt'

   Ⓒ coul'dnt

   Ⓓ I'll

2. Which singular possessive is written correctly?

   Ⓐ Anthonys' behavior

   Ⓑ Samanthas conduct

   Ⓒ Connor's activities

   Ⓓ Katherin'es manners

3. Which plural possessive is written correctly?

   Ⓐ men's shirts

   Ⓑ womens' coats

   Ⓒ girl's dresses

   Ⓓ boys shoes

4. Which time is written correctly?

   Ⓐ 118

   Ⓑ 1:18

   Ⓒ 11:8

   Ⓓ one:18

5. Which greeting is correct for a business letter?

   Ⓐ Dear Julia,

   Ⓑ Dear Sir,

   Ⓒ Dear Sergeant York

   Ⓓ Dear Mrs. Reid:

> Be careful not to confuse subject and object pronouns.
>
> - Subject pronouns should be used as the subject of a sentence or clause.
>
>   **I   you   he   she   it   we   they**
>
>   **Incorrect**   **Her and me** volunteer after school.
>   **Correct**   **She and I** volunteer after school.
>
> - Object pronouns take the place of a word or group of words that are the object of a verb or a preposition.
>
>   **me   you   him   her   it   us   them**
>
>   **Incorrect**   Mr. Okwu asked **she and I** to help.
>   **Correct**   Mr. Okwu asked **her and me** to help.
>
>   **Incorrect**   He gave the forms to **she and I.**
>   **Correct**   He gave the forms to **her and me.**

Complete each sentence using the correct pronoun.

1. Lina and _____ volunteer at the senior center.

2. Mr. Okwu trained Lina and _____.

3. We asked for _____ when we got there.

4. He asked _____ to read to the seniors.

5. _____ were shy at first.

6. The seniors clapped for Lina and _____ when we were done.

Proofread this paragraph. Draw a line through the pronoun errors. Write the correction above.

I read for Mrs. Collins every Saturday. Her loves my reading. Her and me really enjoy spending time together. When it's time for she and I to say goodbye, we're always sad. She gave me a special book for my mother and I. It's called <u>Moms</u>. My mom and me loved it.

> Negatives are words that mean "no." When there are two negatives in the same sentence, it's called a double negative. Avoid double negatives.
>
> **Incorrect** Toby **didn't** have **nothing** to do.
> **Correct** Toby **didn't** have **anything** to do.

Rewrite each sentence so there is no longer a double negative.

1. Toby didn't have no idea about how to spend his Saturday afternoon.

   _____

   _____

2. "I don't have nothing to do," he complained to his grandmother.

   _____

   _____

3. "You haven't got nothing to do?" Grandma said in surprise.

   _____

4. "The back porch hasn't been cleaned out for no time," she continued.

   _____

   _____

5. Since Toby didn't have nothing else to do, he cleaned the back porch for Grandma.

   _____

   _____

People often confuse the words *good*, *well*, *bad*, and *badly*.

- The word *good* is an adjective. It describes a noun or pronoun.

    Greg is a **good** singer.

- The word *well* is an adverb. It describes a verb and sometimes an adjective.

    Greg sings **well.**

- The word *bad* is an adjective. It describes a noun or pronoun. Do not use *bad* as an adverb.

    Miranda is a **bad** singer.

- The word *badly* is an adverb. It describes a verb or adjective.

    Miranda sings **badly.**

Complete each sentence correctly.

1. Choir practice went _____ yesterday.

2. Everyone sang _____ , especially the tenors.

3. However, Greg's solo was really _____.

4. He performed _____ during practice.

Write four sentences using the words in parentheses.

5. (good) _____

6. (well) _____

7. (bad) _____

8. (badly) _____

Fill in the bubble next to the correct answer to each question.

1. Which sentence is written correctly?

   Ⓐ Auntie Meg gave a puppy to my brother and I.

   Ⓑ Me and my brother always wanted a puppy.

   Ⓒ My brother and I promised to take good care of the puppy.

   Ⓓ The puppy chased my brother and I all over the yard.

2. Which sentence is written correctly?

   Ⓐ My dad and I play basketball after dinner.

   Ⓑ Him and me shoot baskets for about an hour.

   Ⓒ My mother joins my dad and I sometimes.

   Ⓓ Her and me like to fake out my dad.

3. Which sentence is written correctly?

   Ⓐ Cercie and Emily didn't hear no key in the door.

   Ⓑ There was no sound as the door opened.

   Ⓒ When Andy walked in the room, she didn't see no cats.

   Ⓓ Cercie and Emily didn't waste no time running to greet Andy.

4. Which sentence is written correctly?

   Ⓐ I wanted to win bad.

   Ⓑ She was well as a chess player.

   Ⓒ Today's game went good.

   Ⓓ I performed badly on the oral quiz.

5. Which sentence is written correctly?

   Ⓐ Sienna is a good writer.

   Ⓑ She writes good whenever we have to hand something in.

   Ⓒ Her writing is always as well anyone's.

   Ⓓ Sienna's has written good since she was in first grade.

The words *can* and *may* are often confused, but they mean different things. Be sure to use the word whose meaning fits what you're trying to say.

- *can* means "able to"

    Stefan **can** jump very far.

- *may* means "allowed to"

    "You **may** try out for the team," Coach said.

Write *can* or *may* to complete each sentence correctly.

1. "How far _____ he jump?" Davey asked Coach Gutierrez.

2. "_____ he jump as far as Jennifer?" asked Davey.

3. "He _____ jump almost six and one-half feet," Coach responded.

4. "Wow! _____ I watch him practice today?" Davey asked.

5. "You _____ if you're very quiet," Coach said.

6. "I _____ be so quiet he won't know I'm here," Davey promised.

7. Coach thinks Stefan _____ definitely break the broad jump record.

8. Stefan's mother said he _____ practice every day if it doesn't hurt his grades.

Write two sentences using the words in parentheses.

9. (can) _____

_____

10. (may) _____

The words *lie* and *lay* are often confused.

- Use *lie* to mean "to rest or recline."
    Cujo **lies** on my bed after dinner.

- Use *lay* to mean "to put or place."
    Sometimes I **lay** down my book and play with him.

Proofread this paragraph. Correct any mistakes.

I like to keep my room very organized so I can find what I need. For instance, as soon as I come home from school, I lie my backpack on the floor by my chair. I take out the books I need for homework and lie those on top of the desk. My hamster's cage is on the right side of my desk. I always greet Hammy and pet him, but he usually just lays there. He's not very exciting. All he does is lie one piece of cedar shaving on top of another. When I finish my homework, I lie the paper on the left side of my desk for my mom to review. Before I lay down at night, I make sure everything is put away in its correct place. My clothes are organized by color, and my books are arranged alphabetically on the shelves. I even lie my glasses in the same place so I can find them in the morning. My friends tell me I should just lay back and relax at home, but I prefer to keep things neat.

Write two sentences using the words in parentheses.

1. (lie) _____

_____

2. (lay) _____

_____

The words *lie* and *lay* are often confused.

- Use *lie* to mean "to rest or recline."

- Use *lay* to mean "to put or place."

	lie	lay
Present Tense	I **lie** down when I'm tired.	I **lay** my books on the table.
Past Tense	Yesterday, I **lay** down for a while.	I know I **laid** them there yesterday.

Write the correct past tense form of *lie* or *lay* to complete each sentence.

1. Yesterday I _____ under the willow tree and read a book.

2. I _____ a bottle of water and a blanket beside me.

3. My dog Amira came outside and _____ down beside me.

4. She _____ her bone at my feet.

5. As we _____ there, it grew cooler.

6. I picked up the blanket from where I _____ it and covered us both.

7. Amira _____ under the blanket and cuddled next to me.

8. After an hour, I _____ my book on the ground and went to sleep.

Write two sentences of your own, using the past tense of *lie* and *lay*.

9. _____

_____

10. _____

_____

The words *who* and *whom* and *who's* and *whose* are often confused.

- Use *who* as the subject of a sentence.

    Who made the cake?   **Who** will clean up after the party?

- Use *whom* as the object of a verb or preposition.

    Whom did you invite?   To **whom** did you send invitations?

- Use *who's* to mean "who is."

    Who's bringing the balloons?   **Who's** going to take you home?

- Use *whose* to show ownership.

    Whose cup is this?   **Whose** shoes are in the backyard?

Write *who*, *whom*, *who's*, or *whose* to complete each sentence.

1. For _____ is that package?

2. _____ taking you on a tour?

3. _____ essay is the best?

4. To _____ is the letter addressed?

5. _____ can take you to karate practice?

6. I wonder _____ the best player on the team.

7. _____ can sing the loudest in the choir?

8. _____ will you take to the party?

9. _____ dishes were left on the table?

10. _____ taking French this year?

Fill in the bubble next to the correct answer to each question.

1. Which sentence is written correctly?

    Ⓐ Can I go horseback riding with Aunt Lourdes?

    Ⓑ You may go if you've finished your chores.

    Ⓒ Can I go swimming on Saturday?

    Ⓓ I may swim.

2. Which sentence is written correctly?

    Ⓐ "May I have the mustard, please?" asked Maeve.

    Ⓑ "Yes, you can," replied Michael.

    Ⓒ "Can I have the pickles, too?" Maeve asked again.

    Ⓓ "No, you cannot," Michael answered.

3. Which sentence is written correctly?

    Ⓐ I lay down on the floor every night when I start my yoga exercises.

    Ⓑ First I lie the mat down on the floor.

    Ⓒ Then I lie down on the mat and stretch.

    Ⓓ Sometimes my cat lays on my stomach while I try to exercise.

4. Which sentence is written correctly?

    Ⓐ Who's going to teach band this year?

    Ⓑ Whom is coming to dinner?

    Ⓒ Whose your favorite singer?

    Ⓓ To who did you write?

5. Which sentence is written correctly?

    Ⓐ I laid down after school because I was very tired.

    Ⓑ He lay his books on the table after the meeting.

    Ⓒ Because I had a headache, I carefully layed my head on the pillow.

    Ⓓ My dad laid his hand on my shoulder to stop me from running into the street.

> A base word, also called a word root, is the main part of a word before word parts are added at the beginning or the end.
>
> **keep**ing   un**happy**
> **friend**ship   pre**view**

Underline the base words.

1. impossible

2. softness

3. seller

4. reread

5. distrust

6. uncertain

7. speeding

8. goodness

Complete each sentence by writing a base word on the line.

9. I decided to re_____ my story to make it more exciting.

10. Martin is _____ing dinner for his family.

11. The teacher will dis_____ the class in ten minutes.

12. That movie has non_____ action.

13. That bouquet of flowers is so _____ful!

14. "I am upset that I can't go to the party," said Maria _____ly.

15. Because I was _____less, I broke Mom's favorite vase.

16. Tanisha can't attend the play. Her sister is also un_____ to come.

A prefix is a word part that comes before a base word.

over– + pay = overpay

A suffix is a word part that comes after a base word.

over– + pay + –ment = overpayment

Make words to complete each sentence by adding a prefix or a suffix to the base word in parentheses.

Prefixes		Suffixes	
pre–	un–	–ment	–ness
re–	dis–	–ful	–ion

1. Elia would like to _____ the seating before the dinner. (arrange)

2. Awards night will be filled with _____ for those nominated. (excite)

3. Joaquin is _____ that he will win the award for best athlete. (hope)

4. Mi Hye hates to get up in front of a crowd, but she is determined to hide

   her _____. (nervous)

5. Mr. Enright is feeling _____ because his ride is late. (frustrate)

6. He does not want to _____ anyone. (appoint)

7. He is _____ if he will make it on time. (sure)

8. Ms. Gray was full of _____ for all the nominees. (encourage)

9. She asked everyone to _____ one more time on the stage. (assemble)

10. Finally, it was time for the _____ of the winners. (announce)

A prefix is a word part that comes before a base word. A prefix changes the meaning of the word. These prefixes mean *not* or *opposite of:*

Prefix	Example	Meaning
mis–	**mis**behave	not behave
un–	**un**answered	not answered
dis–	**dis**comfort	the opposite of comfort
non–	**non**sense	not making sense

Complete each sentence with the correct word from the word box.

nonfiction	uncomfortable	miscounted	nonprofit
discontinue	miscalculation	dishonest	unfair

1. The referee was _____ when he gave a point to the other team.

2. The doctor told her to _____ taking the pills.

3. The teacher _____ when she tallied 19 students.

4. *Marley & Me,* a _____ book, is the true story of a man and his dog.

5. Brianna made a _____ when adding the fractions.

6. The _____ organization did not make money, but performed many good deeds in the community.

7. Dora was _____ when she told a lie.

8. Jason was _____ sleeping without a pillow.

What other words do you know with these prefixes? Write two sentences using at least one word with a prefix in each sentence.

9. _____

10. _____

> A prefix is a word part that comes before a base word. A prefix changes the meaning of the word. These prefixes mean *not* or *opposite of:*

Prefix	Example	Meaning
in–	**in**accurate	not accurate
im–	**im**balance	not balanced
il–	**il**literate	not literate
de–	**de**throne	not on the throne

Complete each word with the correct base word.

1. A person who is not active is _____active.

2. If you remove the value from something, you _____value it.

3. An act that is not legal is _____legal.

4. A person who is not mature is _____mature.

5. Something that is the opposite of activated is _____activated.

6. A person who is not patient is _____patient.

7. An act that is not logical is _____logical.

8. Something that is not complete is _____complete.

What other words do you know with these prefixes? Write two sentences using at least one word with a prefix in each sentence.

9. _____

10. _____

A prefix is a word part that comes before a base word. Some prefixes express number.

Prefix	Meaning	Example
uni–	one	**uni**son
bi–	two	**bi**lingual
tri–	three	**tri**athlete
quadr–	four	**quadra**lateral

Write the definition of each word.

1. univision _____

2. biannual _____

3. tricycle _____

4. quadrangle _____

Write the word for each definition.

5. having three colors _____

6. having one form _____

7. one of four offspring born in a single birth _____

8. having two valves _____

What other words do you know with these prefixes? Write two sentences using at least one word with a prefix in each sentence.

9. _____

10. _____

Knowing the meanings of common prefixes can help you with words you meet in school subjects.

Prefix	Meaning	Example
tele–	far, distant	**tele**graph
poly–	many	**poly**gon
inter–	among, between	**inter**planetary
trans–	across, to pass	**trans**port

Complete each sentence using the correct prefix.

1. _____nesia is a _____syllabic word for a country composed of many

   islands. It is a tropical country, so you would not want to wear heavy _____ester

   clothes there.

2. When I want to get away from the _____phone and _____vision, I look

   through my _____scope to see the stars.

3. Emily _____ferred her _____parency before her _____atlantic trip.

4. Isabelle appreciated the _____mission of the _____national meeting, as

   she had to work hard _____preting the speeches.

What other words do you know with these prefixes? Write two sentences using at least one word with a prefix in each sentence.

5. _____

6. _____

Name _____

Fill in the bubble next to the correct answer.

1. In which list are the number prefixes in order from smallest to largest?
   Ⓐ bi–, quadr–, tri–, uni–
   Ⓑ uni–, bi–, tri–, quadr–
   Ⓒ bi–, tri–, uni–, quadr–
   Ⓓ quadr–, tri–, bi–, uni–

2. What is the base word of *reintroduction?*
   Ⓐ tion
   Ⓑ reintroduce
   Ⓒ introduce
   Ⓓ duct

3. In which list do all the words express a negative condition?
   Ⓐ imbalance, disregard, interpret, nonsense
   Ⓑ deformed, polyester, uncomfortable, impatient
   Ⓒ inaccurate, quadrant, devalue, illegal
   Ⓓ undone, inactive, miscount, illiterate

4. Which word has both a prefix and a suffix?
   Ⓐ dishonest
   Ⓑ basement
   Ⓒ unicorn
   Ⓓ uncomfortable

5. Which word describes a true story?
   Ⓐ illiterate
   Ⓑ inaccurate
   Ⓒ nonfiction
   Ⓓ nonsense

A suffix is a word part that comes after a base word. Adding a suffix to a word changes the word's meaning.

These suffixes form nouns:

Suffix	Meaning	Example
–ment	act of, result of	ammend**ment**
–ness	state of	good**ness**
–ion	act of, state of	perfect**ion**
–ist	one who	violin**ist**

Complete each sentence. Use one suffix for each pair of sentences.

1. The teacher showed her amaze_____. The student's improve_____ was remarkable.

2. The bicycl_____ stopped for a moment. She wanted to talk to the

   biolog_____ conducting an experiment by the creek.

3. Julie's fascinat_____ for the athlete was obvious. He is the champ_____ of his sport.

4. Each spring brings happi_____ to places in the Far North. The dark_____ of the winter months is over.

What other words do you know with these suffixes? Write two sentences of your own using at least one suffix in each sentence.

5. _____

   _____

6. _____

   _____

A suffix is a word part that comes after a base word. Adding a suffix to a word changes the word's meaning.

These suffixes form nouns:

Suffix	Meaning	Example
–ship	state or quality of	friend**ship**
–ism	characteristic of	optim**ism**
–dom	state or quality of	wis**dom**
–ology	study or science of	ge**ology**

Complete each noun with the correct base word for the suffix.

1. A hero shows _____ism.

2. Some people face hard times, but learn to grow from their _____ship.

3. A free nation holds _____dom as a right.

4. The scientists at a zoo study _____ology.

5. A citizen of a country has _____ship.

6. A country with a king is a _____dom.

7. Something that seems real has the characteristic of _____ism.

8. The study of the ecosystem is _____ology.

What other words do you know with these suffixes? Write two sentences of your own using at least one suffix in each sentence.

9. _____

10. _____

A suffix is a word part that comes after a base word. Adding a suffix to a word changes the word's meaning.

These suffixes form adjectives:

Suffix	Meaning	Example
–able	is, can be	do**able**
–al	like	natur**al**
–ic	relating to	angel**ic**
–ous	full of	nerv**ous**

Complete each sentence with the correct word. Use the suffixes from the rule box.

1. If you can return something, it is _____.

2. If you are full of joy, you are _____.

3. If something is like magic, it is _____.

4. If something is related to poetry, it is _____.

5. If something is like the center, it is _____.

6. If something is able to perish, it is _____.

7. If you are full of adventure, you are _____.

8. If something is related to science, it is _____.

What other words do you know with these suffixes? Write two sentences of your own using at least one suffix in each sentence.

9. _____

10. _____

Fill in the bubble next to the correct answer.

1. *Encouragement* most nearly means _____.

Ⓐ an encouraging person

Ⓑ the act of encouraging

Ⓒ able to be encouraged

Ⓓ full of courage

2. Something that can be agreed upon is _____.

Ⓐ agreeist

Ⓑ agreeship

Ⓒ agreeable

Ⓓ agreement

3. Someone who has the characteristics of a patriot shows _____.

Ⓐ patriotic

Ⓑ patriotist

Ⓒ patriotable

Ⓓ patriotism

4. *Symbolic* most nearly means _____.

Ⓐ can be a symbol

Ⓑ study of symbols

Ⓒ state of being a symbol

Ⓓ like a symbol

5. The state of being protected is _____.

Ⓐ protectist

Ⓑ protectous

Ⓒ protection

Ⓓ protectable

Many words used in science have Greek or Latin roots.

Root	Meaning	Example
therm	heat	**therm**al
scope	instrument for viewing	peri**scope**
hydr	water	**hydr**ant
terra	land, earth	**terra**in

Given the meaning of the roots, determine the meaning of these words.

1. terrestrial _____

2. dehydrate _____

3. hydroelectricity _____

4. thermos _____

5. microscope _____

6. hydrology _____

7. thermometer _____

8. terrarium _____

9. hydrate _____

10. telescope _____

11. territory _____

12. hydrotherapy _____

Name _____

Many words used in science have Greek or Latin roots.

Root	Meaning	Example
photo	light	**photo**graph
bio	life	**bio**graphy
geo	earth	**geo**graphy
cycl	wheel, circular	**cycl**e

Match each word in the word box with its definition.

geophysics   photosensitive   cyclical   cyclone   geothermal
biology   recycle   geocentric   antibiotic   photosynthesis

1. sensitive to light _____

2. of the heat of the Earth _____

3. a substance that destroys microorganisms _____

4. violent rotating windstorm _____

5. to reuse or pass through again _____

6. physics of the Earth _____

7. how plants use light as an energy source _____

8. the study of life _____

9. having the Earth as the center _____

10. recurring or moving in circles _____

When you know the meaning of common Greek and Latin word roots, you can figure out the meanings of many words.

Root	Meaning	Example
chron	time	**chron**ology
lum	light	il**lum**inate
phon	sound	tele**phon**e
nym	name	anon**ym**ous

Complete each sentence with the correct word from the word box.

chronic	symphony	synonym	luminescent
phonograph	luminary	chronological	pseudonym

1. The fish that glowed in the deep ocean was _____.

2. Carrie placed the names of the presidents in _____ order.

3. The Boston _____ played beautiful music for its audience.

4. She used a _____ to hide her identity.

5. Maria played some records on a _____ owned by her parents.

6. James has a _____ cough that has lasted for a month.

7. The committee declared Ms. True a _____ because she outshone others in her field.

8. The teacher asked the student to think of a _____ to make her writing more interesting.

Fill in the bubble next to the correct answer.

1. *Thermostat* most nearly means _____.

    Ⓐ doing something quickly

    Ⓑ a device to control the heating and air conditioning

    Ⓒ a container used to keep drinks cold

    Ⓓ measuring the circumference of the Earth

2. *Hydrafoil* most nearly means _____.

    Ⓐ without water

    Ⓑ wrapping your food in aluminum foil

    Ⓒ a boat that skims the surface of the water

    Ⓓ a plant that requires no sunlight or food

3. *Periscope* most nearly means _____.

    Ⓐ an instrument used for viewing over or around objects

    Ⓑ a mechanical device used for transportation

    Ⓒ the inability to walk

    Ⓓ a knife used to cut pears

4. *Anachronism* most nearly means _____.

    Ⓐ a painful disease affecting the joints

    Ⓑ the ability to hear arachnids

    Ⓒ the dark shapes you see when you close you eyes

    Ⓓ something in the incorrect place in time

5. *Phonetic* most nearly means _____.

    Ⓐ moving at an increased and irregular pace

    Ⓑ having the ability to construct towers

    Ⓒ representing the sounds of speech with symbols

    Ⓓ the ability to produce light for photographic purposes

Synonyms are words that have almost the same meaning. You can use synonyms to vary your writing, avoid repetition, or make your use of language more precise.

Synonyms for *make:* create, invent, construct, cause
Synonyms for *laugh:* giggle, guffaw, chortle, chuckle
Synonyms for *hard:* difficult, tough, impossible, dangerous
Synonyms for *small:* tiny, miniscule, minute, miniature

A thesaurus is a reference book that lists synonyms.

Cross out each underlined word and replace it with a synonym.

1. Mackenzie had always wanted to <u>make</u> something to save people time in the kitchen.

2. He tried to figure out what was the <u>toughest</u> task for a cook.

3. His father said that one recipe called for <u>small</u> slivers of garlic.

4. "I can never get them small enough," he <u>laughed</u>.

5. "Maybe I should <u>make</u> a garlic dicer," Mackenzie said.

Write a sentence for each of these synonyms.

6. (sad) _____

_____

7. (depressed) _____

_____

8. (somber) _____

_____

> There are usually slight differences in meaning among synonyms. Think about the meaning you want as you choose just the right word.
>
> As the audience quieted, she began to **speak.**
>
> Samantha **lectured** on the importance of libraries.
>
> *Speak* and *lecture* are synonyms, but each word means something slightly different.

Write synonyms for the underlined words in the paragraph. Cross out the underlined word or words and write the synonym above it. Use a thesaurus if necessary.

After the audience members <u>found</u> their seats, Cassie <u>moved</u> to the

podium. She had never <u>talked</u> in front of a large audience before, and this

audience was <u>very large</u>. Cassie talked about her experiences <u>working</u> in a

reading clinic. She said that helping other people was something that made

her feel <u>good</u>. She <u>worked</u> very hard to learn what would be helpful in

teaching younger readers. One girl, Katrinka, was <u>getting better</u> in her

decoding skills. Another child, Emeka, was showing more <u>belief</u> in himself as

he read aloud for others. Volunteering made a big difference in Cassie's life,

and she wanted to <u>tell</u> other people her age so they would be encouraged to

try to make a difference, too.

> Antonyms are words that have opposite meanings.
>
>   Antonyms for *mumble:* shout, yell, enunciate, speak clearly
>   Antonyms for *cry:* laugh, smile, chuckle, beam
>   Antonyms for *sweet:* mean, nasty, tart, sour
>   Antonyms for *happy:* morose, sad, miserable, depressed

Write an antonym for the word in parentheses to complete each sentence.

1. Mateo's sixth-grade graduation was a very (sad) _____ occasion for Mateo and his family.

2. Mateo's whole family was there, (excluding) _____ his grandparents.

3. Mateo's turn came to give his speech, and he made sure to (mumble)

   _____ .

4. Mateo's grandmother was so moved by his speech she began to (laugh)

   _____ .

5. Everyone clapped (quietly) _____ when Mateo finished his speech.

6. Mateo's parents were very (ashamed) _____ of their son.

Write a sentence for each antonym about movies or TV shows you've watched recently.

7. (funny) _____

   _____

8. (worst) _____

   _____

> Antonyms are words that have opposite meanings. You can use antonyms to compare and contrast things.
>
> The town's library is **old**, but the middle school building is **new**.
>
> The library looks **traditional**, but the middle school building looks **modern**.

Write antonyms for each clue to complete the crossword puzzle.

Across
4. superior
6. awkward
10. common
11. peculiar
12. honor
13. command
14. create

Down
1. public
2. excellent
3. achieve
5. purify
7. simple
8. forbid
9. proud
12. bold

Homophones are words that sound alike but have different spellings and meanings.

The queen sits upon a **throne** made of gold.
The jockey was **thrown** from his horse during the race.

Do you want a **piece** of cake?
Kofi Annan works for **peace** through the United Nations.

Circle the homophone to complete the sentence correctly.

1. Do you know (whether, weather) you can go skiing or not?

2. That shade of green (compliments, complements) your red hair.

3. You must go (threw, through) the tunnel to reach the beach.

4. I need more (lead, led) for my pencil.

5. (Lightening, Lightning) is both beautiful and dangerous.

6. The (principle, principal) reason for the celebration was Lupe's graduation.

7. I must (pedal, peddle) faster if I want to get to school on time!

8. (Witch, Which) route should we take?

Write a sentence for each of these homophones. Make sure you use the correct meaning for the word's spelling in your sentence.

9. (hole) _____

_____

10. (whole) _____

_____

Language Fundamentals • EMC 2756 • © Evan-Moor Corp.

Homophones are words that sound alike but have different spellings and meanings. Homophones are often confused with each other. Make sure your spelling matches the meaning that you intend.

They're is a contraction of *they are.*
Their means "belonging to them."
There indicates a place or position.

They're going to find **their** kneepads over **there.**

Your means "belonging to you."
You're is a contraction of *you are.*

You're going to wear **your** new socks.

Choose the correct homophones to complete the sentences.

Katya and her little brother Rey play soccer for the Tigers. Last year, Rey was too young to play. This year, the coach told him, "_____ old enough to learn the game!" The Tigers are really nice, and _____ looking out for Rey. Katya is _____ captain, since she's the best player.

"This is _____ jersey," she said to Rey, as she handed him a green shirt. "You sit over _____ until the coach tells you what to do," Katya told Rey.

Coach Munras walked over to Rey. "_____ ready to play, right?" she asked Rey.

"You bet, I am!" Rey exclaimed.

"_____ position is keeper," Coach Munras began. "You will keep the other team from scoring. _____ will be plenty of practice for you to get to know _____ position. See the team in the red jerseys? _____ going to kick the balls toward you. Catch, kick, or block the balls as they come toward you. Good luck!"

Fill in the bubble next to the correct answer.

1. Which word is a synonym for *vacant?*
   Ⓐ full
   Ⓑ unoccupied
   Ⓒ thin
   Ⓓ wealthy

2. Which two words are synonyms?
   Ⓐ *create* and *destroy*
   Ⓑ *create* and *beginning*
   Ⓒ *create* and *make*
   Ⓓ *create* and *speak*

3. Which word is an antonym for *solemn?*
   Ⓐ sober
   Ⓑ depressed
   Ⓒ giddiness
   Ⓓ silly

4. Which words are homophones?
   Ⓐ *some* and *sum*
   Ⓑ *broke* and *joke*
   Ⓒ *tell* and *tale*
   Ⓓ *finished* and *done*

5. _____ *going to play hockey with their friends this afternoon.*
   Ⓐ Their
   Ⓑ There
   Ⓒ They're
   Ⓓ Theyre

Language Fundamentals • EMC 2756 • © Evan-Moor Corp.

Proofreading Marks

Use these marks to show corrections.

Mark	Meaning	Example
ℒ	Take this out (delete).	I love to to read.
⊙	Add a period.	It was late⊙
≡	Make this a capital letter.	First prize went to maria.
/	Make this a lowercase letter.	We saw a Black Cat.
___	Fix the spelling.	This is our ~~hause~~ house.
∧	Add a comma.	Goodnight∧Mom.
∨	Add an apostrophe.	That∨s Lil∨s bike.
∨ ∨	Add quotation marks.	∨Come in, he said.
! ? ∧ ∧	Add an exclamation point or a question mark.	Help∧Can you help me∧
⊼	Add a hyphen.	I've read three∧fourths of the book.
⌒	Close the space.	Foot⌒ball is fun.
∧	Add a word or letter.	The∧pen is mine. (red)
___	Underline the words.	We read <u>Old Yeller</u>.
⫶∧	Add a colon.	Alex arrived at 400.

Proofread this paragraph. Use proofreading marks to correct the 10 errors.

Our class will have a Meeting on tuesday. We will vote on issues that affect the lifes of sixth-grade students. Everyone in the sixth grade will cast a secret ballot. The ballots will be collected in sealed boxs. The principal and our teacher will have the power to veto any motion. If a motion receives these two vetos, it cannot pass. There are two political partys in our class. One calls itself the Foxes, and the other calls itself the Wolfs. The Foxs and the Wolves will elect representatives to sit in the class congress. All the class's in our school are holding elections. We are learning about Democracy.

Write the words correctly on the lines below.

1. _____   6. _____

2. _____   7. _____

3. _____   8. _____

4. _____   9. _____

5. _____   10. _____

Language Fundamentals • EMC 2756 • © Evan-Moor Corp.

Proofread this paragraph. Use proofreading marks to correct
the 10 errors.

The art museum in our city is the older one in the state. Paintings by

Monet, Picasso, and Cassatt hang in one gallery. Monet was a french painter,

Picasso a Spanish painter, and Cassatt an american painter. Monet's

paintings have more beautifuller colors than Picasso's paintings. I like the

brightest pinks and pale blues that he used to paint taller cathedrals. Monet's

paintings seem softest than Picasso's. I once saw a Picasso painting about war

in a book. The picasso paintings in our museum are not as scary as this

painting in the book. I think that the Cassatt paintings are the better ones in

the whole museum. I like the sweet scenes of mothers and children. The

expressions are very realistic.

Write the words correctly on the lines below.

1. _____   6. _____

2. _____   7. _____

3. _____   8. _____

4. _____   9. _____

5. _____   10. _____

Use proofreading marks to correct the 10 errors.

My brother and I collect vinyl records, the kind that our grandparents played on machines called record players. I have many records, but my brother has the most than me. I collect older rock-and-roll records. I have the record by Elvis and one by Chubby Checker. These records are my favorites. A old song called "The Twist" is on the checker record. Everyone danced to that song when my grandmother was the girl. She still dances! She dances when my brother plays his records, too. My brother likes recordings of polka music! He says that the polka is the goodest dance in the world. Our family is polish, and we all like a polka.

Find the errors. Write the words correctly on the lines below.

1. _____   6. _____

2. _____   7. _____

3. _____   8. _____

4. _____   9. _____

5. _____   10. _____

Language Fundamentals • EMC 2756 • © Evan-Moor Corp.

Proofread these paragraphs. Find the 10 errors, cross them out, and write the words correctly above them.

Last night, snow fell. My sisters and brothers and me decided to put on our snowshoes and go into the woods today. Snowshoes have been around for a long time. In our barn, we have a really old pair. I took one old snowshoe down from the shelf once. I thought they was a tennis racket! Our modern snowshoes have fancier clamps, but it works the same way. I put on my snowshoes myself, but my youngest brother needs help. He says that it won't be long before he can do it for hisself.

In the woods, my siblings and me found a wide trail. I stopped to adjust Bobby's clamps, and I tightened my, too. The others forged ahead. Bobby and me took our time. We looked for a sign of life along the snowy trail. It wasn't long before we found them. We examined little footprints made by a field mouse. For Bobby and I , the footprints were an exciting discovery. Suddenly, a large crow called from a tree. They reminded us that many creatures live in the winter woods.

Proofread these paragraphs. Find the 10 errors, cross them out, and write the words correctly above them.

On a sunny summer day, many neighbors visit our backyard. Most yards in the neighborhood are small, but our is large. My friends and me have room for running and shady spots for resting. Last night, my dad and mom cooked hot dogs on the grill in the backyard. Some parents don't cook outside, but my like to cook for a crowd in our backyard.

Almost all of the neighbors came over. Ms. Lee brought potato salad. I like potato salad, and her's is the best I've ever tasted. Mr. Carson brought lemonade and soda. Him and Ms. Carson brought lawn chairs, too. There lawn chairs provided all of us places to sit while we waited for a freshly grilled hot dog.

"Whom brought the marshmallows?" I asked after dinner. My older sister Carol brought out a bag of marshmallows for toasting. Her and her friends never forget the marshmallows. Them volunteered to toast a marshmallow for everyone.

As the sun set, the mosquitoes came out. It was time to put on bug spray. The adults talked and laughed while the kids kicked a soccer ball. When it was too dark to see, the other kids and me told stories. What a perfect summer day!

Name _____

Proofread these paragraphs. Use proofreading marks to correct
the 10 errors.

The last imperial ruler of Russia was Tsar Nicholas II. Nicholas inherited
the throne from his father. An assassin shooted Nicholas's father in the
street, making Nicholas the tsar. He never really want to have that awesome
responsibility, but he take his duties seriously. Nicholas marryed Alexandra,
a German princess. A shy person, Alexandra is uncomfortable with her
public position. Still, she support her husband.

Nicholas and Alexandra have a family of four daughters and one son.
Their son was born with a serious illness. He bleeded and bruised at the
slightest bump. The bleeding was difficult to stop and the bruising is quite
painful. Doctors tryed to ease the little boy's pain. Alexandra, the desperate
mother, believed that a mysterious man named Rasputin could save her little
boy. Rasputin was able to ease the boy's suffering, but there was no cure for
his disease.

Write the words correctly on the lines below.

1. _____   6. _____

2. _____   7. _____

3. _____   8. _____

4. _____   9. _____

5. _____   10. _____

Proofread these paragraphs. Find the 10 errors, cross them out, and write the words correctly above them.

Early yesterday morning, James and Marshall go fishing. They baited their hooks with worms and wait. It was very quiet. All at once, a large fish bursted through the surface of the lake. The scales of the fish gleamed like gold in the sun. The golden fish dive deep again. The boys wondered if they might catch that amazing fish. Marshall says that he would cook the fish if he catched it. James said that he would mount the fish and hang it above the fireplace.

The boys settled back with their fishing poles. Suddenly, the big fish breaked the surface of the lake again. The fish fliped his golden fins. He shook his tail. The fish, the boys thought, is having a good time. He's showing off! Over and over the gleaming fish jumped.

By the time the fish was finished with his show, the boys finded that they had put down their poles. "I don't want to catch him," Marshall said to James. "I want to see him jump every time I come to the lake."

"Me, too," said James. "I had an idea! The next time we come here, let's bring binoculars instead of poles and hooks."

Language Fundamentals • EMC 2756 • © Evan-Moor Corp.

Name _____

Proofread these paragraphs. Use proofreading marks to correct the 10 errors.

The first time I seen the room in the attic of our new house, I knowed that I had to make it mine. Our old house were very modern and has only one floor. It was a nice house, but I is thrilled to be moving into our new home.

The attic be a little spooky now, but soon I am making it cozy and cheerful. My dad and mom will help by covering the beams with something called wallboard. Here is some wallpaper samples. I will pick out something pretty to cover the wallboard.

The attic room is huge! There is two windows. Next weekend, Mom helped me find curtains. From one window, I can see big pine trees. The other window is the best part of this attic room. From that window, I can see my best friend's house!

Find the errors. Write the words correctly on the lines below.

1. _____   6. _____

2. _____   7. _____

3. _____   8. _____

4. _____   9. _____

5. _____   10. _____

Proofread these paragraphs. Use proofreading marks to correct
the 10 errors.

This morning, my mom and dad and I are pack for our summer
vacation. Every year, we rents the same cottage at the shore. My dad say the
cottage is "rustic." He means that it is old-fashioned. We likes it that way.

On our first vacation at the cottage, I was surprised not to see a television
in the living room. I wonder what we would do in the evenings, but after a
few days, I liked the quiet. I started reading some old kids' books that I found
in a bookcase. That is when I discover mystery books. Have you ever heared
of Nancy Drew?

Today I am packing two books to read and a board game to play. Earlier
today, I buyed stamps at the post office. Next week, I will sent postcards to
my friends. The cottage do not have a computer connection, so I have no
e-mail!

Find the errors. Write the words correctly on the lines below.

1. _____   6. _____

2. _____   7. _____

3. _____   8. _____

4. _____   9. _____

5. _____   10. _____

Name _____

Proofread these paragraphs. Find the 10 errors, cross them out, and write the words correctly above them.

Monica eager drank the cool water. Maybe running the track at noon, the hottest part of the day, had not been a good idea. Kia had been running, too, but she had run slow than Monica. Now Kia breathed easiest than her friend did. "Monica, let's run in the morning tomorrow," Kia suggested. "We'll be able to run fastest and longest when it is cooler."

Monica hated to get up more early than necessary, but she agreed to try a morning run the next day. "I'll set my alarm," Monica promised.

The next morning, Monica's alarm rang loudest than a fire alarm, and Monica groaned more long than she ever had before. The sleepy girl pushed a button on the alarm clock. She thought it was the snooze button, but she had turned off the alarm altogether. Before long, Monica was sleeping more deeper than her snoring dog, Buster.

Monica slept. She woke up gradually when Buster licked her nose. The phone was ringing. "Oh, no!" she said to Buster, "Look at the time!"

"Hmm," Kia said on the phone, "maybe you'd run gooder in the evening than you do in the morning!"

Proofread this paragraph. Correct the sentence fragments by adding words to make them complete or connecting them to another sentence. Then rewrite the paragraph below.

On July 20, 1969, An American spaceship landed on the moon. My uncle watched the landing on television In his college dorm. Said that everyone was very excited. An astronaut down the spaceship's ladder to step on the surface of the moon. Uncle Tito and his friends cheered. Cheered again when an American flag was planted. On the moon. In the photographs, looks like it is waving in a breeze, but it is not. No wind on the moon. The flag has wires in it to make it look like it is standing out in a breeze. The flag still there, but we cannot see it from Earth. I've tried. My friends and I have started an astronomy club. Will read about the moon and look at it through a telescope.

_____

_____

_____

_____

_____

_____

_____

_____

_____

Find each run-on sentence in these paragraphs and correct it. You can create two sentences or make the run-on into a compound or a complex sentence by using a conjunction.

During her long career, Margaret Chase Smith was one of the most important figures in American politics. She was born in 1897 in Maine she would come to serve that state with distinction. In fact, she would become the first woman to serve in both houses of the United States Congress.

Before Margaret Chase became a well-known politician, she worked as a teacher, a telephone operator, a newspaper circulation manager, and an office manager at a textile mill. During that time, she helped to establish a local club for business and professional women later, she became the president of the state office of that club. Her experiences would serve her well.

Mrs. Smith was a committed public servant with strong principles. She stood up to the infamous Senator McCarthy she strongly objected to his scare tactics in 1964, she became the first woman to be placed in nomination for the presidency of the United States by a major political party. Although she never became president, her country has not forgotten her contributions to its government.

She was instrumental in helping women achieve permanent status in the military she traveled to 23 countries during the cold war to improve relations. She held a perfect attendance record in Congress for many years spent very little money on campaigns. Some people told her she could never hope to achieve many of these goals. In response to those attitudes, Margaret Chase Smith said, "When people keep telling you that you can't do a thing, you kind of like to try it."

Read these paragraphs and then rewrite them below to make them read more smoothly. Combine sentences to avoid choppiness and unnecessary repetition. Use compound sentences, complex sentences, and other sentence-combining techniques.

I have been reading about bees. The honeybee is native to Europe. It is native to Africa, too. It is not native to America. Human travelers brought honeybees to America. They brought bees to America because the bees help with plant pollination. They brought bees to America because honeybees produce honey.

Honey is a sweetener that we can use in tea. We can use it in special desserts. In ancient times, honey was used as a salve for wounds. It was used as a salve for wounds because bacteria cannot live in honey. Bacteria cannot pass through a layer of honey. Honey is used in medicines even today. It is used in medicines since it can cover up bitter tastes.

_____

_____

_____

_____

_____

_____

_____

_____

Name _____

Proofread these paragraphs. Use proofreading marks to correct the 10 errors. Hint: One five-word proper noun counts as one error.

Have you ever been to pittsburgh? Pittsburgh is in pennsylvania. My friend katelyn lives there, and I visit her every november. Last saturday, her parents took us into the city to see the awesome dinosaur skeletons at the carnegie museum of natural history. The huge skeletons tower over the museum visitors. I wanted to study the skeletons, but katelyn's little brother was scared, so we moved on.

Next we went to see the exhibit of minerals and gems. We saw everything from coal to emeralds. The guide had a special machine that clicked and crackled as it measured the amount of radioactivity in the different minerals. the machine is called a Geiger counter because it was invented by a german professor named geiger. I think it would be fun to have a Geiger counter. I would use it to look for special minerals in my backyard.

Find the errors. Write the words correctly on the lines below.

1. _____   6. _____

2. _____   7. _____

3. _____   8. _____

4. _____   9. _____

5. _____   10. _____

Name _____

Proofread these paragraphs. Use proofreading marks to correct the 10 errors. Hint: Multiple-word proper nouns count as one error.

My cat's name is Tiger Lily. She is both independent and affectionate. I adopted tiger lily from garver animal friends, a shelter on ferry road. It was a cold friday afternoon in early february when my mom and I went to the shelter. Ms. cindric, one of the volunteers at the shelter, told us that a little cat had been found in a recent snowstorm. The cat had not had enough to eat and was very cold.

I called to my mom, "can we keep her?"

"Of course, we can," Mom answered. "we can give her the love and care she needs."

At first, Tiger Lily was very shy, and she hid from us. However, it did not take long for her to learn that the sound of a can opener meant gourmet kitty, her favorite brand of cat food. By presidents' day, Tiger Lily had become a healthy and happy cat. She knows that we love her and will never let her be cold and hungry again.

Find the errors. Write the words correctly on the lines below.

1. _____ 6. _____

2. _____ 7. _____

3. _____ 8. _____

4. _____ 9. _____

5. _____ 10. _____

Name _____

Proofread these paragraphs. Use proofreading marks to correct the
10 errors. Hint: Multiple-word proper nouns count as one error.

In the year 1914, a war began in europe. That war would become known
first as the Great War, then as the World War, and finally as world war I.
War was declared on Serbia by austria on July 28 at 11 o'clock. That was the
time when Archduke franz Ferdinand died after being shot as he rode
through the streets of sarajevo. The war that began with a shot fired in a
small city in serbia would soon engulf much of the world. The united states
entered the war in 1917. Many people died. The world would never be
the same.

Every year, we honor the veterans of all wars on November 11, veterans
day. This holiday was originally called armistice day. The agreement that
ended the great war was signed in 1918 on the eleventh day of the eleventh
month. At 11 o'clock that day, the guns fell silent.

Find the errors. Write the words correctly on the lines below.

1. _____   6. _____

2. _____   7. _____

3. _____   8. _____

4. _____   9. _____

5. _____   10. _____

Proofread these paragraphs. Use proofreading marks to correct the 10 errors. Hint: Multiple-word proper nouns count as one error.

Nathaniel Hawthorne wrote one of my favorite books. Published in 1853, the book is called <u>tanglewood tales</u>. In that Book, Hawthorne wrote stories based on famous greek myths. He wrote them so that the boys and girls of his century would enjoy them. Today, hawthorne's writing style seems a little old-fashioned, but that is one of the reasons I like it. My favorite story in the book is "the minotaur."

I want to read <u>the house of the seven gables</u>, a novel Hawthorne wrote about a real house in salem, Massachusetts. I visited that amazing house last year. It is a bit spooky. It even has a secret passageway! after I visited the house, I started to read the novel, but it was a little too hard for me then. On monday, I'll ask mr. brown, our school librarian, if he thinks I could read it now.

Find the errors. Write the words correctly on the lines below.

1. _____   6. _____

2. _____   7. _____

3. _____   8. _____

4. _____   9. _____

5. _____   10. _____

Proofread this letter. Use proofreading marks to correct the
10 errors.

January 5, 2008

Dear Aunt Lee:

What a surprise it was to receive that package from you. Dad and I could

not imagine what it might be. Because the box was so heavy we thought that

it might be full of big books. Of course we both love books but we love

cookies and cakes, too. How did you know we would not have time to bake

for ourselves.

You know that my favorite cookies are the ones with green icing. Thank

you, Aunt Lee for including those. My dads favorite cookies are the ones that

look like pinwheels. We are looking forward to trying the new kinds of

cookies in the box.

We are grateful for that fruitcake, too. The pieces of candied fruit in the

cake look like little jewels. Dad and I think the fruitcake might be too pretty

to eat. Did you use Great-grandpa's recipe! I'm guessing that you did!

Love

Terry

Proofread these paragraphs. Use proofreading marks to correct
the 10 errors.

I have a piano lesson on Saturday at 10-30 in the morning. I'm a new

student. I have learned three scales so far. I can play a C-major scale a

G-major scale, and a D-major scale. I can only play the scales with my right

hand but next week my piano teacher will teach me how to play the scales

with my left hand. The pieces I am learning to play are easy and a little silly. I

have learned "Teddy's Picnic," "Dance Tune, and "Sunny Day." My teacher

says that it won't be long before I can learn more interesting music. I want to

play the great pieces of Bach, Beethoven Brahms, and the Beatles.

Musical talent runs in our family. Mom plays the cello in an orchestra

and dad plays the trumpet in a Dixieland band. Because she is still very small

my little sister plays a tiny violin. Did you know that violins come in

different sizes for kids. When she first started taking violin lessons my little

sister practiced on a violin made from a cardboard box. It had just one

string! My little sister is glad that I am taking piano lessons. "We can play

duets, she says.

Proofread this business letter. Use proofreading marks to correct the 10 errors.

Mr Paul Pecan, President

Bake-Oh Company

30 Drury Lane

Middleville ME 00001

Dec 21 2006

Dear Mr. Pecan,

For many years, I have been a fan of your companys products. My favorite is the Morning Madness Muffin I often pack one of these nutritious muffins in my backpack. Because your product is full of fruit, fiber, and nuts it gives me the energy that I need to walk to school.

I am writing to ask if you might consider giving a tour of your factory. I am the president of the Good Food for Good Fun Club at Middleville Middle School and I have been telling the club members about your fabulous products All of the members have agreed that they would be interested in seeing how the Morning Madness Muffin is made.

Thank you for considering my request.

Sincerely

P. J. Wetzel

Proofread these paragraphs. Use proofreading marks to correct the 10 errors.

Since the beginning of this school year I have been reviewing books for the Sixth Grade Gazette. Its now time for me to offer my recommendations for fun summer reading. What should you read first.

If you have not read <u>Blue Willow</u> start there The book was written by Doris Gates. The main character, Janey, is the daughter of migrant workers. Although I had learned about migrant workers in school. I did not know about what it might be like to grow up in a migrant family until I read this book. Blue Willow is at the very top of my list. Ill read it for a second time this summer.

Short stories can be fun to read, too. On a hot day, read Jack Londons story To Build a Fire." Once you read that story about a man being lost in the Arctic ice and snow you will never complain about the summer heat again!

Language Fundamentals • EMC 2756 • © Evan-Moor Corp.

Name _____

Proofread this paragraph. Use proofreading marks to correct the
10 errors.

What are you doing on this rainy Saturday I'm going to watch an old

movie on television. Its called Plan Nine from Outer Space. I like science

fiction movies. Before the movie comes on I'll watch an old science fiction

television show called Lost in Space. I've seen a few episodes and they were

pretty silly. One episode, was called Invasion from the Fifth Dimension. Do

you want to come over to watch TV with me. You can have some of my

moms famous pizza! Send me an e-mail or an instant message. I'll be writing

e-mails until Lost in Space comes on.

Rewrite the paragraph on the lines below. Remember to include all of the correct
punctuation.

_____

_____

_____

_____

_____

_____

_____

_____

_____

_____

Proofread these paragraphs. Use proofreading marks to correct the
10 errors.

"Are you coming to the talent show tonight, Mr. Robson? Cindy asked.

"I will" she continued, "be reading a poem I wrote"

Thank you, Cindy for reminding me. I'll be there!"

Cindy was glad that her language arts teacher would be coming to hear

her read poetry tonight. Before taking Mr. Robsons class, Cindy didn't even

know that she liked poetry. Now she was writing her own poetry and reading

it out loud!

That evening, the auditorium was crowded. Cindys parents and her sister

were there. At first Cindy was very nervous, but then she saw her parents

smiling faces. Mr. Robson was there, too, and he gave a thumbs-up sign and

grinned. Cindy began reading her poem "My Cat Mimi with confidence.

Language Fundamentals • EMC 2756 • © Evan-Moor Corp.

Proofread these paragraphs. Use proofreading marks to correct the
10 errors.

I like it when my dad drives me to school in his really old car. He keeps

the radio tuned to a station that only plays old songs and he sings along. He

knows almost all the words. When he doesn't know a word he just makes

something up. Its always something funny that doesn't make any sense at all

When my big brother drives me to school, it's not as much fun. He

listens to the radio, too but I dont like the music he listens to very much. He

never sings along. He just keeps time by tapping his fingers on the steering

wheel. Maybe hes nervous because he just earned his license.

When Mom drives me to school she turns the radio off. She wants to

talk. "What will you do in school today" she asks I don't always want to talk,

but sometimes it's nice.

Rewrite the first paragraph with the correct punctuation.

_____

_____

_____

_____

_____

_____

_____

Proofread these paragraphs. Find the 10 errors, cross them out, and write the words correctly above them.

Last winter, my neighbors lost their home to a fire. Life has been pretty rough for them the past few months. Today, people in the community have joined together to help rebuild their house. I'm one of several kids who decided to help.

"Can I carry that for you?" I asked one of the workers.

"Yes, you may," she replied. "Thank you. Now I can help with the framing."

I decided I could help most by doing little things for the workers. Pretty soon, I hardly had time to set down!

"Lie that bag of sand by the wheelbarrow, please!"

I layed the sand by the wheelbarrow and ran back to the workers. "What's next?"

"Find out whose pouring the concrete," requested Rick.

"And who's hammer is this?" asked Gina.

"And to who does this hard hat belong?" Will called.

I don't think I never ran around so much in one day! When I went in my room that night, I laid down and went to sleep right away. I knew I needed to work just as hard for a whole week. However, I was happy to help make our neighbors' lives more good than before.

Language Fundamentals • EMC 2756 • © Evan-Moor Corp.

Proofread these paragraphs. Find the 10 errors, cross them out, and write the words correctly above them.

Our class put on a play for the whole school yesterday. It went pretty good. My friends and me had a lot of fun!

All the actors remembered their lines, and the audience set still in their seats for the whole hour. I didn't have no lines to memorize because I worked backstage. I like being behind the scenes better than being on stage. Being in front of all those people would be too nerve-racking!

I was the prop master. My job was to make sure all the props were where they needed to be and were returned to the right places. During a play, things can get pretty hectic! At one point, we lost some props!

Before the show, I layed the swords by the prop table. Kerry and Catalina picked them up for their scene. They said they lay them in the same place after the scene, but no one could find them. Whom could have moved them?

It turned out that Kevin thought he needed them for the next scene, but he wasn't supposed to be onstage until the next act! He had stayed up all night rehearsing his lines and was confused. Thankfully, we found them in time and didn't have no more problems.

Kevin laid down for a nap this afternoon, so he is ready to go for our next performance. Our director and him had a talk about getting enough sleep before a performance!

Proofread these paragraphs. Find the 10 errors, cross them out, and write the words correctly above them.

My soccer coach retired this year. He was my coach for several years, so I wanted to do something special for him. My mom makes the better chocolate chip cookies in the world, so I decided to ask her to help me bake some for him. It was an interesting experience because I had never baked before!

"Mom, may you help me bake some cookies?" I asked.

"What? You, bake? For who?" she asked, shocked.

"I want to make them for Coach Brewer's retirement party."

Mom taught me the basics of baking. I think I did pretty good! I insisted on doing most of it myself. Mom showed me how to measure the ingredients, told me what the abbreviations meant, and reminded me to keep an eye on the cookies in the oven. My only big mistake was when I lay the butter on the table and our cat ate it. That went bad.

I thought the cookies were really well. I hope Coach likes them. I don't have no other presents!

"Who's cookies are these?" Coach asked, with a cookie in his mouth.

"They're mine," I answered. "I baked them."

"You're kidding!" he exclaimed. "I might have to retire again next year just to get some more of these cookies!"

My favorite picture from the party is of Coach and I with cookie crumbs all over our faces!

Language Fundamentals • EMC 2756 • © Evan-Moor Corp.

Answer Key

Page 11

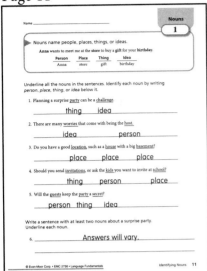

Nouns 1

Nouns name people, places, things, or ideas.

Anna wants to meet me at the **store** to buy a **gift** for your **birthday.**

Person	Place	Thing	Idea
Anna	store	gift	birthday

Underline all the nouns in the sentences. Identify each noun by writing *person, place, thing,* or *idea* below it.

1. Planning a surprise <u>party</u> can be a <u>challenge</u>.
   thing   idea

2. There are many <u>worries</u> that come with being the <u>host</u>.
   idea   person

3. Do you have a good <u>location</u>, such as a <u>house</u> with a big <u>basement</u>?
   place   place   place

4. Should you send <u>invitations</u>, or ask the <u>kids</u> you want to invite at <u>school</u>?
   thing   person   place

5. Will the <u>guests</u> keep the <u>party</u> a <u>secret</u>?
   person   thing   idea

Write a sentence with at least two nouns about a surprise party. Underline each noun.

6. _____ Answers will vary. _____

Identifying Nouns   11

Page 12

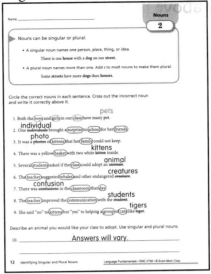

Nouns 2

Nouns can be singular or plural.

- A singular noun names one person, place, thing, or idea.
  There is one **house** with a **dog** on our **street**.
- A plural noun names more than one. Add *s* to most nouns to make them plural.
  Some **streets** have more **dogs** than **houses**.

Circle the correct nouns in each sentence. Cross out the incorrect noun and write it correctly above it.

1. Both the (boys) and (girls) in our (class) have many (pet).
   pets
2. One ~~individuals~~ brought a (surprise) to (school) for her (friends).
   individual
   photo
3. It was a ~~photos~~ of (kittens) that her (family) could not keep.
   kittens
4. There was a yellow (basket) with two white (kitten) inside.
   kittens
5. Several (students) asked if the (class) could adopt an (animals).
   animal
6. The (teacher) suggested (whales) and other endangered ~~creature~~.
   creatures
   confusion
7. There was ~~confusions~~ in the (classroom) that (day).
   students
8. The (teacher) improved the (communication) with the (student).
   tigers
9. She said "no" to (kittens) but "yes" to helping a (group) of (cats) like (tiger).

Describe an animal you would like your class to adopt. Use singular and plural nouns.

10. _____ Answers will vary. _____

12   Identifying Singular and Plural Nouns

Page 13

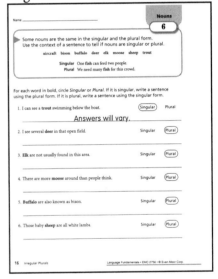

Nouns 3

Nouns that end in *sh, ch, x, s,* and *z* require *es* to form the plural.
One class is in the auditorium, while other **classes** are waiting to enter.
If I had one wish, I would ask for more **wishes!**

Underline the nouns that have the *es* plural form. Circle the nouns that have the *s* plural ending.

1. All of the (houses) have <u>porches</u> and (bushes) around them.
2. All of the (beaches) have sand and (shells).
3. All of the <u>lunches</u> are (choices) with sandwiches.
4. All of the (dances) at the ball are (waltzes).
5. All of the <u>dishes</u> have matching (cups) and glasses.
6. All of the <u>dresses</u> have (ruffles) and <u>patches</u> of lace.
7. All of the <u>foxes</u> are being chased by (hunters) and (hounds).
8. All of the <u>lynxes</u> are related to (cougars) and mountain (lions).
9. All of the football (players) who missed the <u>passes</u> feel like (klutzes).

Complete the sentence with at least one noun with the *es* plural ending.

10. All of the _____ Answers will vary. _____

Plural Nouns (adding es)   13

Page 14

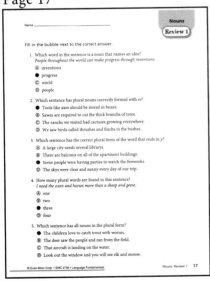

Nouns 4

To form the plural of nouns that end in a consonant and *y*, change the *y* to *i* and add *es*.

Singular	Plural
library	libraries
balcony	balconies

If a noun ends in a vowel and *y*, just add *s*.

Singular	Plural
key	keys
joy	joys

Rewrite each sentence with the correct plural form of the underlined words.

1. Many <u>country</u> celebrate different <u>holiday</u>.
   Many countries celebrate different holidays.

2. They have different <u>story</u> and <u>custom</u>.
   They have different stories and customs.

3. The youngest <u>baby</u> through oldest <u>adult</u> celebrate with <u>family</u>.
   The youngest babies to the oldest adults celebrate in families.

4. The <u>alley</u> and <u>avenue</u> are decorated in <u>city</u>.
   The alleys and avenues are decorated in cities.

5. All the <u>bakery</u> are busy selling <u>box</u> and <u>tray</u> of <u>treat</u>.
   All the bakeries are busy selling boxes and trays of treats.

6. There are <u>candy</u> and <u>cake</u> for <u>boy</u> and <u>girl</u> to enjoy.
   There are candies and cakes for boys and girls to enjoy.

14   Plural Nouns (changing y to i and adding es)

Page 15

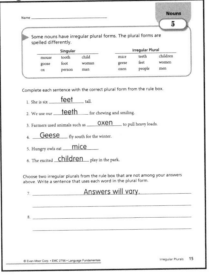

Nouns 5

Some nouns have irregular plural forms. The plural forms are spelled differently.

Singular			Irregular Plural		
mouse	tooth	child	mice	teeth	children
goose	foot	woman	geese	feet	women
ox	person	man	oxen	people	men

Complete each sentence with the correct plural form from the rule box.

1. She is six _feet_ tall.
2. We use our _teeth_ for chewing and smiling.
3. Farmers used animals such as _oxen_ to pull heavy loads.
4. _Geese_ fly south for the winter.
5. Hungry owls eat _mice_.
6. The excited _children_ play in the park.

Choose two irregular plurals from the rule box that are not among your answers above. Write a sentence that uses each word in the plural form.

7. _____ Answers will vary. _____

8. _____

Irregular Plurals   15

Page 16

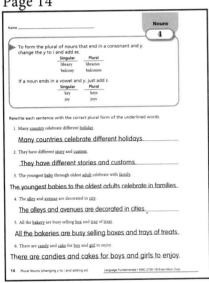

Nouns 6

Some nouns are the same in the singular and the plural form. Use the context of a sentence to tell if nouns are singular or plural.

aircraft   bison   buffalo   deer   elk   moose   sheep   trout

Singular One **fish** can feed two people.
Plural We many **fish** for this crowd.

For each word in bold, circle *Singular* or *Plural*. If it is singular, write a sentence using the plural form. If it is plural, write a sentence using the singular form.

1. I can see a **trout** swimming below the boat.   (Singular)   Plural
   _____ Answers will vary. _____

2. I see several **deer** in that open field.   Singular   (Plural)

3. **Elk** are not usually found in this area.   Singular   (Plural)

4. There are more **moose** around than people think.   Singular   (Plural)

5. **Buffalo** are also known as bison.   Singular   (Plural)

6. Those baby **sheep** are all white lambs.   Singular   (Plural)

16   Irregular Plurals

Page 17

Nouns Review 1

Fill in the bubble next to the correct answer.

1. Which word in the sentence is a noun that names an idea?
   People throughout the world can make progress through inventions.
   Ⓐ inventions
   ● progress
   Ⓒ world
   Ⓓ people

2. Which sentence has plural nouns correctly formed with *es*?
   ● Tools like axes should be stored in boxes.
   Ⓑ Sawes are required to cut the thick branchs of trees.
   Ⓒ The ranchs we visited had cactuses growing everywhere.
   Ⓓ We saw birds called thrushes and finchs in the bushes.

3. Which sentence has the correct plural form of the word that ends in *y*?
   Ⓐ A large city needs several librarys.
   Ⓑ There are balconis on all of the apartment buildings.
   ● Some people were having parties to watch the fireworks.
   Ⓓ The skys were clear and sunny every day of our trip.

4. How many plural words are found in this sentence?
   I need the oxen and horses more than a sheep and geese.
   Ⓐ one
   Ⓑ two
   ● three
   Ⓓ four

5. Which sentence has all nouns in the plural form?
   ● The children love to catch trout with worms.
   Ⓑ The deer saw the people and ran from the field.
   Ⓒ That aircraft is landing on the water.
   Ⓓ Look out the window and you will see elk and moose.

Nouns: Review 1   17

Page 18

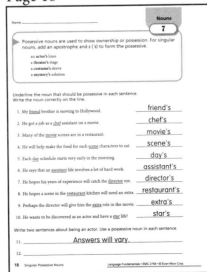

Nouns 7

Possessive nouns are used to show ownership or possession. For singular nouns, add an apostrophe and *s* ('s) to form the possessive.

an actor's lines
a theater's stage
a costume's sleeve
a mystery's solution

Underline the noun that should be possessive in each sentence. Write the noun correctly on the line.

1. My <u>friend</u> brother is moving to Hollywood.   friend's
2. He got a job as a <u>chef</u> assistant on a movie.   chef's
3. Many of the <u>movie</u> scenes are in a restaurant.   movie's
4. He will help make the food for each <u>scene</u> characters to eat.   scene's
5. Each <u>day</u> schedule starts very early in the morning.   day's
6. He says that an <u>assistant</u> life involves a lot of hard work.   assistant's
7. He hopes his years of experience will catch the <u>director</u> eye.   director's
8. He hopes a scene in the <u>restaurant</u> kitchen will need an extra.   restaurant's
9. Perhaps the director will give him the <u>extra</u> role in the movie.   extra's
10. He wants to be discovered as an actor and have a <u>star</u> life!   star's

Write two sentences about being an actor. Use a possessive noun in each sentence.

11. _____ Answers will vary. _____
12. _____

18   Singular Possessive Nouns

Page 19

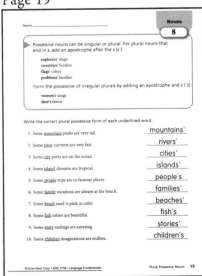

Nouns 8

Possessive nouns can be singular or plural. For plural nouns that end in *s*, add an apostrophe after the *s* (*s'*).

explorers' ships
countries' borders
flags' colors
problems' hurdles

Form the possessive of irregular plurals by adding an apostrophe and *s* ('s).

women's songs
deer's fawns

Write the correct plural possessive form of each underlined word.

1. Some <u>mountain</u> peaks are very tall.   mountains'
2. Some <u>river</u> currents are very fast.   rivers'
3. Some <u>city</u> ports are on the ocean.   cities'
4. Some <u>island</u> climates are tropical.   islands'
5. Some <u>people</u> trips are to faraway places.   people's
6. Some <u>family</u> vacations are always at the beach.   families'
7. Some <u>beach</u> sand is pink in color.   beaches'
8. Some <u>fish</u> colors are beautiful.   fish's
9. Some <u>story</u> endings are amazing.   stories'
10. Some <u>children</u> imaginations are endless.   children's

Plural Possessive Nouns   19

Page 20

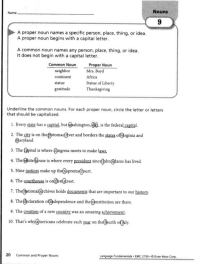

Nouns 9

A proper noun names a specific person, place, thing, or idea.
A proper noun begins with a capital letter.

A common noun names any person, place, thing, or idea.
It does not begin with a capital letter.

Common Noun	Proper Noun
neighbor	Mrs. Boyd
continent	Africa
statue	Statue of Liberty
gratitude	Thanksgiving

Underline the common nouns. For each proper noun, circle the letter or letters that should be capitalized.

1. Every state has a capital, but washington, D.C., is the federal capital.
2. The city is on the potomac river and borders the states of virginia and maryland.
3. The capitol is where congress meets to make laws.
4. The white house is where every president since john adams has lived.
5. Nine justices make up the supreme court.
6. The courthouse is on first street.
7. The national archives holds documents that are important to our history.
8. The declaration of independence and the constitution are there.
9. The creation of a new country was an amazing achievement.
10. That's why americans celebrate each year on the fourth of july.

Page 21

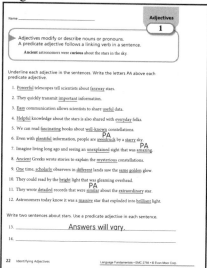

Nouns Review 2

Fill in the bubble next to the correct answer.

1. Choose the correct possessive noun to complete the sentence.
A _____ outcome is always better with teamwork.
- Ⓐ game's
- Ⓑ players'
- ● teams'
- Ⓓ assignment's

2. Choose the correct plural possessive for *fish*.
- Ⓐ fishies
- Ⓑ fishie's
- Ⓒ fish's
- ● fish

3. Which sentence has singular and plural possessive nouns?
- Ⓐ The knight's armor was heavy and the horses were big.
- Ⓑ The lord's robes and ladies' dresses were made of rich fabric.
- Ⓒ The castle's moat was a form of protection.
- Ⓓ Castles' windows were small and the rooms' light was dim.

4. Choose the correct proper noun to complete the sentence.
My _____ is Dad's brother.
- Ⓐ best friend
- Ⓑ Coach
- Ⓒ uncle
- ● Uncle Dan

5. How many proper nouns are in this sentence?
Grandma said she will take our family to a play or a musical.
- Ⓐ none
- ● one
- Ⓒ three
- Ⓓ four

Page 22

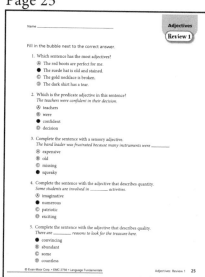

Adjectives 1

Adjectives modify or describe nouns or pronouns.
A predicate adjective follows a linking verb in a sentence.
Ancient astronomers were **curious** about the stars in the sky.

Underline each adjective in the sentences. Write the letters PA above each predicate adjective.

1. Powerful telescopes tell scientists about faraway stars.
2. They quickly transmit important information.
3. Easy communication allows scientists to share useful data.
4. Helpful knowledge about the stars is also shared with everyday folks.
5. We can read fascinating books about well-known constellations.
6. Even with plentiful information, people are awestruck by a starry sky. [PA]
7. Imagine living long ago and seeing an unexplained sight that was amazing. [PA]
8. Ancient Greeks wrote stories to explain the mysterious constellations.
9. One time, scholarly observers in different lands saw the same golden glow.
10. They could read by the bright light that was gleaming overhead.
11. They wrote detailed records that were similar about the extraordinary star.
12. Astronomers today know it was a massive star that exploded into brilliant light.

Write two sentences about stars. Use a predicate adjective in each sentence.
13. _____ Answers will vary. _____
14. _____

Page 23

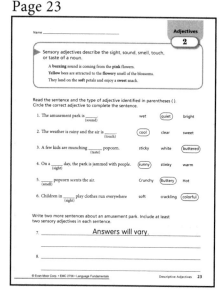

Adjectives 2

Sensory adjectives describe the sight, sound, smell, touch, or taste of a noun.
A **buzzing** sound is coming from the **pink** flowers.
Yellow bees are attracted to the **flowery** smell of the blossoms.
They land on the **soft** petals and enjoy a **sweet** snack.

Read the sentence and the type of adjective identified in parentheses ( ). Circle the correct adjective to complete the sentence.

1. The amusement park is _____ (sound). — wet / (quiet) / bright
2. The weather is rainy and the air is _____ (touch). — (cool) / clear / sweet
3. A few kids are munching _____ (taste) popcorn. — sticky / white / (buttered)
4. On a _____ (sight) day, the park is jammed with people. — (sunny) / stinky / warm
5. _____ (smell) popcorn scents the air. — Crunchy / (Buttery) / Hot
6. Children in _____ (sight) play clothes run everywhere. — soft / crackling / (colorful)

Write two more sentences about an amusement park. Include at least two sensory adjectives in each sentence.
7. _____ Answers will vary. _____
8. _____

Page 24

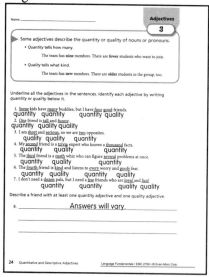

Adjectives 3

Some adjectives describe the quantity or quality of nouns or pronouns.
- *Quantity* tells how many.
The team has **nine** members. There are **fewer** students who want to join.
- *Quality* tells what kind.
The team has **new** members. There are **older** students in the group, too.

Underline all the adjectives in the sentences. Identify each adjective by writing quantity or quality below it.

1. Some kids have many buddies, but I have four good friends. — quantity quantity quantity quality
2. One friend is tall and funny. — quantity quality quality
3. I am short and serious, so we are two opposites. — quality quality quantity
4. My second friend is a trivia expert who knows a thousand facts. — quantity quality quantity
5. The third friend is a math whiz who can figure several problems at once. — quantity quality quantity
6. The fourth friend is kind and listens to every worry and goofy fear. — quantity quality quality quality
7. I don't need a dozen pals, but I need a few friends who are loyal and fun! — quantity quantity quality quality

Describe a friend with at least one quantity adjective and one quality adjective.
8. _____ Answers will vary. _____

Page 25

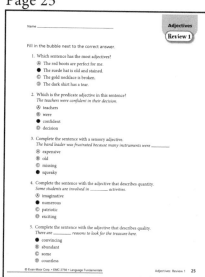

Adjectives Review 1

Fill in the bubble next to the correct answer.

1. Which sentence has the most adjectives?
- Ⓐ The red boots are perfect for me.
- ● The suede hat is old and stained.
- Ⓒ The gold necklace is broken.
- Ⓓ The dark shirt has a tear.

2. Which is the predicate adjective in this sentence?
The teachers were confident in their decision.
- Ⓐ teachers
- Ⓑ were
- ● confident
- Ⓓ decision

3. Complete the sentence with a sensory adjective.
The band leader was frustrated because many instruments were _____.
- Ⓐ expensive
- Ⓑ old
- Ⓒ missing
- ● squeaky

4. Complete the sentence with the adjective that describes quantity.
Some students are involved in _____ activities.
- Ⓐ imaginative
- ● numerous
- Ⓒ patriotic
- Ⓓ exciting

5. Complete the sentence with the adjective that describes quality.
There are _____ reasons to look for the treasure here.
- ● convincing
- Ⓑ abundant
- Ⓒ some
- Ⓓ countless

Page 26

Adjectives 4

Adjectives are used to make comparisons.
- Comparative adjectives use *er* to compare two people, places, things, or ideas.
loud + er = louder
The siren is **louder** today than yesterday.
- Superlative adjectives use *est* to compare three or more people, places, things, or ideas.
old + est = oldest
This is the **oldest** tree in the yard.

Circle the correct form of the adjective to complete each sentence. On the line, write C for comparative or S for superlative to identify the type of adjective.

1. The Rocky Mountains are [C] _____ than the Appalachians. — (taller) / tallest
2. The Mississippi is the [S] _____ river and the most famous. — mightier / (mightiest)
3. Chicago is the [S] _____ city, according to its nickname. — windier / (windiest)
4. I visited New York City, and it was [C] _____ than where I live. — (noisier) / noisiest
5. Florida, the "Sunshine State," must be [C] _____ than Illinois. — (sunnier) / sunniest
6. Alaska must be the [S] _____ state, being so far north. — colder / (coldest)
7. Many places could claim to be the [S] _____ in America. — prettier / (prettiest)
8. I would like to live in the place that is the [S] _____. — friendlier / (friendliest)

Write two sentences about the place where you live. Include a comparative adjective in one sentence and a superlative adjective in the other.
9. _____ Answers will vary. _____
10. _____

Page 27

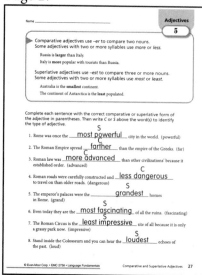

Adjectives 5

Comparative adjectives use –*er* to compare two nouns.
Some adjectives with two or more syllables use *more* or *less*.
Russia is **larger** than Italy.
Italy is **more** popular with tourists than Russia.

Superlative adjectives use –*est* to compare three or more nouns.
Some adjectives with two or more syllables use *most* or *least*.
Australia is the **smallest** continent.
The continent of Antarctica is the **least** populated.

Complete each sentence with the correct comparative or superlative form of the adjective in parentheses. Then write C or S above the word(s) to identify the type of adjective.

1. Rome was once the [S] **most powerful** city in the world. (powerful)
2. The Roman Empire spread [C] **farther** than the empire of the Greeks. (far)
3. Roman law was [C] **more advanced** than other civilizations' because it established order. (advanced)
4. Roman roads were carefully constructed and [C] **less dangerous** to travel on than older roads. (dangerous)
5. The emperor's palaces were the [S] **grandest** homes in Rome. (grand)
6. Even today they are the [S] **most fascinating** of all the ruins. (fascinating)
7. The Roman Circus is the [S] **least impressive** site of all because it is only a grassy park now. (impressive)
8. Stand inside the Colosseum and you can hear the [S] **loudest** echoes of the past. (loud)

Page 28

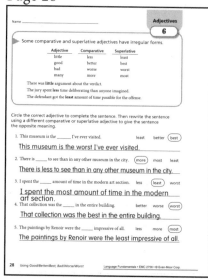

Adjectives 6

Some comparative and superlative adjectives have irregular forms.

Adjective	Comparative	Superlative
little	less	least
good	better	best
bad	worse	worst
many	more	most

There was **little** argument about the verdict.
The jury spent **less** time deliberating than anyone imagined.
The defendant got the **least** amount of time possible for the offense.

Circle the correct adjective to complete the sentence. Then rewrite the sentence using a different comparative or superlative adjective to give the sentence the opposite meaning.

1. This museum is the _____ I've ever visited. — least / better / (best)
This museum is the worst I've ever visited.
2. There is _____ to see than in any other museum in the city. — (more) / most / least
There is less to see than in any other museum in the city.
3. I spent the _____ amount of time in the modern art section. — more / (least) / worst
I spent the most amount of time in the modern art section.
4. That collection was the _____ in the entire building. — better / worse / (worst)
That collection was the best in the entire building.
5. The paintings by Renoir were the _____ impressive of all. — less / more / (most)
The paintings by Renoir were the least impressive of all.

Page 29

Name ______________________

Adjectives
Review 2

Fill in the bubble next to the correct answer.

1. Complete the sentence with the correct form of the adjective.
   This camera is the ______ we can afford to buy.
   - ● most expensive
   - Ⓑ less expensive
   - Ⓒ more expensive
   - Ⓓ expensivest
2. Which sentence has a comparative adjective and a superlative adjective?
   - Ⓐ They have the newest house but the oldest car in the neighborhood.
   - Ⓑ There are more trees in their yard and more flowers in ours.
   - Ⓒ The person with cleanest bedroom in our family wins a prize each week.
   - ● The best solution for my messy bedroom may be a bigger closet.
3. Which adjective could be used to compare three friends?
   - Ⓐ blonder
   - ● funniest
   - Ⓒ more athletic
   - Ⓓ less patient
4. Choose the correct adjective to complete the sentence.
   The winning team is always ______ than its opponent.
   - Ⓐ most strategic
   - Ⓑ less competitive
   - ● more successful
   - Ⓓ best focused
5. Which statement about adjectives is correct?
   - Ⓐ Adjectives usually follow a noun.
   - Ⓑ Most adjectives have three syllables.
   - ● Adjectives that make comparisons may end in *er*.
   - Ⓓ Irregular comparative adjectives compare irregular nouns.

© Evan-Moor Corp. • EMC 2756 • Language Fundamentals   Adjectives: Review 2   29

Page 30

Name ______________________

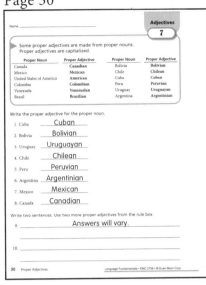

Adjectives
7

Some proper adjectives are made from proper nouns.
Proper adjectives are capitalized.

Proper Noun	Proper Adjective	Proper Noun	Proper Adjective
Canada	**Canadian**	Bolivia	**Bolivian**
Mexico	**Mexican**	Chile	**Chilean**
United States of America	**American**	Cuba	**Cuban**
Colombia	**Colombian**	Peru	**Peruvian**
Venezuela	**Venezuelan**	Uruguay	**Uruguayan**
Brazil	**Brazilian**	Argentina	**Argentinian**

Write the proper adjective for the proper noun.

1. Cuba — Cuban
2. Bolivia — Bolivian
3. Uruguay — Uruguayan
4. Chile — Chilean
5. Peru — Peruvian
6. Argentina — Argentinian
7. Mexico — Mexican
8. Canada — Canadian

Write two sentences. Use two more proper adjectives from the rule box.

9. Answers will vary.
10. ______________________

30   Proper Adjectives   Language Fundamentals • EMC 2756 • © Evan-Moor Corp.

Page 31

Name ______________________

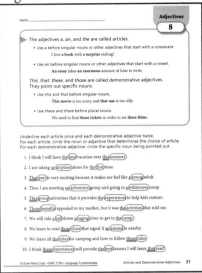

Adjectives
8

The adjectives *a*, *an*, and *the* are called articles.

- Use *a* before singular nouns or other adjectives that start with a consonant.
  I love **a book** with **a surprise** ending!
- Use *an* before singular nouns or other adjectives that start with a vowel.
  An essay takes **an enormous** amount of time to write.

This, *that*, *these*, and *those* are called demonstrative adjectives.
They point out specific nouns.

- Use *this* and *that* before singular nouns.
  This movie is too scary, and **that one** is too silly.
- Use *these* and *those* before plural nouns.
  We need to find **those tickets** in order to see **these films**.

Underline each article once and each demonstrative adjective twice.
For each article, circle the noun or adjective that determines the choice of article.
For each demonstrative adjective, circle the specific noun being pointed out.

1. I think I will have the best vacation ever this summer.
2. I am taking an airplane alone for the first time.
3. That part is very exciting because it makes me feel like a young adult.
4. Then I am meeting an adventure group and going to a wilderness camp.
5. This group advertises that it provides the experiences to help kids mature.
6. Those benefits appealed to my mother, but it was the activities that sold me.
7. We will ride a raft down a raging river to get to the camp.
8. We learn to read those clues that signal if an animal is nearby.
9. We learn all the rules for camping and how to follow those rules.
10. I think these experiences will provide the best lessons I will learn this year!

© Evan-Moor Corp. • EMC 2756 • Language Fundamentals   Articles and Demonstrative Adjectives   31

Page 32

Name ______________________

Adjectives
Review 3

Fill in the bubble next to the correct answer.

1. Which word is the correct proper adjective for Canada?
   - Ⓐ Canadese
   - Ⓑ Canadish
   - ● Canadian
   - Ⓓ Canadan
2. Which pair is not correct?
   - Ⓐ Peru: Peruvian
   - Ⓑ America: American
   - Ⓒ Colombia: Colombian
   - ● Brazil: Brazilish
3. Which sentence has the most articles?
   - ● An elevator is stuck in the store with a crowd inside.
   - Ⓑ A technician has gone to the ninth floor to fix it.
   - Ⓒ An older woman got off just in the nick of time.
   - Ⓓ An episode like this reminds me to always take the stairs.
4. Which sentence correctly uses demonstrative adjectives?
   - Ⓐ These shoe are too old to wear again this year.
   - ● Those sandals were put in that box for donations.
   - Ⓒ This coat is made of those itchy wool I can't wear.
   - Ⓓ The shopping trip will take more time than we expected.
5. How many adjectives are in this sentence?
   These Hawaiian flowers are the kind you see on a tropical island.
   - Ⓐ three
   - Ⓑ four
   - ● five
   - Ⓓ six

32   Adjectives: Review 3   Language Fundamentals • EMC 2756 • © Evan-Moor Corp.

Page 33

Name ______________________

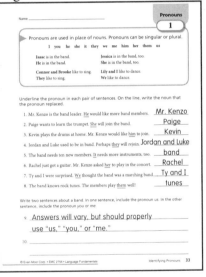

Pronouns
1

Pronouns are used in place of nouns. Pronouns can be singular or plural.

I you he she it they we me him her them us

Isaac is in the band.
He is in the band.

Jessica is in the band, too.
She is in the band, too.

Connor and Brooke like to sing.
They like to sing.

Lily and I like to dance.
We like to dance.

Underline the pronoun in each pair of sentences. On the line, write the noun that the pronoun replaced.

1. Mr. Kenzo is the band leader. He would like more band members. — Mr. Kenzo
2. Paige wants to learn the trumpet. She will join the band. — Paige
3. Kevin plays the drums at home. Mr. Kenzo would like him to join. — Kevin
4. Jordan and Luke used to be in band. Perhaps they will rejoin. — Jordan and Luke
5. The band needs ten new members. It needs more instruments, too. — band
6. Rachel just got a guitar. Mr. Kenzo asked her to play in the concert. — Rachel
7. Ty and I were surprised. We thought the band was a marching band. — Ty and I
8. The band knows rock tunes. The members play them well! — tunes

Write two sentences about a band. In one sentence, include the pronoun *us*. In the other sentence, include the pronoun *you* or *me*.

9. Answers will vary, but should properly use "us," "you," or "me."
10. ______________________

© Evan-Moor Corp. • EMC 2756 • Language Fundamentals   Identifying Pronouns   33

Page 34

Name ______________________

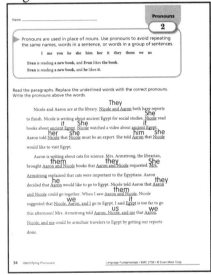

Pronouns
2

Pronouns are used in place of nouns. Use pronouns to avoid repeating the same names, words in a sentence, or words in a group of sentences.

I me you he she him her it they them we us

Evan is reading **a new book,** and **Evan** likes **the book.**
Evan is reading **a new book,** and **he** likes **it.**

Read the paragraphs. Replace the underlined words with the correct pronouns. Write the pronouns above the words.

Nicole and Aaron are at the library. Nicole and Aaron [They] both have reports to finish. Nicole is writing about ancient Egypt for social studies. Nicole [She] read books about ancient Egypt [it]. Nicole [She] watched a video about ancient Egypt [it]. Aaron told Nicole [her] that Nicole [she] must be an expert. She told Aaron [him] that Nicole [she] would like to visit Egypt.

Aaron is writing about cats for science. Mrs. Armstrong, the librarian, brought Aaron and Nicole [them] books that Aaron and Nicole [they] requested. Mrs. Armstrong [She] explained that cats were important to the Egyptians. Aaron decided that Aaron [he] would like to go to Egypt. Nicole told Aaron that Aaron and Nicole [they] could go together. When I saw Aaron and Nicole [them], Nicole suggested that Nicole, Aaron, and I [we] go to Egypt. I said Egypt [it] is too far to go this afternoon! Mrs. Armstrong told Aaron, Nicole, and me [us] that Aaron, Nicole, and me [we] could be armchair travelers to Egypt by getting our reports done.

34   Identifying Pronouns   Language Fundamentals • EMC 2756 • © Evan-Moor Corp.

Page 35

Name ______________________

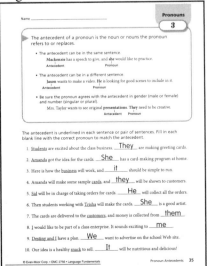

Pronouns
3

The antecedent of a pronoun is the noun or nouns the pronoun refers to or replaces.

- The antecedent can be in the same sentence.
  Mackenzie (Antecedent) has a speech to give, and **she** (Pronoun) would like to practice.
- The antecedent can be in a different sentence.
  Jason (Antecedent) wants to make a video. **He** (Pronoun) is looking for good scenes to include in it.
- Be sure the pronoun agrees with the antecedent in gender (male or female) and number (singular or plural).
  Mrs. Taylor wants to see original **presentations** (Antecedent). **They** (Pronoun) need to be creative.

The antecedent is underlined in each sentence or pair of sentences. Fill in each blank line with the correct pronoun to match the antecedent.

1. Students are excited about the class business. They are making greeting cards.
2. Amanda got the idea for the cards. She has a card-making program at home.
3. Here is how the business will work, and it should be simple to run.
4. Amanda will make some sample cards, and they will be shown to customers.
5. Sid will be in charge of taking orders for cards. He will collect all the orders.
6. Then students working with Trisha will make the cards. She is a good artist.
7. The cards are delivered to the customers, and money is collected from them.
8. I would like to be part of a class enterprise. It sounds exciting to me.
9. Destiny and I have a plan. We want to advertise on the school Web site.
10. Our idea is a healthy snack to sell. It will be nutritious and delicious!

© Evan-Moor Corp. • EMC 2756 • Language Fundamentals   Pronoun Antecedents   35

Page 36

Name ______________________

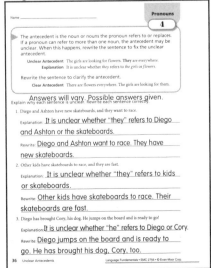

Pronouns
4

The antecedent is the noun or nouns the pronoun refers to or replaces. If a pronoun can refer to more than one noun, the antecedent may be unclear. When this happens, rewrite the sentence to fix the unclear antecedent.

Unclear Antecedent The girls are looking for flowers. **They** are everywhere.
Explanation It is unclear whether *they* refers to *the girls* or *flowers*.

Rewrite the sentence to clarify the antecedent.

Clear Antecedent There are flowers everywhere. The girls are looking for them.

Answers will vary. Possible answers given.

Explain why each sentence is unclear. Rewrite each sentence correctly.

1. Diego and Ashton have new skateboards, and they want to race.
   Explanation: It is unclear whether "they" refers to Diego and Ashton or the skateboards.
   Rewrite: Diego and Ashton want to race. They have new skateboards.
2. Other kids have skateboards to race, and they are fast.
   Explanation: It is unclear whether "they" refers to kids or skateboards.
   Rewrite: Other kids have skateboards to race. Their skateboards are fast.
3. Diego has brought Cory, his dog. He jumps on the board and is ready to go!
   Explanation: It is unclear whether "he" refers to Diego or Cory.
   Rewrite: Diego jumps on the board and is ready to go. He has brought his dog, Cory, too.

36   Unclear Antecedents   Language Fundamentals • EMC 2756 • © Evan-Moor Corp.

Page 37

Name ______________________

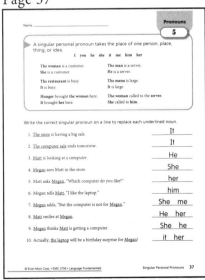

Pronouns
5

A singular personal pronoun takes the place of one person, place, thing, or idea.

I you he she it me him her

The woman is a customer.
She is a customer.

The man is a server.
He is a server.

The restaurant is busy.
It is busy.

The menu is large.
It is large.

Hunger brought **the woman** here.
It brought **her** here.

The woman called to the **server.**
She called to **him.**

Write the correct singular pronoun on a line to replace each underlined noun.

1. The store is having a big sale. — It
2. The computer sale ends tomorrow. — It
3. Matt is looking at a computer. — He
4. Megan sees Matt in the store. — She
5. Matt asks Megan, "Which computer do you like?" — her
6. Megan tells Matt, "I like the laptop." — him
7. Megan adds, "But the computer is not for Megan." — She me
8. Matt smiles at Megan. — He her
9. Megan thinks Matt is getting a computer. — She he
10. Actually, the laptop will be a birthday surprise for Megan! — it her

© Evan-Moor Corp. • EMC 2756 • Language Fundamentals   Singular Personal Pronouns   37

Page 38

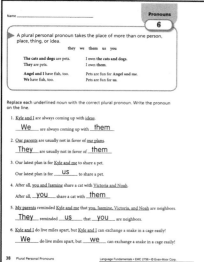

Pronouns 6

A plural personal pronoun takes the place of more than one person, place, thing, or idea.

they   we   them   us   you

The cats and dogs are pets.	I own the cats and dogs.
They are pets.	I own them.
Angel and I are fun for Angel and me, too.	Pets are fun for Angel and me.
We have fish, too.	Pets are fun for us.

Replace each underlined noun with the correct plural pronoun. Write the pronoun on the line.

1. Kyle and I are always coming up with ideas.
   We are always coming up with them.

2. Our parents are usually not in favor of our plans.
   They are usually not in favor of them.

3. Our latest plan is for Kyle and me to share a pet.
   Our latest plan is for us to share a pet.

4. After all, you and Jasmine share a cat with Victoria and Noah.
   After all, you share a cat with them.

5. My parents reminded Kyle and me that you, Jasmine, Victoria, and Noah are neighbors.
   They reminded us that you are neighbors.

6. Kyle and I do live miles apart, but Kyle and I can exchange a snake in a cage easily!
   We do live miles apart, but we can exchange a snake in a cage easily!

38 Plural Personal Pronouns

Page 39

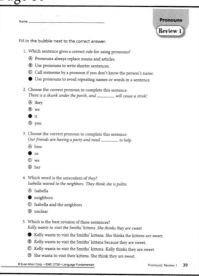

Pronouns Review 1

Fill in the bubble next to the correct answer.

1. Which sentence gives a correct rule for using pronouns?
   - Ⓐ Pronouns always replace nouns and articles.
   - Ⓑ Use pronouns to write shorter sentences.
   - Ⓒ Call someone by a pronoun if you don't know the person's name.
   - ● Use pronouns to avoid repeating names or words in a sentence.

2. Choose the correct pronoun to complete this sentence:
   There is a skunk under the porch, and _____ will cause a stink!
   - Ⓐ they
   - Ⓑ we
   - ● it
   - Ⓓ you

3. Choose the correct pronoun to complete this sentence:
   Our friends are having a party and need _____ to help.
   - Ⓐ him
   - ● us
   - Ⓒ we
   - Ⓓ her

4. Which word is the antecedent of *they*?
   Isabella waved to the neighbors. They think she is polite.
   - Ⓐ Isabella
   - ● neighbors
   - Ⓒ Isabella and the neighbors
   - Ⓓ unclear

5. Which is the best revision of these sentences?
   Kelly wants to visit the Smiths' kittens. She thinks they are sweet.
   - ● Kelly wants to visit the Smiths' kittens. She thinks the kittens are sweet.
   - Ⓑ Kelly wants to visit the Smiths' kittens because they are sweet.
   - Ⓒ Kelly wants to visit the Smiths' kittens. Kelly thinks they are sweet.
   - Ⓓ She wants to visit their kittens. Kelly think they are sweet.

Pronouns: Review 1 39

Page 40

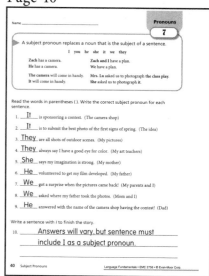

Pronouns 7

A subject pronoun replaces a noun that is the subject of a sentence.

I   you   he   she   it   we   they

Zach has a camera.	Zach and I have a plan.
He has a camera.	We have a plan.
The camera will come in handy.	Mrs. Lu asked us to photograph the class play.
It will come in handy.	She asked us to photograph it.

Read the words in parentheses ( ). Write the correct subject pronoun for each sentence.

1. It is sponsoring a contest. (The camera shop)
2. It is to submit the best photo of the first signs of spring. (The idea)
3. They are all shots of outdoor scenes. (My pictures)
4. They always say I have a good eye for color. (My art teachers)
5. She says my imagination is strong. (My mother)
6. He volunteered to get my film developed. (My father)
7. We got a surprise when the pictures came back! (My parents and I)
8. We asked where my father took the photos. (Mom and I)
9. He answered with the name of the camera shop having the contest! (Dad)

Write a sentence with I to finish the story.

10. Answers will vary, but sentence must include I as a subject pronoun.

40 Subject Pronouns

Page 41

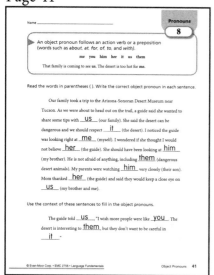

Pronouns 8

An object pronoun follows an action verb or a preposition (words such as *about, at, for, of, to,* and *with*).

me   you   him   her   it   us   them

That family is coming to see us. The desert is too hot for me.

Read the words in parentheses ( ). Write the correct object pronoun in each sentence.

Our family took a trip to the Arizona-Sonoran Desert Museum near Tucson. As we were about to head out on the trail, a guide said she wanted to share some tips with us (our family). She said the desert can be dangerous and we should respect it (the desert). I noticed the guide was looking right at me (myself). I wondered if she thought I would not believe her (the guide). She should have been looking at him (my brother). He is not afraid of anything, including them (dangerous desert animals). My parents were watching him very closely (their son). Mom thanked her (the guide) and said they would keep a close eye on us (my brother and me).

Use the context of these sentences to fill in the object pronouns.

The guide told us, "I wish more people were like you. The desert is interesting to them, but they don't want to be careful in it."

Object Pronouns 41

Page 42

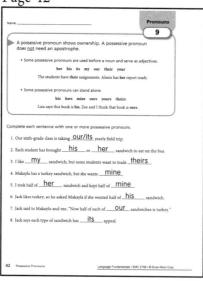

Pronouns 9

A possessive pronoun shows ownership. A possessive pronoun does not need an apostrophe.

- Some possessive pronouns are used before a noun and serve as adjectives.

  her   his   its   my   our   their   your

  The students have their assignments. Alexis has her report ready.

- Some possessive pronouns can stand alone.

  his   hers   mine   ours   yours   theirs

  Luis says this book is his. Zoe and I think that book is ours.

Complete each sentence with one or more possessive pronouns.

1. Our sixth-grade class is taking our/its yearly field trip.
2. Each student has brought his or her sandwich to eat on the bus.
3. I like my sandwich, but some students want to trade theirs.
4. Makayla has a turkey sandwich, but she wants mine.
5. I took half of her sandwich and kept half of mine.
6. Jack likes turkey, so he asked Makayla if she wanted half of his sandwich.
7. Jack said to Makayla and me, "Now half of each of our sandwiches is turkey."
8. Jack says each type of sandwich has its appeal.

42 Possessive Pronouns

Page 43

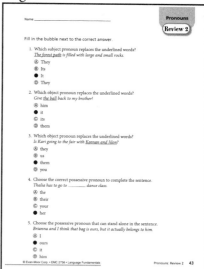

Pronouns Review 2

Fill in the bubble next to the correct answer.

1. Which subject pronoun replaces the underlined words?
   The forest path is filled with large and small rocks.
   - Ⓐ They
   - Ⓑ Its
   - ● It
   - Ⓓ They

2. Which object pronoun replaces the underlined words?
   Give the ball back to my brother!
   - Ⓐ him
   - ● it
   - Ⓒ its
   - Ⓓ them

3. Which object pronoun replaces the underlined words?
   Is Kari going to the fair with Keenan and Jilon?
   - Ⓐ they
   - Ⓑ us
   - ● them
   - Ⓓ you

4. Choose the correct possessive pronoun to complete the sentence.
   Thalia has to go to _____ dance class.
   - Ⓐ the
   - Ⓑ their
   - Ⓒ your
   - ● her

5. Choose the possessive pronoun that can stand alone in the sentence.
   Brianna and I think that bag is ours, but it actually belongs to him.
   - Ⓐ I
   - ● ours
   - Ⓒ it
   - Ⓓ him

Pronouns: Review 2 43

Page 44

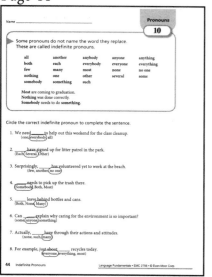

Pronouns 10

Some pronouns do not name the word they replace. These are called indefinite pronouns.

all	another	anybody	anyone	anything
both	each	everybody	everyone	everything
few	many	most	none	no one
nothing	one	other	several	some
somebody	something	such		

Most are coming to graduation.
Nothing was done correctly.
Somebody needs to do something.

Circle the correct indefinite pronoun to complete the sentence.

1. We need _____ to help out this weekend for the class cleanup.
   (one, **everybody**, all)
2. _____ have signed up for litter patrol in the park.
   (Each, **Several**, Other)
3. Surprisingly, _____ has volunteered yet to work at the beach.
   (few, another, **no one**)
4. _____ needs to pick up the trash there.
   (**Somebody**, Both, Most)
5. _____ leave behind bottles and cans.
   (Both, None, **Many**)
6. Can _____ explain why caring for the environment is so important?
   (some, **anyone**, something)
7. Actually, _____ have through their actions and attitudes.
   (none, such, **many**)
8. For example, just about _____ recycles today.
   (**everyone**, everything, most)

44 Indefinite Pronouns

Page 45

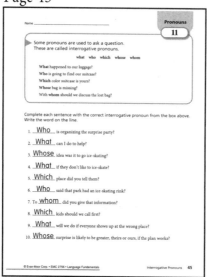

Pronouns 11

Some pronouns are used to ask a question. These are called interrogative pronouns.

what   who   which   whose   whom

What happened to our luggage?
Who is going to find our suitcase?
Which color suitcase is yours?
Whose bag is missing?
With whom should we discuss the lost bag?

Complete each sentence with the correct interrogative pronoun from the box above. Write the word on the line.

1. Who is organizing the surprise party?
2. What can I do to help?
3. Whose idea was it to go ice-skating?
4. What if they don't like to ice-skate?
5. Which place did you tell them?
6. Who said that park had an ice-skating rink?
7. To whom did you give that information?
8. Which kids should we call first?
9. What will we do if everyone shows up at the wrong place?
10. Whose surprise is likely to be greater, theirs or ours, if the plan works?

Interrogative Pronouns 45

Page 46

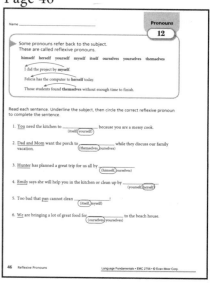

Pronouns 12

Some pronouns refer back to the subject. These are called reflexive pronouns.

himself   herself   yourself   myself   itself   ourselves   yourselves   themselves

I did the project by myself.
Felicia has the computer to herself today.
Those students found themselves without enough time to finish.

Read each sentence. Underline the subject, then circle the correct reflexive pronoun to complete the sentence.

1. You need the kitchen to _____ because you are a messy cook.
   (itself, **yourself**)
2. Dad and Mom want the porch to _____ while they discuss our family vacation.
   (**themselves**, ourselves)
3. Hunter has planned a great trip for us all by _____.
   (**himself**, ourselves)
4. Emily says she will help you in the kitchen or clean up by _____.
   (yourself, **herself**)
5. Too bad that pan cannot clean _____.
   (**itself**, myself)
6. We are bringing a lot of great food for _____ to the beach house.
   (**ourselves**, yourselves)

46 Reflexive Pronouns

Page 47

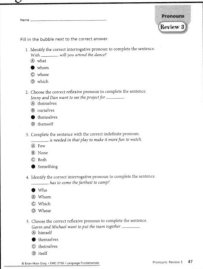

Name _____

Pronouns — Review 3

Fill in the bubble next to the correct answer.

1. Identify the correct interrogative pronoun to complete the sentence.
   With _____ will you attend the dance?
   Ⓐ what
   ● whom
   Ⓒ whose
   Ⓓ which

2. Choose the correct reflexive pronoun to complete the sentence.
   Jenny and Dan want to see the project for _____.
   Ⓐ theirselves
   Ⓑ ourselves
   ● themselves
   Ⓓ themself

3. Complete the sentence with the correct indefinite pronoun.
   _____ is needed in that play to make it more fun to watch.
   Ⓐ Few
   Ⓑ None
   Ⓒ Both
   ● Something

4. Identify the correct interrogative pronoun to complete the sentence.
   _____ has to come the farthest to camp?
   ● Who
   Ⓑ Whom
   Ⓒ Which
   Ⓓ Whose

5. Choose the correct reflexive pronoun to complete the sentence.
   Gavin and Michael want to put the team together _____.
   Ⓐ himself
   ● themselves
   Ⓒ theirselves
   Ⓓ itself

© Evan-Moor Corp. • EMC 2756 • Language Fundamentals   Pronouns: Review 3   47

Page 48

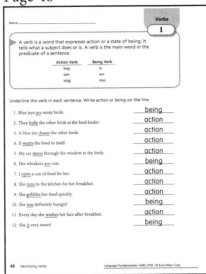

Name _____

Verbs — 1

A verb is a word that expresses action or a state of being. It tells what a subject does or is. A verb is the main word in the predicate of a sentence.

Action Verb	Being Verb
leap	is
saw	are
sing	was

Underline the verb in each sentence. Write *action* or *being* on the line.

1. Blue jays <u>are</u> noisy birds. — being
2. They <u>bully</u> the other birds at the bird feeder. — action
3. A blue jay <u>chases</u> the other birds. — action
4. It <u>wants</u> the food to itself. — action
5. My cat <u>stares</u> through the window at the birds. — action
6. Her whiskers <u>are</u> cute. — being
7. I <u>open</u> a can of food for her. — action
8. She <u>runs</u> to the kitchen for her breakfast. — action
9. She <u>gobbles</u> her food quickly. — action
10. She <u>was</u> definitely hungry! — being
11. Every day she <u>washes</u> her face after breakfast. — action
12. She <u>is</u> very sweet! — being

48   Identifying Verbs   Language Fundamentals • EMC 2756 • © Evan-Moor Corp.

Page 49

Name _____

Verbs — 2

An action verb tells what the subject does.
- Some action verbs tell about actions that can be seen or heard.
  We **trod** along the wooded path. We **sang** a lively hiking song.
- Some action verbs tell about actions that cannot be seen or heard.
  Mr. Krebs **thinks** about resting. He **wants** a snack.

Write the action verb in each sentence.

1. The Nature Club hikes in the woods. — hikes
2. Our leaders teach us about plants and animals. — teach
3. Ms. Curtis points to some poison ivy. — points
4. Avoid those shiny green leaves! — Avoid
5. Ms. Curtis leads us away from the dangerous plant. — leads

Choose an action verb from the word box below to complete each sentence. Circle *yes* if the action can be seen or heard or *no* if it cannot be seen or heard.

| flowed   hope   will explore   waded   are planning |

6. Yesterday we __waded__ in a creek in the woods.   (yes) no
7. The water __flowed__ over our toes and ankles.   (yes) no
8. We __are planning__ another hike.   yes (no)
9. The club __will explore__ another trail with Mr. Krebs and Ms. Curtis.   (yes) no
10. We all __hope__ for a sunny day.   yes (no)

© Evan-Moor Corp. • EMC 2756 • Language Fundamentals   Action Verbs   49

Page 50

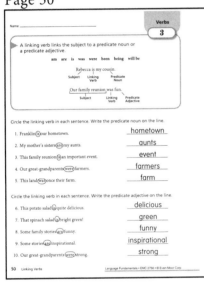

Name _____

Verbs — 3

A linking verb links the subject to a predicate noun or a predicate adjective.

am are is was were been being will be

Rebecca is my cousin.
Subject / Linking Verb / Predicate Noun

Our family reunion was fun.
Subject / Linking Verb / Predicate Adjective

Circle the linking verb in each sentence. Write the predicate noun on the line.

1. Franklin (is) our hometown. — hometown
2. My mother's sisters (are) my aunts. — aunts
3. This family reunion (is) an important event. — event
4. Our great-grandparents (were) farmers. — farmers
5. This land (was) once their farm. — farm

Circle the linking verb in each sentence. Write the predicate adjective on the line.

6. This potato salad (is) quite delicious. — delicious
7. That spinach salad (is) bright green! — green
8. Some family stories (are) funny. — funny
9. Some stories (are) inspirational. — inspirational
10. Our great-grandparents (were) strong. — strong

50   Linking Verbs   Language Fundamentals • EMC 2756 • © Evan-Moor Corp.

Page 51

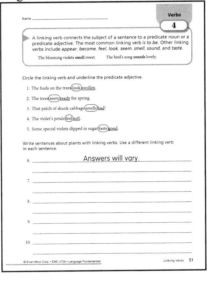

Name _____

Verbs — 4

A linking verb connects the subject of a sentence to a predicate noun or a predicate adjective. The most common linking verb is *to be*. Other linking verbs include *appear, become, feel, look, seem, smell, sound,* and *taste*.

The blooming violets **smell** sweet.   The bird's song **sounds** lovely.

Circle the linking verb and underline the predicate adjective.

1. The buds on the trees (look) <u>swollen</u>.
2. The trees (seem) <u>ready</u> for spring.
3. That patch of skunk cabbage (smells) <u>bad</u>!
4. The violet's petals (feel) <u>soft</u>.
5. Some special violets dipped in sugar (taste) <u>good</u>.

Write sentences about plants with linking verbs. Use a different linking verb in each sentence.

6. _____ Answers will vary. _____
7. _____
8. _____
9. _____
10. _____

© Evan-Moor Corp. • EMC 2756 • Language Fundamentals   Linking Verbs   51

Page 52

Name _____

Verbs — Review 1

Fill in the bubble next to the correct answer.

1. In which sentence is the verb underlined?
   Ⓐ Miners dig <u>coal</u> from deep holes in the Earth.
   Ⓑ Mining is a dangerous <u>job</u>.
   Ⓒ The coal <u>dust</u> gets in the miners' lungs.
   ● The miners <u>arrive</u> for work.

2. Which sentence below contains an action verb?
   ● The miners wear lights on their hard hats.
   Ⓑ The right equipment is important.
   Ⓒ Miners are serious about safety.
   Ⓓ The crew seems ready to go.

3. Which sentence contains a linking verb?
   Ⓐ Old furnaces burned coal.
   ● The buildings were black with coal dust.
   Ⓒ Trucks delivered coal to homes.
   Ⓓ Furnaces glowed with fire.

4. Which sentence contains a linking verb?
   Ⓐ Coal smoke rose over a town.
   ● Sometimes the days looked as dark as night.
   Ⓒ Look at these old photographs.
   Ⓓ I can see the mine entrance in the distance.

5. Which of the verbs below can be a linking verb?
   Ⓐ dance
   Ⓑ jump
   Ⓒ hurry
   ● taste

52   Verbs: Review 1   Language Fundamentals • EMC 2756 • © Evan-Moor Corp.

Page 53

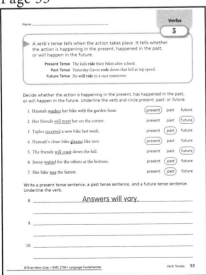

Name _____

Verbs — 5

A verb's tense tells when the action takes place. It tells whether the action is happening in the present, happened in the past, or will happen in the future.

Present Tense The kids <u>ride</u> their bikes after school.
Past Tense Yesterday Gavin <u>rode</u> down that hill at top speed.
Future Tense He <u>will ride</u> in a race tomorrow.

Decide whether the action is happening in the present, has happened in the past, or will happen in the future. Underline the verb and circle *present*, *past*, or *future*.

1. Hannah <u>washes</u> her bike with the garden hose. — (present) past future
2. Her friends <u>will meet</u> her on the corner. — present past (future)
3. Taylor <u>received</u> a new bike last week. — present (past) future
4. Hannah's clean bike <u>gleams</u> like new. — (present) past future
5. The friends <u>will coast</u> down the hill. — present past (future)
6. Jenny <u>waited</u> for the others at the bottom. — present (past) future
7. Her bike <u>was</u> the fastest. — present (past) future

Write a present tense sentence, a past tense sentence, and a future tense sentence. Underline the verb.

8. _____ Answers will vary. _____
9. _____
10. _____

© Evan-Moor Corp. • EMC 2756 • Language Fundamentals   Verb Tenses   53

Page 54

Name _____

Verbs — 6

The present tense tells that the action or state of being is happening now or happens regularly.

Is Happening Now My favorite television show is on.
Happens Regularly The main character gets in trouble each week.

Read each sentence. Underline the present tense verb. Write *now* or *regularly*.

1. I <u>watch</u> my favorite show on Wednesday evenings. — regularly
2. On those nights, my family <u>sits</u> on the couch together. — regularly
3. We <u>pause</u> for a commercial. — now
4. During the commercial, my dad <u>gets</u> a snack in the kitchen. — now
5. Sometimes, we <u>eat</u> ice cream during the show. — regularly
6. I <u>enjoy</u> the jokes and funny situations on the show. — regularly
7. In every episode, the dad in the show <u>gets</u> the last word. — regularly

Write three sentences in the present tense to show action that is happening now and regularly.

8. _____ Answers will vary. _____
9. _____
10. _____

54   Present Tense Verbs   Language Fundamentals • EMC 2756 • © Evan-Moor Corp.

Page 55

Name _____

Verbs — 7

A past tense verb tells that an action or state of being took place in the past and is over.

My family **traveled** to Germany last summer.
We **went** on a boat down a river.
The guide **pointed** to old castles on the shore.

Circle the past tense verb in each pair of sentences.

1. Here are the pictures of our trip to Europe. We (boarded) this enormous plane.
2. My parents (gave) me this camera before the trip. I like taking pictures.
3. This picture shows a town square in Germany. We (ate) lunch in that town.
4. I (tried) a dish of sauerkraut. You are wrinkling your nose.
5. I (liked) the sauerkraut! I want to have it again soon.
6. In this picture, we are in Berlin. We (saw) many monuments there.
7. This bomb-damaged church is a war monument now. People (were) quiet there.
8. We (brought) these spicy cookies back with us. I'll share them with you.

Write sentences in the past tense about something that happened and is over.

9. _____ Answers will vary. _____
10. _____

© Evan-Moor Corp. • EMC 2756 • Language Fundamentals   Past Tense Verbs   55

Page 56

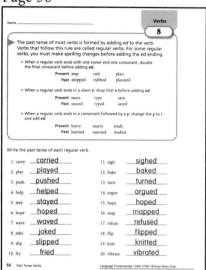

Verbs 8

The past tense of most verbs is formed by adding *ed* to the verb. Verbs that follow this rule are called regular verbs. For some regular verbs, you must make spelling changes before adding the *ed* ending.

- When a regular verb ends with one vowel and one consonant, double the final consonant before adding *ed*.

Present	stop	rub	plan
Past	stopped	rubbed	planned

- When a regular verb ends in a silent *e*, drop the *e* before adding *ed*.

Present	snore	type	save
Past	snored	typed	saved

- When a regular verb ends in a consonant followed by a *y*, change the *y* to *i* and add *ed*.

Present	hurry	marry	study
Past	hurried	married	studied

Write the past tense of each regular verb.

1. carry — **carried**
2. play — **played**
3. push — **pushed**
4. help — **helped**
5. stay — **stayed**
6. hope — **hoped**
7. wave — **waved**
8. joke — **joked**
9. slip — **slipped**
10. fry — **fried**
11. sigh — **sighed**
12. bake — **baked**
13. turn — **turned**
14. argue — **argued**
15. hope — **hoped**
16. map — **mapped**
17. refuse — **refused**
18. flip — **flipped**
19. knit — **knitted**
20. vibrate — **vibrated**

Page 57

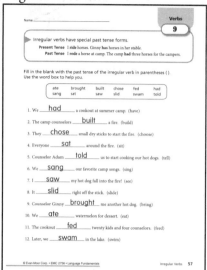

Verbs 9

Irregular verbs have special past tense forms.

Present Tense I **ride** horses. Ginny **has** horses in her stable.
Past Tense I **rode** at camp. The camp **had** three horses for the campers.

Fill in the blank with the past tense of the irregular verb in parentheses ( ). Use the word box to help you.

| ate | brought | built | chose | fed | had |
| sang | sat | saw | slid | swam | told |

1. We **had** a cookout at summer camp. (have)
2. The camp counselors **built** a fire. (build)
3. They **chose** small dry sticks to start the fire. (choose)
4. Everyone **sat** around the fire. (sit)
5. Counselor Adam **told** us to start cooking our hot dogs. (tell)
6. We **sang** our favorite camp songs. (sing)
7. I **saw** my hot dog fall into the fire! (see)
8. It **slid** right off the stick. (slide)
9. Counselor Ginny **brought** me another hot dog. (bring)
10. We **ate** watermelon for dessert. (eat)
11. The cookout **fed** twenty kids and four counselors. (feed)
12. Later, we **swam** in the lake. (swim)

Page 58

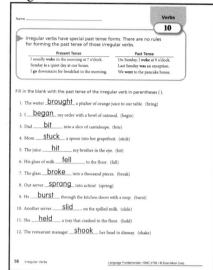

Verbs 10

Irregular verbs have special past tense forms. There are no rules for forming the past tense of those irregular verbs.

Present Tense	Past Tense
I usually **wake** in the morning at 7 o'clock.	On Sunday, I **woke** at 9 o'clock.
Sunday is a quiet day at our house.	Last Sunday **was** an exception.
I **go** downstairs for breakfast in the morning.	We **went** to the pancake house.

Fill in the blank with the past tense of the irregular verb in parentheses ( ).

1. The waiter **brought** a pitcher of orange juice to our table. (bring)
2. I **began** my order with a bowl of oatmeal. (begin)
3. Dad **bit** into a slice of cantaloupe. (bite)
4. Mom **stuck** a spoon into her grapefruit. (stick)
5. The juice **hit** my brother in the eye. (hit)
6. His glass of milk **fell** to the floor. (fall)
7. The glass **broke** into a thousand pieces. (break)
8. Our server **sprang** into action! (spring)
9. He **burst** through the kitchen doors with a mop. (burst)
10. Another server **slid** on the spilled milk. (slide)
11. She **held** a tray that crashed to the floor. (hold)
12. The restaurant manager **shook** her head in dismay. (shake)

Page 59

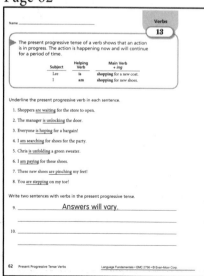

Verbs Review 2

Fill in the bubble next to the correct answer.

1. Which sentence is in the present tense?
   - Ⓐ Ms. Reed strode into the room.
   - Ⓑ She was on a mission.
   - Ⓒ She cleared her throat.
   - ● Her voice rings strong and clear now.

2. Which sentence is in the past tense?
   - Ⓐ Ms. Reed is the chemistry teacher at the high school.
   - Ⓑ She shows our class a big chart.
   - Ⓒ She calls it the periodic table of elements.
   - ● My older sister studied this chart last year.

3. Which sentence contains a regular verb in the past tense?
   - ● The table looked complicated to me.
   - Ⓑ There was a symbol in every square.
   - Ⓒ Ms. Reed tells us about the elements.
   - Ⓓ She brought some test tubes to our classroom, too.

4. What is the past tense of *stay*?
   - Ⓐ stayyed
   - Ⓑ staied
   - ● stayed
   - Ⓓ staied

5. Which sentence contains the correct past tense form of its verb?
   - Ⓐ My brother forgetted his chemistry book.
   - ● My mother became a chemist.
   - Ⓒ I finded the subject interesting.
   - Ⓓ I will read more about it.

Page 60

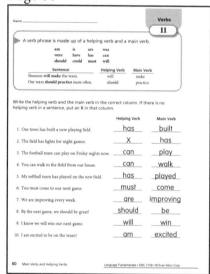

Verbs 11

A verb phrase is made up of a helping verb and a main verb.

am	is	are	was
were	have	has	can
should	could	must	will

Sentence	Helping Verb	Main Verb
Shannon **will make** the team.	will	make
Our team **should practice** more often.	should	practice

Write the helping verb and the main verb in the correct column. If there is no helping verb in a sentence, put an X in that column.

	Helping Verb	Main Verb
1. Our town has built a new playing field.	has	built
2. The field has lights for night games.	X	has
3. The football team can play on Friday nights now.	can	play
4. You can walk to the field from our house.	can	walk
5. My softball team has played on the new field.	has	played
6. You must come to our next game.	must	come
7. We are improving every week.	are	improving
8. By the next game, we should be great!	should	be
9. I know we will win our next game.	will	win
10. I am excited to be on the team!	am	excited

Page 61

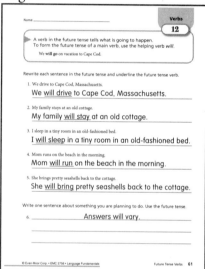

Verbs 12

A verb in the future tense tells what is going to happen. To form the future tense of a main verb, use the helping verb *will*.

We **will go** on vacation to Cape Cod.

Rewrite each sentence in the future tense and underline the future tense verb.

1. We drive to Cape Cod, Massachusetts.
   We <u>will drive</u> to Cape Cod, Massachusetts.

2. My family stays at an old cottage.
   My family <u>will stay</u> at an old cottage.

3. I sleep in a tiny room in an old-fashioned bed.
   I <u>will sleep</u> in a tiny room in an old-fashioned bed.

4. Mom runs on the beach in the morning.
   Mom <u>will run</u> on the beach in the morning.

5. She brings pretty seashells back to the cottage.
   She <u>will bring</u> pretty seashells back to the cottage.

Write one sentence about something you are planning to do. Use the future tense.

6. **Answers will vary.**

Page 62

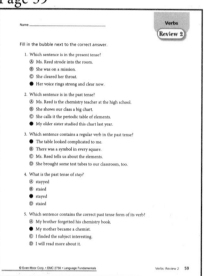

Verbs 13

The present progressive tense of a verb shows that an action is in progress. The action is happening now and will continue for a period of time.

Subject	Helping Verb	Main Verb + *ing*
Lee	is	**shopping** for a new coat.
I	am	**shopping** for new shoes.

Underline the present progressive verb in each sentence.

1. Shoppers <u>are waiting</u> for the store to open.
2. The manager <u>is unlocking</u> the door.
3. Everyone <u>is hoping</u> for a bargain!
4. I <u>am searching</u> for shoes for the party.
5. Chris <u>is unfolding</u> a green sweater.
6. I <u>am paying</u> for these shoes.
7. These new shoes <u>are pinching</u> my feet!
8. You <u>are stepping</u> on my toe!

Write two sentences with verbs in the present progressive tense.

9. **Answers will vary.**

10. _____

Page 63

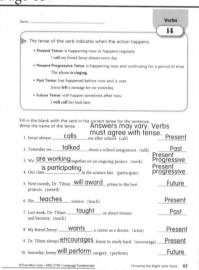

Verbs 14

The tense of the verb indicates when the action happens.

- **Present Tense:** is happening now or happens regularly
  I call my friend Jenny almost every day.
- **Present Progressive Tense:** is happening now and continuing for a period of time
  The phone is **ringing**.
- **Past Tense:** has happened before now and is over
  Jenny **left** a message for me yesterday.
- **Future Tense:** will happen sometime after now
  I will **call** her back later.

Fill in the blank with the verb in the correct tense for the sentence. Write the name of the tense.

Answers may vary. Verbs must agree with tense.

1. Jenny always **calls** me after school. (call) — **Present**
2. Yesterday we **talked** about a school assignment. (talk) — **Past**
3. We **are working** together on an ongoing project. (work) — **Present Progressive**
4. Our class **is participating** in the science fair. (participate) — **Present Progressive**
5. Next month, Dr. Tilton **will award** prizes to the best projects. (award) — **Future**
6. She **teaches** science. (teach) — **Present**
7. Last week, Dr. Tilton **taught** us about viruses and bacteria. (teach) — **Past**
8. My friend Jenny **wants** a career as a doctor. (want) — **Present**
9. Dr. Tilton always **encourages** Jenny to study hard. (encourage) — **Present**
10. Someday, Jenny **will perform** surgery. (perform) — **Future**

Page 64

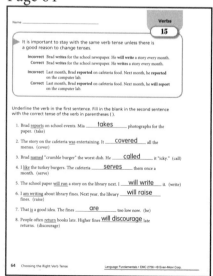

Verbs 15

It is important to stay with the same verb tense unless there is a good reason to change tenses.

Incorrect Brad **writes** for the school newspaper. He **will write** a story every month.
Correct Brad **writes** for the school newspaper. He **writes** a story every month.

Incorrect Last month, Brad **reported** on cafeteria food. Next month, he **reported** on the computer lab.
Correct Last month, Brad **reported** on cafeteria food. Next month, he **will report** on the computer lab.

Underline the verb in the first sentence. Fill in the blank in the second sentence with the correct tense of the verb in parentheses ( ).

1. Brad <u>reports</u> on school events. Mia **takes** photographs for the paper. (take)
2. The story on the cafeteria <u>was</u> entertaining. It **covered** all the menus. (cover)
3. Brad <u>named</u> "crumble burger" the worst dish. He **called** it "icky." (call)
4. I <u>like</u> the turkey burgers. The cafeteria **serves** them once a month. (serve)
5. The school paper <u>will run</u> a story on the library next. I **will write** it. (write)
6. I <u>am writing</u> about library fines. Next year, the library **will raise** fines. (raise)
7. That <u>is</u> a good idea. The fines **are** too low now. (be)
8. People often <u>return</u> books late. Higher fines **will discourage** late returns. (discourage)

Verbs — Review 3

Fill in the bubble next to the correct answer.

1. Which sentence is in the future tense?
   Ⓐ George is playing soccer.
   ● He will walk the dog later.
   Ⓒ Charlie waits for George by the back door.
   Ⓓ He wags his tail when he sees George.

2. In which sentence is the main verb underlined?
   Ⓐ Charlie will chase squirrels in the yard.
   Ⓑ That one has scampered up a tree.
   ● The squirrel is chattering at Charlie from a branch.
   Ⓓ George is tugging at the leash.

3. In which sentence is the helping verb underlined?
   Ⓐ George and Charlie will follow a path through the woods.
   Ⓑ They have walked this path many times.
   Ⓒ Charlie is nervous.
   ● He is sniffing at the air.

4. Which sentence is in the present progressive tense?
   Ⓐ Charlie has spotted a rabbit in the underbrush.
   Ⓑ Charlie is very still.
   ● George is holding tight to the leash.
   Ⓓ The rabbit escapes into the woods.

5. In which sentence is the verb in the correct tense?
   ● Yesterday, Charlie almost caught the rabbit.
   Ⓑ Before, George will chase him through the woods.
   Ⓒ Yesterday, George is remembering Charlie's leash.
   Ⓓ Yesterday, Charlie takes off after a rabbit.

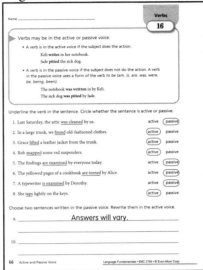

Verbs 16

Verbs may be in the active or passive voice.
- A verb is in the active voice if the subject does the action.
  Keli **writes** in her notebook.
  Jade **pitied** the sick dog.
- A verb is in the passive voice if the subject does not do the action. A verb in the passive voice uses a form of the verb to be (am, is, are, was, were, be, being, been).
  The notebook **was written** in by Keli.
  The sick dog **was pitied** by Jade.

Underline the verb in the sentence. Circle whether the sentence is active or passive.

1. Last Saturday, the attic was cleaned by us. — active (passive)
2. In a large trunk, we found old-fashioned clothes. — (active) passive
3. Grace lifted a leather jacket from the trunk. — (active) passive
4. Rob snapped some red suspenders. — (active) passive
5. The findings are examined by everyone today. — active (passive)
6. The yellowed pages of a cookbook are turned by Alice. — active (passive)
7. A typewriter is examined by Dorothy. — active (passive)
8. She taps lightly on the keys. — (active) passive

Choose two sentences written in the passive voice. Rewrite them in the active voice.

9. Answers will vary.

10.

Verbs 17

Verbs may be in the active or passive voice. Using the active voice in your writing makes it more interesting.
- A verb is in the active voice if the subject does the action.
  The team **wears** red uniforms for home games.
  Delia **wrote** a letter to me about her decision.
- A verb is in the passive voice if the subject does not do the action. A verb in the passive voice uses a form of the verb to be (am, is, are, was, were, be, being, been).
  Red shirts **are worn** by the team for home games.
  A letter **was written** to me by Delia about her decision.

Write a paragraph of at least four sentences about your family. Use the active voice.

Answers will vary.

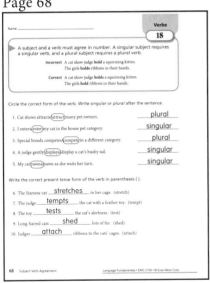

Verbs 18

A subject and a verb must agree in number. A singular subject requires a singular verb, and a plural subject requires a plural verb.

Incorrect A cat show judge **hold** a squirming kitten.
The girls **holds** ribbons in their hands.

Correct A cat show judge **holds** a squirming kitten.
The girls **hold** ribbons in their hands.

Circle the correct form of the verb. Write singular or plural after the sentence.

1. Cat shows attracts/(attract) many pet owners. — plural
2. I enters/(enter) my cat in the house pet category. — singular
3. Special breeds competes/(compete) in a different category. — plural
4. A judge gently (displays)/display a cat's bushy tail. — singular
5. My cat (yawns)/yawn as she waits her turn. — singular

Write the correct present tense form of the verb in parentheses ( ).

6. The Siamese cat __stretches__ in her cage. (stretch)
7. The judge __tempts__ the cat with a feather toy. (tempt)
8. The toy __tests__ the cat's alertness. (test)
9. Long-haired cats __shed__ lots of fur. (shed)
10. Judges __attach__ ribbons to the cats' cages. (attach)

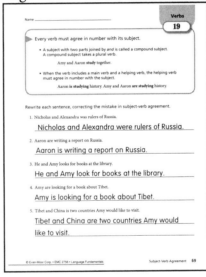

Verbs 19

Every verb must agree in number with its subject.
- A subject with two parts joined by and is called a compound subject. A compound subject takes a plural verb.
  Amy and Aaron **study** together.
- When the verb includes a main verb and a helping verb, the helping verb must agree in number with the subject.
  Aaron **is studying** history. Amy and Aaron **are studying** history.

Rewrite each sentence, correcting the mistake in subject-verb agreement.

1. Nicholas and Alexandra was rulers of Russia.
   Nicholas and Alexandra were rulers of Russia.

2. Aaron are writing a report on Russia.
   Aaron is writing a report on Russia.

3. He and Amy looks for books at the library.
   He and Amy look for books at the library.

4. Amy are looking for a book about Tibet.
   Amy is looking for a book about Tibet.

5. Tibet and China is two countries Amy would like to visit.
   Tibet and China are two countries Amy would like to visit.

Verbs — Review 4

Use what you know about verb tenses to answer each question.

1. Which sentence is in the passive voice?
   Ⓐ The store clerk returns change to a customer.
   Ⓑ The shelves are full.
   ● The shopping is being done by Dylan today.
   Ⓓ The fresh bread smells good.

2. Which sentence is in the active voice?
   Ⓐ A box of cereal was taken from the shelf by Dylan.
   Ⓑ The information on nutrition was checked.
   Ⓒ The box of Sugar Shock was placed back on the shelf.
   ● He chose a box of Whole Wheat Wonder instead.

3. Which one is the best revision from passive to active voice?
   A cart is being pushed by Dylan with a squeaky wheel.
   Ⓐ The cart with a squeaky wheel is being pushed by Dylan.
   ● Dylan pushes a cart with a squeaky wheel.
   Ⓒ The cart pushed by Dylan has a squeaky wheel.
   Ⓓ Squeaky wheels on the cart are pushed by Dylan.

4. In which sentence does the verb agree with its subject?
   Ⓐ Dylan choose a large purple eggplant.
   Ⓑ He are planning an Italian meal.
   ● Dylan and his dad cook together.
   Ⓓ They makes great tomato sauce.

5. In which sentence does the verb agree with its subject?
   Ⓐ In the kitchen, Dylan consult a cookbook.
   Ⓑ He take a large pan from the cupboard.
   Ⓒ This recipe has a long list of ingredients.
   ● The instructions are complicated.

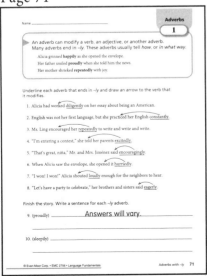

Adverbs 1

An adverb can modify a verb, an adjective, or another adverb. Many adverbs end in –ly. These adverbs usually tell how, or in what way.
Alicia grinned **happily** as she opened the envelope.
Her father smiled **proudly** when he told her the news.
Her mother shrieked **repeatedly** with joy.

Underline each adverb that ends in –ly and draw an arrow to the verb that it modifies.

1. Alicia had worked diligently on her essay about being an American.
2. English was not her first language, but she practiced her English constantly.
3. Ms. Ling encouraged her repeatedly to write and write and write.
4. "I'm entering a contest," she told her parents excitedly.
5. "That's great, niña," Mr. and Mrs. Jimenez said encouragingly.
6. When Alicia saw the envelope, she opened it hurriedly.
7. "I won! I won!" Alicia shouted loudly enough for the neighbors to hear.
8. "Let's have a party to celebrate," her brothers and sisters said eagerly.

Finish the story. Write a sentence for each –ly adverb.

9. (proudly) Answers will vary.

10. (sleepily)

Adverbs 2

Many adverbs don't end in –ly. These adverbs often tell where, when, and to what extent. The words tomorrow, there, soon, here, very, and too are all adverbs.

Where Gina was tired once she got there.
When Yesterday she had finished her drawing.
To What Extent She was very pleased with her final version.

Find the adverb in each sentence and circle it. Then write where, when, or to what extent on the line.

1. Gina drew (daily) trying to finish her self-portrait for the state fair. — when
2. First prize was something she wanted (very) much. — to what extent
3. If she won, she and her family would be (so) happy. — to what extent
4. First prize was a trip to New York, and she and her family would fly (there). — where
5. Gina was going to learn (tomorrow) who won the contest. — when

Complete each sentence with the type of adverb in parentheses.

6. Gina looked __everywhere__ (where) to see if she could find the judges.
7. She knew they would be on stage __soon__ (when).
8. __Then__ (when) one of the judges spoke.
9. Gina's family was __very__ (to what extent) proud to hear her name announced.
10. Gina was __too__ (to what extent) stunned to move!

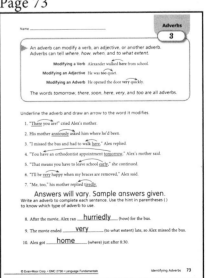

Adverbs 3

An adverb can modify a verb, an adjective, or another adverb. Adverbs can tell where, how, when, and to what extent.

Modifying a Verb Alexander walked **here** from school.
Modifying an Adjective He was **too** quiet.
Modifying an Adverb He opened the door **very** quickly.

The words tomorrow, there, soon, here, very, and too are all adverbs.

Underline the adverb and draw an arrow to the word it modifies.

1. "There you are!" cried Alex's mother.
2. His mother anxiously asked him where he'd been.
3. "I missed the bus and had to walk here," Alex replied.
4. "You have an orthodontist appointment tomorrow," Alex's mother said.
5. "That means you have to leave school early," she continued.
6. "I'll be very happy when my braces are removed," Alex said.
7. "Me, too," his mother replied tiredly.

Answers will vary. Sample answers given.

Write an adverb to complete each sentence. Use the hint in parentheses ( ) to know which type of adverb to use.

8. After the movie, Alex ran __hurriedly__ (how) for the bus.
9. The movie ended __very__ (to what extent) late, so Alex missed the bus.
10. Alex got __home__ (where) just after 8:30.

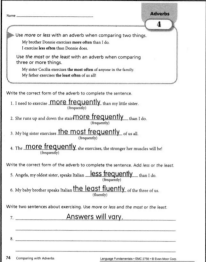

Adverbs 4

Use *more* or *less* with an adverb when comparing two things.
My brother Donnie exercises **more often** than I do.
I exercise **less often** than Donnie does.

Use the *most* or the *least* with an adverb when comparing three or more things.
My sister Cecilia exercises **the most often** of anyone in the family.
My father exercises **the least often** of us all!

Write the correct form of the adverb to complete the sentence.

1. I need to exercise **more frequently** than my little sister.
(frequently)

2. She runs up and down the stairs **more frequently** than I do.
(frequently)

3. My big sister exercises **the most frequently** of us all.
(frequently)

4. The **more frequently** she exercises, the stronger her muscles will be!
(frequently)

Write the correct form of the adverb to complete the sentence. Add *less* or the *least*.

5. Angela, my oldest sister, speaks Italian **less frequently** than I do.
(frequently)

6. My baby brother speaks Italian **the least fluently** of the three of us.
(fluently)

Write two sentences about exercising. Use *more* or *less* and the *most* or the *least*.

7. **Answers will vary.**

8.

74 Comparing with Adverbs

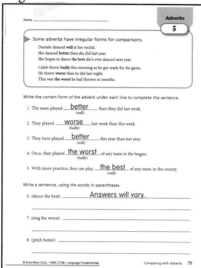

Adverbs 5

Some adverbs have irregular forms for comparisons.
Daniele danced **well** at her recital.
She danced **better** than she did last year.
She hopes to dance **the best** she's ever danced next year.
Caleb threw **badly** this morning as he got ready for the game.
He threw **worse** than he did last night.
This was **the worst** he had thrown in months.

Write the correct form of the adverb under each line to complete the sentence.

1. The team played **better** than they did last week.
(well)

2. They played **worse** last week than this week.
(badly)

3. They have played **better** this year than last year.
(well)

4. Once, they played **the worst** of any team in the league.
(badly)

5. With more practice, they can play **the best** of any team in the county.
(well)

Write a sentence, using the words in parentheses.

6. (dance the best) **Answers will vary.**

7. (sing the worst)

8. (pitch better)

Comparing with Adverbs 75

Adverbs 6

Negatives are words that mean "no" or "not."
Celinda asked her teacher **not** to call on her today.
She had **never** been unprepared before.
She had looked for her homework, and it was **nowhere** to be found.

Complete each sentence with a negative.

1. Celinda **never** forgot her homework.

2. She was **not** the kind of person who came to class unprepared.

3. This morning, she could **not** find her homework.

4. She had **never** forgotten her homework before, so her teacher was understanding.

5. She had looked high and low, but her homework was **nowhere** to be found.

6. From now on, Celinda was going **nowhere** without her homework.

7. This was **never/not** going to happen again.

Write a sentence for each negative.

8. (not) **Answers will vary.**

9. (never)

10. (nowhere)

76 Negative Adverbs

Adverbs Review

Fill in the bubble next to the correct answer.

1. Which underlined adverb tells *where*?
   Ⓐ We left *quickly* after the show was over.
   Ⓑ It was *decidedly* the worst show ever!
   Ⓒ Mom is going to see it *tomorrow*.
   ● It's playing *there* until Saturday.

2. Which underlined adverb tells *how*?
   ● Eric shouted *loudly* when he won first place.
   Ⓑ Steffi called *home* when she heard the news.
   Ⓒ Brian said he'd be there *tomorrow*.
   Ⓓ Cara sang *yesterday* at the spring concert.

3. Which underlined adverb tells *to what extent*?
   Ⓐ Zoe tiptoed *quietly* into the room.
   Ⓑ Her little brother, Liam, was sleeping *soundly*.
   ● She was *so* happy to have a little brother.
   Ⓓ *Tomorrow* they were going to the park together.

4. Which sentence is written correctly?
   Ⓐ Zachary snores more loud than all of us.
   Ⓑ When we camp, no one cooks more oftener than Luis.
   Ⓒ Robert digs the most quicker than anyone setting up the trenches.
   ● Wang pitches his tent the most rapidly of anyone.

5. Which word is a negative in this sentence?
   Nonah never knotted knots before.
   ● never
   Ⓑ knotted
   Ⓒ knots
   Ⓓ Nonah

Adverbs: Review 77

Prepositions 1

A preposition is used to show the relationship of a noun or pronoun to another word. Prepositions can show position, direction, or other relationships.

above	across	after	around	at	before	behind
below	beside	between	during	for	from	inside
off	on	through	to	toward	under	with

The team is playing **in** the championship game.
The fans **inside** the gym are very excited.
The player with the ball dribbled **across** the court.

Underline the prepositions in the sentences.

1. Our basketball coach had a surprise *for* us *during* practice today.

2. We met *with* a professional player named Verry Tawl.

3. Verry arrived *after* our main workout and *before* our practice game.

4. Coach wanted Verry to watch us shoot *from* the foul line.

5. We are good shots and usually get the ball *through* the hoop.

6. Many players bounced the ball *off* the rim or hit it *on* the backboard *before* making the basket.

7. Verry watched us run *around* the court and pass the ball *between* players.

8. We dribbled *down* the court, moving the ball *toward* our basket to score.

9. Team members *at* practice were photographed standing *beside* Verry.

10. There was space *above* my head for Verry Tawl to sign the picture!

78 Identifying Prepositions

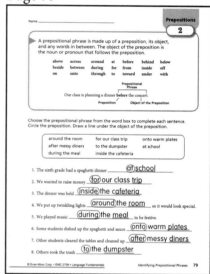

Prepositions 2

A prepositional phrase is made up of a preposition, its object, and any words in between. The object of the preposition is the noun or pronoun that follows the preposition.

above	across	around	at	before	behind	below
beside	between	during	for	from	inside	off
on	onto	through	to	toward	under	with

Our class is planning a dinner **before** the concert.

Choose the prepositional phrase from the word box to complete each sentence. Circle the preposition. Draw a line under the object of the preposition.

around the room	for our class trip	onto warm plates
after messy diners	to the dumpster	at school
during the meal	inside the cafeteria	

1. The sixth grade had a spaghetti dinner **(at)** school

2. We wanted to raise money **(for)** our class trip

3. The dinner was held **(inside)** the cafeteria

4. We put up twinkling lights **(around)** the room so it would look special.

5. We played music **(during)** the meal to be festive.

6. Some students dished up the spaghetti and sauce **(onto)** warm plates

7. Other students cleared the tables and cleaned up **(after)** messy diners

8. Others took the trash **(to)** the dumpster

Identifying Prepositional Phrases 79

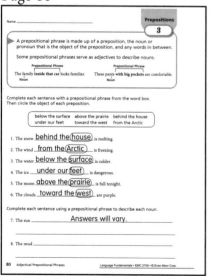

Prepositions 3

A prepositional phrase is made up of a preposition, the noun or pronoun that is the object of the preposition, and any words in between.

Some prepositional phrases serve as adjectives to describe nouns.

The family **inside that car** looks familiar.
These pants **with big pockets** are comfortable.

Complete each sentence with a prepositional phrase from the word box. Then circle the object of each preposition.

| below the surface | above the prairie | behind the house |
| under our feet | toward the west | from the Arctic |

1. The snow **behind the (house)** is melting.

2. The wind **from the (Arctic)** is freezing.

3. The water **below the (surface)** is colder.

4. The ice **under our (feet)** is dangerous.

5. The moon **above the (prairie)** is full tonight.

6. The clouds **toward the (west)** are purple.

Complete each sentence using a prepositional phrase to describe each noun.

7. The sun **Answers will vary.**

8. The mud

80 Adjectival Prepositional Phrases

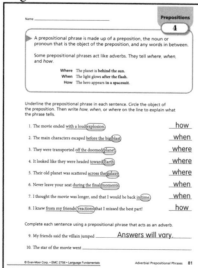

Prepositions 4

A prepositional phrase is made up of a preposition, the noun or pronoun that is the object of the preposition, and any words in between.

Some prepositional phrases act like adverbs. They tell *where*, *when*, and *how*.

Where The planet is **behind the sun**.
When The light glows **after the flash**.
How The hero appears **in a spacesuit**.

Underline the prepositional phrase in each sentence. Circle the object of the preposition. Then write *how*, *when*, or *where* on the line to explain what the phrase tells.

1. The movie ended *with a loud (explosion)* **how**

2. The main characters escaped *before the big (blast)* **when**

3. They were transported *off the doomed (planet)* **where**

4. It looked like they were headed *toward (Earth)* **where**

5. Their old planet was scattered *across the (galaxy)* **where**

6. Never leave your seat *during the final (moments)* **when**

7. I thought the movie was longer, and that I would be back *in (time)* **when**

8. I knew *from my friends' (reaction)* that I missed the best part! **how**

Complete each sentence using a prepositional phrase that acts as an adverb.

9. My friends said the villain jumped **Answers will vary.**

10. The star of the movie went

Adverbial Prepositional Phrases 81

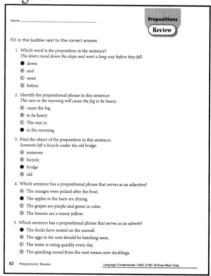

Prepositions Review

Fill in the bubble next to the correct answer.

1. Which word is the preposition in the sentence?
   The skiers raced down the slope and went a long way before they fell.
   ● down
   Ⓑ and
   Ⓒ went
   Ⓓ before

2. Identify the prepositional phrase in this sentence:
   The rain in the morning will cause the fog to be heavy.
   Ⓐ cause the fog
   Ⓑ to be heavy
   Ⓒ The rain in
   ● in the morning

3. Find the object of the preposition in this sentence:
   Someone left a bicycle under the old bridge.
   Ⓐ someone
   Ⓑ bicycle
   ● bridge
   Ⓓ old

4. Which sentence has a prepositional phrase that serves as an adjective?
   Ⓐ The oranges were picked after the frost.
   ● The apples in the barn are drying.
   Ⓒ The grapes are purple and green in color.
   Ⓓ The lemons are a sunny yellow.

5. Which sentence has a prepositional phrase that serves as an adverb?
   ● The ducks have nested on the seawall.
   Ⓑ The eggs in the nest should be hatching soon.
   Ⓒ The water is rising quickly every day.
   Ⓓ The quacking sound from the nest means new ducklings.

82 Prepositions: Review

220

Page 83

Sentences 1

A sentence is a group of words that expresses a complete thought or statement. A declarative sentence tells something and ends with a period. Declarative sentences are the most common kind of sentences.

The clash of warm air with cold air causes thunder.
Thunder and lightning make me nervous.
I think we should go inside.

Write a declarative sentence about each topic. Be sure to begin your statement with a capital letter and end it with a period.

Answers will vary.

1. (a game) _____
2. (a holiday) _____
3. (a historic event) _____
4. (a friend) _____
5. (a movie) _____
6. (a hero) _____
7. (a personal goal) _____
8. (a memory) _____
9. (your school) _____
10. (a book) _____

Page 84

Sentences 2

An interrogative sentence asks a question and ends with a question mark (?).

• Many interrogative sentences begin with a helping verb. The subject is between the helping verb and the main verb.
  Do you **play** a musical instrument?
  Are you **going** to the concert?
• Many interrogative sentences begin with one of these common question words: who, what, when, where, why, or how.
  Who is playing? **What** kind of music will we hear? **When** does the concert begin?
  Where is the concert hall? **Why** aren't we going in the car? **How** will we get there?

Answers will vary. Sample answers are given.
Write an interrogative sentence to go with each answer. Place a question mark at the end of each one.

1. Question: **Who is that?**
   Answer: That is Ravi Shankar, a famous musician.
2. Question: **What does he play?**
   Answer: He plays an instrument called the sitar.
3. Question: **What is a sitar?**
   Answer: A sitar is a stringed instrument.
4. Question: **Where is Ravi Shankar from?**
   Answer: Mr. Shankar is from India.
5. Question: **Do you know how to play the sitar?**
   Answer: No, I can't play the sitar.
6. Question: **Would you like to learn?**
   Answer: Yes, I'd love to learn how to play the sitar!

Page 85

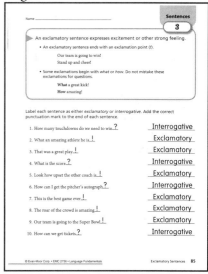

Sentences 3

An exclamatory sentence expresses excitement or other strong feeling.

• An exclamatory sentence ends with an exclamation point (!).
  Our team is going to win!
  Stand up and cheer!
• Some exclamations begin with what or how. Do not mistake these exclamations for questions.
  What a great kick!
  How amazing!

Label each sentence as either exclamatory or interrogative. Add the correct punctuation mark to the end of each sentence.

1. How many touchdowns do we need to win **?** — Interrogative
2. What an amazing athlete he is **!** — Exclamatory
3. That was a great play **!** — Exclamatory
4. What is the score **?** — Interrogative
5. Look how upset the other coach is **!** — Exclamatory
6. How can I get the pitcher's autograph **?** — Interrogative
7. This is the best game ever **!** — Exclamatory
8. The roar of the crowd is amazing **!** — Exclamatory
9. Our team is going to the Super Bowl **!** — Exclamatory
10. How can we get tickets **?** — Interrogative

Page 86

Sentences 4

An imperative sentence gives a command. It ends with a period (.).

Pay attention to the directions.
Use a pencil for the test.
Do not skip questions.

An imperative sentence may include the courtesy word please. An imperative sentence might also include the name of the person or animal being addressed.

Take out a piece of paper, please.
Students, please fill in the circles carefully.
Work quietly, Pam.

Label the sentence as declarative or imperative.

1. The test will take one hour to complete. — declarative
2. Close your books, please. — imperative
3. Do not talk during the test. — imperative
4. This test is important. — declarative
5. Concentrate, please. — imperative

Write an imperative sentence that someone might say in each setting.

Answers will vary.

6. (a restaurant) _____
7. (a movie theater) _____
8. (a school bus) _____
9. (a store) _____
10. (a swimming pool) _____

Page 87

Sentences 5

A sentence is a group of words that expresses a complete thought. There are four kinds of sentences.

• A declarative sentence states something and ends with a period.
• An interrogative sentence asks a question and ends with a question mark.
• An imperative sentence gives a command and ends with a period.
• An exclamatory sentence expresses strong feeling and ends with an exclamation point.

Add the correct end mark to each sentence. Then label the sentence declarative, interrogative, imperative, or exclamatory.

1. I carry my artwork in a large case called a portfolio **.** — declarative
2. Help me with my easel **.** — imperative
3. Have you ever drawn a self-portrait **?** — interrogative
4. Does this look like me **?** — interrogative
5. This kind of drawing is called a still life **.** — declarative
6. What an amazing painting **!** — exclamatory

Write one of each kind of sentence. Be sure to use correct punctuation.

Answers will vary.

7. Declarative: _____
8. Interrogative: _____
9. Imperative: _____
10. Exclamatory: _____

Page 88

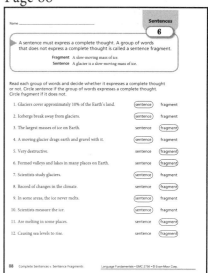

Sentences 6

A sentence must express a complete thought. A group of words that does not express a complete thought is called a sentence fragment.

Fragment A slow-moving mass of ice.
Sentence A glacier is a slow-moving mass of ice.

Read each group of words and decide whether it expresses a complete thought or not. Circle sentence if the group of words expresses a complete thought. Circle fragment if it does not.

1. Glaciers cover approximately 10% of the Earth's land. — (sentence) fragment
2. Icebergs break away from glaciers. — (sentence) fragment
3. The largest masses of ice on Earth. — sentence (fragment)
4. A moving glacier drags earth and gravel with it. — (sentence) fragment
5. Very destructive. — sentence (fragment)
6. Formed valleys and lakes in many places on Earth. — sentence (fragment)
7. Scientists study glaciers. — (sentence) fragment
8. Record of changes in the climate. — sentence (fragment)
9. In some areas, the ice never melts. — (sentence) fragment
10. Scientists measure the ice. — (sentence) fragment
11. Are melting in some places. — sentence (fragment)
12. Causing sea levels to rise. — sentence (fragment)

Page 89

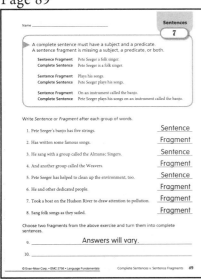

Sentences 7

A complete sentence must have a subject and a predicate. A sentence fragment is missing a subject, a predicate, or both.

Sentence Fragment Pete Seeger a folk singer.
Complete Sentence Pete Seeger is a folk singer.

Sentence Fragment Plays his songs.
Complete Sentence Pete Seeger plays his songs.

Sentence Fragment On an instrument called the banjo.
Complete Sentence Pete Seeger plays his songs on an instrument called the banjo.

Write Sentence or Fragment after each group of words.

1. Pete Seeger's banjo has five strings. — Sentence
2. Has written some famous songs. — Fragment
3. He sang with a group called the Almanac Singers. — Sentence
4. And another group called the Weavers. — Fragment
5. Pete Seeger has helped to clean up the environment, too. — Sentence
6. He and other dedicated people. — Fragment
7. Took a boat on the Hudson River to draw attention to pollution. — Fragment
8. Sang folk songs as they sailed. — Fragment

Choose two fragments from the above exercise and turn them into complete sentences.

Answers will vary.

9. _____
10. _____

Page 90

Sentences Review 1

Fill in the bubble next to the correct answer.

1. Which group of words is a declarative sentence?
   Ⓐ Have you seen my autograph book?
   ● I want to collect the signatures of famous people.
   Ⓒ How exciting it would be to meet a movie star!
   Ⓓ Be polite when you ask for an autograph.

2. Which group of words is an interrogative sentence?
   Ⓐ I will start with famous people in our town.
   Ⓑ What a great person our mayor is!
   ● Do you think she will give me her autograph?
   Ⓓ The town meeting will be a good place to meet her.

3. Which group of words is an exclamatory sentence punctuated correctly?
   Ⓐ What should I say to her?
   Ⓑ She should sign my book.
   Ⓒ Will you sign my autograph book!
   ● How kind she was!

4. Which group of words is an imperative sentence?
   Ⓐ I should send her a thank-you note.
   ● Choose a nice piece of stationery.
   Ⓒ Should I write with red ink?
   Ⓓ I think blue ink would be better.

5. Which group of words is a complete sentence?
   ● There are no movie stars living in our town.
   Ⓑ Ms. Guzzo, the director of the community theater.
   Ⓒ Kindly gave her my autograph.
   Ⓓ The actors in this production.

Page 91

Sentences 8

Every sentence has two parts, a subject and a predicate.

• The subject tells who or what the sentence is about.
• The predicate tells what the subject is or does.

Subject	Predicate
Everyone in our school	rode the bus to Rainbow Park.
Even the teachers	were excited about the school picnic.

Divide each sentence into its two parts and write them on the lines.

1. Rainbow Park is a popular place for school picnics.
   Subject: Rainbow Park
   Predicate: is a popular place for school picnics

2. The park has roller coasters and other rides.
   Subject: The park
   Predicate: has roller coasters and other rides

3. Dennis and Jimmy took Ms. White on the merry-go-round.
   Subject: Dennis and Jimmy
   Predicate: took Ms. White on the merry-go-round

4. Some kids from my class rowed a boat on the lake.
   Subject: Some kids from my class
   Predicate: rowed a boat on the lake

5. I won a stuffed bear at the game tent.
   Subject: I
   Predicate: won a stuffed bear at the game tent

Page 92

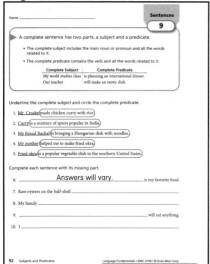

Sentences 9

A complete sentence has two parts, a subject and a predicate.
- The complete subject includes the main noun or pronoun and all the words related to it.
- The complete predicate contains the verb and all the words related to it.

Complete Subject	Complete Predicate
My world studies class	is planning an international dinner.
Our teacher	will make an exotic dish.

Underline the complete subject and circle the complete predicate.
1. Mr. Crosby **made chicken curry with rice.**
2. Curry **is a mixture of spices popular in India.**
3. My friend Rachel **is bringing a Hungarian dish with noodles.**
4. My mother **helped me to make fried okra.**
5. Fried okra **is a popular vegetable dish in the southern United States.**

Complete each sentence with its missing part.
6. ___ Answers will vary. ___ is my favorite food.
7. Raw oysters on the half-shell ___
8. My family ___
9. ___ will eat anything.
10. I ___

92   Subjects and Predicates

Page 93

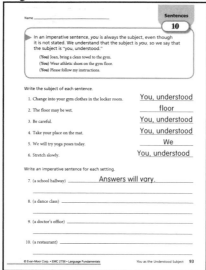

Sentences 10

In an imperative sentence, *you* is always the subject, even though it is not stated. We understand that the subject is *you*, so we say that the subject is "you, understood."

(You) Joan, bring a clean towel to the gym.
(You) Wear athletic shoes on the gym floor.
(You) Please follow my instructions.

Write the subject of each sentence.
1. Change into your gym clothes in the locker room.   _You, understood_
2. The floor may be wet.   _floor_
3. Be careful.   _You, understood_
4. Take your place on the mat.   _You, understood_
5. We will try yoga poses today.   _We_
6. Stretch slowly.   _You, understood_

Write an imperative sentence for each setting.
7. (a school hallway)   _Answers will vary._
8. (a dance class) ___
9. (a doctor's office) ___
10. (a restaurant) ___

You as the Understood Subject   93

Page 94

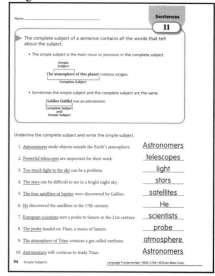

Sentences 11

The complete subject of a sentence contains all the words that tell about the subject.
- The simple subject is the main noun or pronoun in the complete subject.

The atmosphere of this planet contains oxygen.
Complete Subject

- Sometimes the simple subject and the complete subject are the same.

Galileo Galilei was an astronomer.
Complete Subject and Simple Subject

Underline the complete subject and write the simple subject.
1. Astronomers study objects outside the Earth's atmosphere.   _Astronomers_
2. Powerful telescopes are important for their work.   _telescopes_
3. Too much light in the sky can be a problem.   _light_
4. The stars can be difficult to see in a bright night sky.   _stars_
5. The four satellites of Jupiter were discovered by Galileo.   _satellites_
6. He discovered the satellites in the 17th century.   _He_
7. European scientists sent a probe to Saturn in the 21st century.   _scientists_
8. The probe landed on Titan, a moon of Saturn.   _probe_
9. The atmosphere of Titan contains a gas called methane.   _atmosphere_
10. Astronomers will continue to study Titan.   _Astronomers_

94   Simple Subjects

Page 95

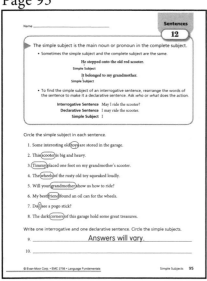

Sentences 12

The simple subject is the main noun or pronoun in the complete subject.
- Sometimes the simple subject and the complete subject are the same.

He stepped onto the old red scooter.
Simple Subject

It belonged to my grandmother.
Simple Subject

- To find the simple subject of an interrogative sentence, rearrange the words of the sentence to make it a declarative sentence. Ask who or what does the action.

Interrogative Sentence   May I ride the scooter?
Declarative Sentence   I may ride the scooter.
Simple Subject   I

Circle the simple subject in each sentence.
1. Some interesting old **toys** are stored in the garage.
2. This **scooter** is big and heavy.
3. **Timmy** placed one foot on my grandmother's scooter.
4. The **wheels** of the rusty old toy squeaked loudly.
5. Will your **grandmother** show us how to ride?
6. My best **friend** found an oil can for the wheels.
7. Do **I** see a pogo stick?
8. The dark **corners** of this garage hold some great treasures.

Write one interrogative and one declarative sentence. Circle the simple subjects.
9. _Answers will vary._
10. ___

Simple Subjects   95

Page 96

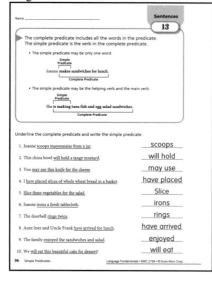

Sentences 13

The complete predicate includes all the words in the predicate. The simple predicate is the verb in the complete predicate.
- The simple predicate may be only one word.

Joanne **makes** sandwiches for lunch.
Simple Predicate
Complete Predicate

- The simple predicate may be the helping verb and the main verb.

She **is making** tuna fish and egg salad sandwiches.
Simple Predicate
Complete Predicate

Underline the complete predicate and write the simple predicate.
1. Joanne scoops mayonnaise from a jar.   _scoops_
2. This china bowl will hold a tangy mustard.   _will hold_
3. You may use this knife for the cheese.   _may use_
4. I have placed slices of whole wheat bread in a basket.   _have placed_
5. Slice these vegetables for the salad.   _Slice_
6. Joanne irons a fresh tablecloth.   _irons_
7. The doorbell rings twice.   _rings_
8. Aunt Inez and Uncle Frank have arrived for lunch.   _have arrived_
9. The family enjoyed the sandwiches and salad.   _enjoyed_
10. We will eat this beautiful cake for dessert!   _will eat_

96   Simple Predicates

Page 97

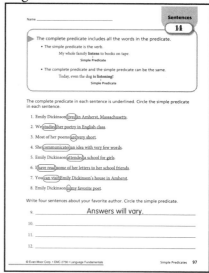

Sentences 14

The complete predicate includes all the words in the predicate.
- The simple predicate is the verb.

My whole family **listens** to books on tape.
Simple Predicate

- The complete predicate and the simple predicate can be the same.

Today, even the dog **is listening**!
Simple Predicate

The complete predicate in each sentence is underlined. Circle the simple predicate in each sentence.
1. Emily Dickinson **lived** in Amherst, Massachusetts.
2. We **studied** her poetry in English class.
3. Most of her poems **are** very short.
4. She **communicated** an idea with very few words.
5. Emily Dickinson **attended** a school for girls.
6. I **have read** some of her letters to her school friends.
7. You **can visit** Emily Dickinson's house in Amherst.
8. Emily Dickinson **is** my favorite poet.

Write four sentences about your favorite author. Circle the simple predicate.
9. _Answers will vary._
10. ___
11. ___
12. ___

Simple Predicates   97

Page 98

Sentences Review 2

Fill in the bubble next to the correct answer.
1. In which sentence is the subject "you, understood"?
   Ⓐ Don't you know about the concert?
   Ⓑ You should give those comics to Michael.
   ● Please wait for me.
   Ⓓ You will arrive early.
2. In which sentence is the complete subject underlined?
   Ⓐ I met Megan in grammar school.
   ● Megan's family moved last year.
   Ⓒ They now live in a small town.
   Ⓓ Our friendship is important to me.
3. In which sentence is the complete predicate underlined?
   Ⓐ We stay in touch by e-mail and telephone.
   Ⓑ I will write a short e-mail tonight.
   ● I will tell her about my homework.
   Ⓓ Mr. Amata gave us a big assignment.
4. In which sentence is the simple subject underlined?
   Ⓐ Megan sometimes helps me with my math homework.
   Ⓑ She is a whiz at math!
   ● My favorite subject is history.
   Ⓓ I can help Megan with her history project.
5. In which sentence is the simple predicate underlined?
   Ⓐ Good friends help each other.
   Ⓑ I have missed Megan this year.
   Ⓒ Our e-mails are important.
   Ⓓ I will press "send" now.

98   Sentences: Review 2

Page 99

Sentences 15

A compound sentence is made by joining two or more simple sentences containing related information. The sentences are joined by a comma and a coordinating conjunction, such as *and, or,* or *but.*

Will is the best bowler, **and** Andy is the worst bowler.
The bowling alley is empty, **but** it will be busy soon.

Other coordinating conjunctions: nor   for   so   yet

Underline the coordinating conjunction in each compound sentence. Add a comma where it belongs.
1. I like to bowl, **but** I am not a good bowler.
2. I like wearing a bowling shirt, **but** I hate those ugly bowling shoes!
3. I like throwing the ball, **but** I'm not very good.
4. I would like to knock down all the pins, **yet** I am happy if any pins fall.
5. I want the ball to go straight, **so** I aim carefully.
6. Most of the time the ball goes off to the side, **or** it will drop into the gutter.
7. You don't score when that happens, **so** it's not good to throw a gutter ball.

Write a compound sentence about how it would feel to knock down all the pins in bowling.
8. _Answers will vary._

Compound Sentences   99

Page 100

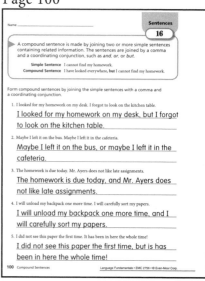

Sentences 16

A compound sentence is made by joining two or more simple sentences containing related information. The sentences are joined by a comma and a coordinating conjunction, such as *and, or,* or *but.*

Simple Sentence   I cannot find my homework.
Compound Sentence   I have looked everywhere, but I cannot find my homework.

Form compound sentences by joining the simple sentences with a comma and a coordinating conjunction.
1. I looked for my homework on my desk. I forgot to look on the kitchen table.
   I looked for my homework on my desk, but I forgot to look on the kitchen table.
2. Maybe I left it on the bus. Maybe I left it in the cafeteria.
   Maybe I left it on the bus, or maybe I left it in the cafeteria.
3. The homework is due today. Mr. Ayers does not like late assignments.
   The homework is due today, and Mr. Ayers does not like late assignments.
4. I will unload my backpack one more time. I will carefully sort my papers.
   I will unload my backpack one more time, and I will carefully sort my papers.
5. I did not see this paper the first time. It has been in here the whole time!
   I did not see this paper the first time, but is has been in here the whole time!

100   Compound Sentences

Page 101

Name ______________

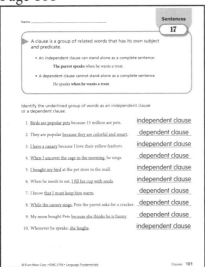

Sentences **17**

A clause is a group of related words that has its own subject and predicate.

- An independent clause can stand alone as a complete sentence.

  The parrot speaks when he wants a treat.

- A dependent clause cannot stand alone as a complete sentence.

  He speaks **when he wants a treat**.

Identify the underlined group of words as an independent clause or a dependent clause.

1. Birds are popular pets because 15 million are pets. independent clause
2. They are popular because they are colorful and smart. dependent clause
3. I have a canary because I love their yellow feathers. independent clause
4. When I uncover the cage in the morning, he sings. dependent clause
5. I bought my bird at the pet store in the mall. independent clause
6. When he needs to eat, I fill his cup with seeds. independent clause
7. I know that I must keep him warm. dependent clause
8. While the canary sings, Pete the parrot asks for a cracker. dependent clause
9. My mom bought Pete because she thinks he is funny. dependent clause
10. Whenever he speaks, she laughs. independent clause

© Evan-Moor Corp. • EMC 2756 • Language Fundamentals   Clauses 101

Page 102

Name ______________

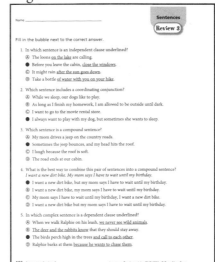

Sentences **Review 3**

Fill in the bubble next to the correct answer.

1. In which sentence is an independent clause underlined?
   - Ⓐ The loons on the lake are calling.
   - ● Before you leave the cabin, close the windows.
   - Ⓒ It might rain after the sun goes down.
   - Ⓓ Take a bottle of water with you on your hike.
2. Which sentence includes a coordinating conjunction?
   - Ⓐ While we sleep, our dogs like to play.
   - Ⓑ As long as I finish my homework, I am allowed to be outside until dark.
   - Ⓒ I want to go to the movie rental store.
   - ● I always want to play with my dog, but sometimes she wants to sleep.
3. Which sentence is a compound sentence?
   - Ⓐ My mom drives a jeep on the country roads.
   - ● Sometimes the jeep bounces, and my head hits the roof.
   - Ⓒ I laugh because the roof is soft.
   - Ⓓ The road ends at our cabin.
4. What is the best way to combine this pair of sentences into a compound sentence?
   I want a new dirt bike. My mom says I have to wait until my birthday.
   - ● I want a new dirt bike, but my mom says I have to wait until my birthday.
   - Ⓑ I want a new dirt bike, my mom says I have to wait until my birthday.
   - Ⓒ My mom says I have to wait until my birthday, I want a new dirt bike.
   - Ⓓ I want a new dirt bike but my mom says I have to wait until my birthday.
5. In which complex sentence is a dependent clause underlined?
   - Ⓐ When we walk Ralphie on his leash, we never see wild animals.
   - Ⓑ The deer and the rabbits know that they should stay away.
   - ● The birds perch high in the trees and call to each other.
   - Ⓓ Ralphie barks at them because he wants to chase them.

102 Sentences: Review 3   Language Fundamentals • EMC 2756 • © Evan-Moor Corp.

Page 103

Name ______________

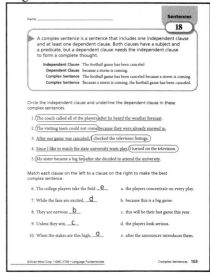

Sentences **18**

A complex sentence is a sentence that includes one independent clause and at least one dependent clause. Both clauses have a subject and a predicate, but a dependent clause needs the independent clause to form a complete thought.

Independent Clause	The football game has been canceled
Dependent Clause	because a storm is coming.
Complex Sentence	The football game has been canceled because a storm is coming.
Complex Sentence	Because a storm is coming, the football game has been canceled.

Circle the independent clause and underline the dependent clause in these complex sentences.

1. The coach called all of the players after he heard the weather forecast.
2. The visiting team could not come because they were already snowed in.
3. After our game was canceled, I checked the television listings.
4. Since I like to watch the state university team play, I turned on the television.
5. My sister became a big fan after she decided to attend the university.

Match each clause on the left to a clause on the right to make the best complex sentence.

6. The college players take the field e	a. the players concentrate on every play.
7. While the fans are excited, d	b. because this is a big game.
8. They are nervous b	c. this will be their last game this year.
9. Unless they win, c	d. the players look serious.
10. When the stakes are this high, a	e. after the announcer introduces them.

© Evan-Moor Corp. • EMC 2756 • Language Fundamentals   Complex Sentences 103

Page 104

Name ______________

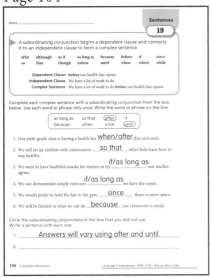

Sentences **19**

A subordinating conjunction begins a dependent clause and connects it to an independent clause to form a complex sentence.

after	although	as if	as long as	because	before	if	since
so	that	though	unless	until	when	where	while

Dependent Clause	**before** our health fair opens.
Independent Clause	We have a lot of work to do
Complex Sentence	We have a lot of work to do **before** our health fair opens.

Complete each complex sentence with a subordinating conjunction from the box below. Use each word or phrase only once. Write the word or phrase on the line.

as long as   so that   (after)   if
because   when   since   (until)

1. Our sixth-grade class is having a health fair when/after this unit ends.
2. We will set up exhibits with information so that other kids learn how to stay healthy.
3. We want to have healthful snacks for visitors to try if/as long as our teacher agrees.
4. We can demonstrate simple exercises if/as long as we have the room.
5. We would prefer to hold the fair in the gym since there is more space.
6. We will be limited in what we can do because our classroom is small.

Circle the subordinating conjunctions in the box that you did not use. Write a sentence with each one.

7. Answers will vary using after and until.
8. ______________

104 Complete Sentences   Language Fundamentals • EMC 2756 • © Evan-Moor Corp.

Page 105

Name ______________

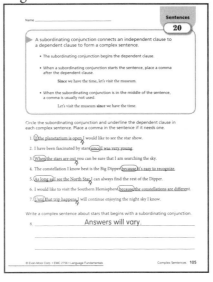

Sentences **20**

A subordinating conjunction connects an independent clause to a dependent clause to form a complex sentence.

- The subordinating conjunction begins the dependent clause.
- When a subordinating conjunction starts the sentence, place a comma after the dependent clause.

  Since we have the time, let's visit the museum.

- When the subordinating conjunction is in the middle of the sentence, a comma is usually not used.

  Let's visit the museum **since** we have the time.

Circle the subordinating conjunction and underline the dependent clause in each complex sentence. Place a comma in the sentence if it needs one.

1. If the planetarium is open, I would like to see the star show.
2. I have been fascinated by stars since I was very young.
3. When the stars are out, you can be sure that I am searching the sky.
4. The constellation I know best is the Big Dipper because it's easy to recognize.
5. As long as I see the North Star, I can always find the rest of the Dipper.
6. I would like to visit the Southern Hemisphere because the constellations are different.
7. Until that trip happens, I will continue enjoying the night sky I know.

Write a complex sentence about stars that begins with a subordinating conjunction.

8. Answers will vary.

© Evan-Moor Corp. • EMC 2756 • Language Fundamentals   Complex Sentences 105

Page 106

Name ______________

Sentences **21**

A dependent clause in a complex sentence may begin with a subordinating conjunction or a signal word.

after	although	as	as if	as long as	because	before	if
once	since	so	that	though	unless	until	what
when	whenever	where	wherever	which	while	who	whoever

Complex Sentence	**Before** European settlers arrived, native people tapped maples for syrup.
Dependent Clause	**Before** European settlers arrived
Independent Clause	native people tapped maples for syrup.
Complex Sentence	I don't know **which** house is theirs.
Dependent Clause	**which** house is theirs.
Independent Clause	I don't know

Complete each complex sentence with a subordinating conjunction or signal word.

1. Teachers reward students who do their homework.
2. Before spring is fully underway, the sap in the maple trees begins to flow.
3. We won't find the trail unless we use the map.
4. Once we learn the steps, the dance will be easy.

Choose a subordinating conjunction and a signal word from the rule box. Write two sentences that contain dependent clauses.

5. Answers will vary.
6. ______________

106 Complex Sentences   Language Fundamentals • EMC 2756 • © Evan-Moor Corp.

Page 107

Name ______________

Sentences **Review 4**

Fill in the bubble next to the correct answer.

1. Which complex sentence is written correctly?
   - Ⓐ Before you leave the cabin close the windows.
   - ● Before you leave the cabin, close the windows.
   - Ⓒ Close the windows, before you leave the cabin.
   - Ⓓ Close the windows before, you leave the cabin.
2. In which sentence is a clause underlined?
   - Ⓐ Our cabin on the lake is made of logs.
   - Ⓑ We sleep in bunk beds.
   - Ⓒ In the living room, there is a big fireplace.
   - ● Since the weather is chilly today, we will build a fire.
3. Where does the comma belong in the following sentence?
   Because the jeep bounces my head hits the roof.
   - Ⓐ a comma is not needed
   - Ⓑ after *because*
   - ● after *bounces*
   - Ⓓ after *head*
4. Which sentence is a complex sentence?
   - Ⓐ We like to hike through the woods.
   - Ⓑ My dad knows every tree and flower in the woods.
   - Ⓒ My mom studies the insects, and I study animal tracks.
   - ● If we see an animal, we stand very still.
5. Choose the correct subordinating conjunction for the sentence.
   Mom feels better, we won't be able to go on vacation.
   - ● Unless
   - Ⓑ After
   - Ⓒ Since
   - Ⓓ As if

© Evan-Moor Corp. • EMC 2756 • Language Fundamentals   Sentences: Review 4 107

Page 108

Name ______________

Sentences **22**

Combine two short sentences to make your writing more interesting. One way to do this is to move key words and phrases from one sentence to another.

Two Sentences	The Pilgrims fed lobsters to their pigs. They fed them on the beach.
Combined Sentence	The Pilgrims fed lobsters to their pigs on the beach.
Two Sentences	Lobsters were washed ashore. They were washed ashore by the surf.
Combined Sentences	Lobsters were washed ashore by the surf.

Answers will vary, suggested answers given.

Combine the sentences by making a phrase in the second sentence part of the first.

1. The Pilgrims sailed from England. They sailed on the *Mayflower*.
   Combined: The Pilgrims sailed from England on the Mayflower.
2. The Pilgrims had a kind of corn. This corn was called flint corn.
   Combined: The Pilgrims had a kind of corn called flint corn.
3. They probably cooked the flint corn. They probably cooked it by boiling it.
   Combined: They probably cooked the flint corn by boiling.
4. The Wampanoag Indians helped the Pilgrims. They helped them with their crops.
   Combined: The Wampanoag Indians helped the Pilgrims with their crops.
5. The Wampanoag built round houses. They built them with tree bark and reeds.
   Combined: The Wampanoag built round houses with tree bark and reeds.
6. Men and women built the houses together. They built them in the spring.
   Combined: Men and women built the houses together in the spring.

108 Combining Sentences   Language Fundamentals • EMC 2756 • © Evan-Moor Corp.

Page 109

Name ______________

Sentences **23**

Combine simple sentences with related ideas to form compound and complex sentences.

- You can use a comma and coordinating conjunction to form a compound sentence.

Simple Sentences	The drama club is presenting a play. Tara is the director.
Compound Sentence	The drama club is presenting a play, **and** Tara is the director.

- Use a subordinating conjunction to build a complex sentence.

Simple Sentences	I will be the star. I am the best actor in school.
Complex Sentence	**Because** I am the best actor in school, I will be the star.

Build a compound sentence or a complex sentence by connecting the simple sentences with the conjunction in parentheses.

1. Our class had a contest. Everyone wrote a play. (and)
   Our class had a contest, and everyone wrote a play.
2. Our director chose my play. It was the best one. (because)
   Our director chose my play because it was the best one.
3. I wrote the play. I don't need to practice. (since)
   Since I wrote the play, I don't need to practice.
4. I took the stage at rehearsal with confidence. I couldn't remember anything! (but)
   I took the stage at rehearsal with confidence, but I couldn't remember anything!
5. I could let someone else star in the play. I could study my lines. (or)
   I could let someone else star in the play, or I could study my lines.

© Evan-Moor Corp. • EMC 2756 • Language Fundamentals   Combining Sentences 109

Page 110

Name ______________________

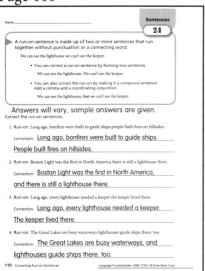

Sentences 24

A run-on sentence is made up of two or more sentences that run together without punctuation or a connecting word.

We can see the lighthouse we can't see the keeper.

- You can correct a run-on sentence by forming two sentences.

We can see the lighthouse. We can't see the keeper.

- You can also correct the run-on by making it a compound sentence. Add a comma and a coordinating conjunction.

We can see the lighthouse, **but** we can't see the keeper.

Answers will vary, sample answers are given.

Correct the run-on sentences.

1. Run-on: Long ago, bonfires were built to guide ships people built fires on hillsides.

   Correction: Long ago, bonfires were built to guide ships. People built fires on hillsides.

2. Run-on: Boston Light was the first in North America there is still a lighthouse there.

   Correction: Boston Light was the first in North America, and there is still a lighthouse there.

3. Run-on: Long ago, every lighthouse needed a keeper the keeper lived there.

   Correction: Long ago, every lighthouse needed a keeper. The keeper lived there.

4. Run-on: The Great Lakes are busy waterways lighthouses guide ships there, too.

   Correction: The Great Lakes are busy waterways, and lighthouses guide ships there, too.

110 Correcting Run-on Sentences Language Fundamentals • EMC 2756 • © Evan-Moor Corp.

Page 111

Name ______________________

Sentences 25

A run-on sentence is two sentences run together as if they were one.

- In a "fused" run-on, two sentences are fused together without any punctuation.

We spent the day at the mall we went to every store.

- In a "comma splice" run-on, a comma alone is used to separate two sentences.

We spent the day at the mall, we went to every store.

You can correct both kinds of run-ons by turning them into two sentences or by forming a compound or a complex sentence.

Simple Sentences We spent the day at the mall. We went to every store.
Compound Sentence We spent the day at the mall, and we went to every store.
Complex Sentence Since we spent the day at the mall, we went to every store.

Correct and rewrite each run-on sentence in the suggested way.

1. Patty and I went to the shoe store we tried on lots of shoes.
   Patty and I went to the shoe store. We tried on lots of shoes.
   Simple sentences:

2. We went to the card store, I needed a birthday card.
   We went to the card store because I needed a birthday card.
   Complex sentence:

3. Patty likes to try on clothes, I would rather try on shoes.
   Patty likes to try on clothes, but I would rather try on shoes.
   Compound sentence:

4. The candle store is my favorite store it smells so good.
   The candle store is my favorite store because it smells so good.
   Complex sentence:

5. The food court has great food we ate tuna sandwiches.
   The food court has great food. We ate tuna sandwiches.
   Simple sentences:

© Evan-Moor Corp. • EMC 2756 • Language Fundamentals Correcting Run-on Sentences 111

Page 112

Name ______________________

Sentences Review 5

Fill in the bubble next to the correct answer.

1. Which one combines the short sentences by moving a phrase?
   Aunt Sara opened an antique shop. She opened it on Liberty Street.
   - ● Aunt Sara opened an antique shop on Liberty Street.
   - Ⓑ Aunt Sara opened an antique shop, and she opened it on Liberty Street.
   - Ⓒ Aunt Sara opened an antique shop she opened it on Liberty Street.
   - Ⓓ Aunt Sara opened an antique shop, she opened it on Liberty Street.

2. Which one combines the sentences by forming a compound sentence?
   She specializes in old jewelry. She carries many other antiques, too.
   - Ⓐ She specializes in old jewelry she carries other antiques, too.
   - ● She specializes in old jewelry, but she carries other antiques, too.
   - Ⓒ She specializes in old jewelry and other antiques, too.
   - Ⓓ While she carries many other antiques, she specializes in old jewelry.

3. Which one combines the sentences by forming a complex sentence?
   - Ⓐ I like the antique radio, and it doesn't work.
   - Ⓑ I like the antique radio it doesn't work.
   - Ⓒ I like the antique radio, but it doesn't work.
   - ● Although it doesn't work, I like the antique radio.

4. Which one is a run-on sentence?
   - Ⓐ Dad bought a set of fancy cuff links, and I saw him looking at the radio.
   - Ⓑ He had a radio just like this one when he was a kid.
   - Ⓒ He decided to buy the radio to fix up for me.
   - ● It might be hard to get parts Aunt Sara has just a few old radio tubes.

5. Which one corrects this run-on?
   Mom is excited to see the old radio she remembers one just like it.
   - ● Mom is excited to see the old radio because she remembers one just like it.
   - Ⓑ Mom is excited to see the old radio, she remembers one just like it.
   - Ⓒ Mom is excited to see the old radio she remembers. One just like it.
   - Ⓓ Mom is excited to see the old radio she remembers one just like it.

112 Sentences: Review 5 Language Fundamentals • EMC 2756 • © Evan-Moor Corp.

Page 113

Name ______________________

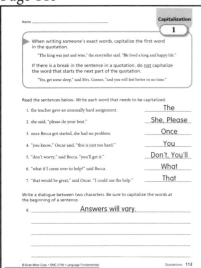

Capitalization 1

When writing someone's exact words, capitalize the first word in the quotation.

"The king was just and wise," the storyteller said. "**H**e lived a long and happy life."

If there is a break in the sentence in a quotation, do not capitalize the word that starts the next part of the quotation.

"Yes, get some sleep," said Mrs. Gomez, "and you will feel better in no time."

Read the sentences below. Write each word that needs to be capitalized.

1. the teacher gave an unusually hard assignment. — The
2. she said, "please do your best." — She, Please
3. once Becca got started, she had no problem. — Once
4. "you know," Oscar said, "this is just too hard." — You
5. "don't worry," said Becca. "you'll get it." — Don't, You'll
6. "what if I come over to help?" said Becca. — What
7. "that would be great," said Oscar. "I could use the help." — That

Write a dialogue between two characters. Be sure to capitalize the words at the beginning of a sentence.

8. Answers will vary.

© Evan-Moor Corp. • EMC 2756 • Language Fundamentals Quotations 113

Page 114

Name ______________________

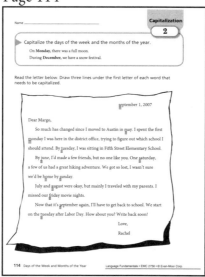

Capitalization 2

Capitalize the days of the week and the months of the year.

On **Monday**, there was a full moon.
During **December**, we have a snow festival.

Read the letter below. Draw three lines under the first letter of each word that needs to be capitalized.

september 1, 2007

Dear Margo,

So much has changed since I moved to Austin in may. I spent the first monday I was here in the district office, trying to figure out which school I should attend. By tuesday, I was sitting in Fifth Street Elementary School.

By june, I'd made a few friends, but no one like you. One saturday, a few of us had a great hiking adventure. We got so lost, I wasn't sure we'd be home by sunday.

July and august were okay, but mainly I traveled with my parents. I missed our friday movie nights.

Now that it's september again, I'll have to get back to school. We start on the tuesday after Labor Day. How about you? Write back soon!

Love,

Rachel

114 Days of the Week and Months of the Year Language Fundamentals • EMC 2756 • © Evan-Moor Corp.

Page 115

Name ______________________

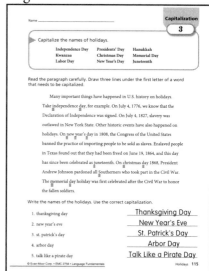

Capitalization 3

Capitalize the names of holidays.

Independence Day	Presidents' Day	Hanukkah
Kwanzaa	Christmas Day	Memorial Day
Labor Day	New Year's Day	Juneteenth

Read the paragraph carefully. Draw three lines under the first letter of a word that needs to be capitalized.

Many important things have happened in U.S. history on holidays. Take independence day, for example. On July 4, 1776, we know that the Declaration of Independence was signed. On July 4, 1827, slavery was outlawed in New York State. Other historic events have also happened on holidays. On new year's day in 1808, the Congress of the United States banned the practice of importing people to be sold as slaves. Enslaved people in Texas found out that they had been freed on June 19, 1864, and this day has since been celebrated as juneteenth. On christmas day 1868, President Andrew Johnson pardoned all Southerners who took part in the Civil War. The memorial day holiday was first celebrated after the Civil War to honor the fallen soldiers.

Write the names of the holidays. Use the correct capitalization.

1. thanksgiving day — Thanksgiving Day
2. new year's eve — New Year's Eve
3. st. patrick's day — St. Patrick's Day
4. arbor day — Arbor Day
5. talk like a pirate day — Talk Like a Pirate Day

© Evan-Moor Corp. • EMC 2756 • Language Fundamentals Holidays 115

Page 116

Name ______________________

Capitalization Review 1

Fill in the bubble next to the correct answer.

1. Which sentence has the correct capitalization?
   - Ⓐ Ari said, "the new principal is strict."
   - ● Naomi said, "I hear that she's fair, though."
   - Ⓒ "she wants to make a lot of changes," said Ari.
   - Ⓓ "maybe it's time for changes," Said Naomi.

2. Which sentence has the correct punctuation?
   - Ⓐ "The school is really warm," Hayden said, "Because the air conditioning is broken."
   - Ⓑ "It's too hot in the spring," said Madison, "it's too cold in winter."
   - Ⓒ "it's not so bad," said Hayden, "since it doesn't even get that hot here."
   - ● "I guess you're right," said Madison. "I'm just sensitive to the heat."

Fill in the bubble next to the word or words that should begin with capital letters.

3. Ⓐ week / Ⓑ morning / ● tuesday / Ⓓ month
4. Ⓐ autumn / ● november / Ⓒ fall / Ⓓ week
5. Ⓐ holiday / Ⓑ occasion / ● christmas / Ⓓ day

116 Capitalization: Review 1 Language Fundamentals • EMC 2756 • © Evan-Moor Corp.

Page 117

Name ______________________

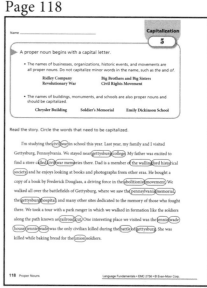

Capitalization 4

Proper nouns begin with capital letters.

- Names of people and pets are proper nouns and should be capitalized.

Opal Rex

- The title before a person's name should also be capitalized.

Doctor Galindez Uncle William

- Names of specific places are also proper nouns and should be capitalized.

Kansas City Niagara Falls Rensselaer New York

For each sentence, choose the word or words that should be capitalized. Rewrite it correctly.

1. David, there is josephine. — Josephine
2. Did you tell aunt jean that she was here? — Aunt Jean
3. No, she's busy walking her dog, inky. — Inky
4. Josephine brought her friend, carmen. — Carmen
5. Carmen brought missy, her dog. — Missy
6. I hope that she will get along with our bird, tiny. — Tiny
7. Did you know that Carmen's aunt is doctor Olivares? — Doctor
8. I'd like to ask her about grandpa's illness. — Grandpa's
9. Maybe if he moved to arizona, he would feel better. — Arizona
10. I don't think moving to phoenix would help him. — Phoenix

© Evan-Moor Corp. • EMC 2756 • Language Fundamentals Proper Nouns 117

Page 118

Name ______________________

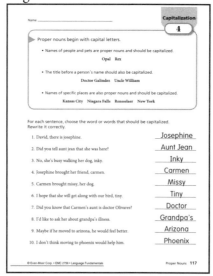

Capitalization 5

A proper noun begins with a capital letter.

- The names of businesses, organizations, historic events, and movements are all proper nouns. Do not capitalize minor words in the name, such as *the* and *of*.

Ridley Company Big Brothers and Big Sisters
Revolutionary War Civil Rights Movement

- The names of buildings, monuments, and schools are also proper nouns and should be capitalized.

Chrysler Building Soldier's Memorial Emily Dickinson School

Read the story. Circle the words that need to be capitalized.

I'm studying the civil war in school this year. Last year, my family and I visited Gettysburg, Pennsylvania. We stayed near gettysburg college. My father was excited to find a store called civil war memories there. Dad is a member of the wallingford historical society and he enjoys looking at books and photographs from other eras. He bought a copy of a book by Frederick Douglass, a driving force in the abolitionist movement. We walked all over the battlefields of Gettysburg, where we saw the pennsylvania memorial, the gettysburg hospital, and many other sites dedicated to the memory of those who fought there. We took a tour with a park ranger in which we walked in formation like the soldiers along the path known as railroad cut. One interesting place we visited was the jennie wade house. jennie wade was the only civilian killed during the battle of gettysburg. She was killed while baking bread for the union soldiers.

118 Proper Nouns Language Fundamentals • EMC 2756 • © Evan-Moor Corp.

Page 119

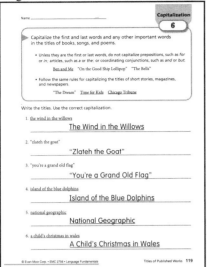

Capitalization 6

Capitalize the first and last words and any other important words in the titles of books, songs, and poems.

- Unless they are the first or last words, do not capitalize prepositions, such as *for* or *in*; articles, such as *a* or *the*; or coordinating conjunctions, such as *and* or *but*.

Ben and Me   "On the Good Ship Lollipop"   "The Bells"

- Follow the same rules for capitalizing the titles of short stories, magazines, and newspapers.

"The Dream"   Time for Kids   Chicago Tribune

Write the titles. Use the correct capitalization.

1. the wind in the willows
The Wind in the Willows

2. "zlateh the goat"
"Zlateh the Goat"

3. "you're a grand old flag"
"You're a Grand Old Flag"

4. island of the blue dolphins
Island of the Blue Dolphins

5. national geographic
National Geographic

6. a child's christmas in wales
A Child's Christmas in Wales

Page 120

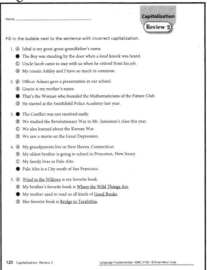

Capitalization Review 2

Fill in the bubble next to the sentence with incorrect capitalization.

1. Ⓐ Jubal is my great-great-grandfather's name.
   ● The Boy was standing by the door when a loud knock was heard.
   Ⓒ Uncle Jacob came to stay with us when he retired from his job.
   Ⓓ My cousin Ashley and I have so much in common.

2. Ⓐ Officer Adams gave a presentation at our school.
   Ⓑ Gracie is my mother's name.
   ● That's the Woman who founded the Mathematicians of the Future Club.
   Ⓓ He started at the Smithfield Police Academy last year.

3. ● The Conflict was not resolved easily.
   Ⓑ We studied the Revolutionary War in Mr. Jamieson's class this year.
   Ⓒ We also learned about the Korean War.
   Ⓓ We saw a movie on the Great Depression.

4. Ⓐ My grandparents live in New Haven, Connecticut.
   Ⓑ My oldest brother is going to school in Princeton, New Jersey.
   Ⓒ My family lives in Palo Alto.
   ● Palo Alto is a City south of San Francisco.

5. Ⓐ Wind in the Willows is my favorite book.
   Ⓑ My brother's favorite book is Where the Wild Things Are.
   ● My mother used to read us all kinds of Good Books.
   Ⓓ Her favorite book is Bridge to Terabithia.

Page 121

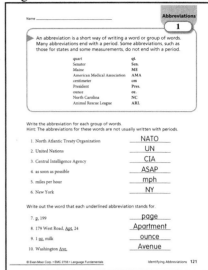

Abbreviations 1

An abbreviation is a short way of writing a word or group of words. Many abbreviations end with a period. Some abbreviations, such as those for states and some measurements, do not end with a period.

quart	qt.
Senator	Sen.
Maine	ME
American Medical Association	AMA
centimeter	cm
President	Pres.
ounce	oz.
North Carolina	NC
Animal Rescue League	ARL

Write the abbreviation for each group of words.
Hint: The abbreviations for these words are not usually written with periods.

1. North Atlantic Treaty Organization   NATO
2. United Nations   UN
3. Central Intelligence Agency   CIA
4. as soon as possible   ASAP
5. miles per hour   mph
6. New York   NY

Write out the word that each underlined abbreviation stands for.

7. p. 199   page
8. 179 West Road, Apt. 24   Apartment
9. 1 oz. milk   ounce
10. Washington Ave.   Avenue

Page 122

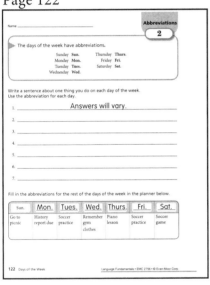

Abbreviations 2

The days of the week have abbreviations.

Sunday	Sun.	Thursday	Thurs.
Monday	Mon.	Friday	Fri.
Tuesday	Tues.	Saturday	Sat.
Wednesday	Wed.		

Write a sentence about one thing you do on each day of the week.
Use the abbreviation for each day.

1. _____ Answers will vary. _____
2. _____
3. _____
4. _____
5. _____
6. _____
7. _____

Fill in the abbreviations for the rest of the days of the week in the planner below.

Sun.	Mon.	Tues.	Wed.	Thurs.	Fri.	Sat.
Go to picnic	History report due	Soccer practice	Remember gym clothes	Piano lesson	Soccer practice	Soccer game

Page 123

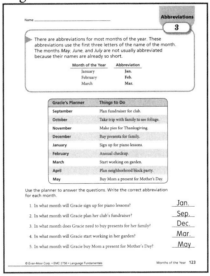

Abbreviations 3

There are abbreviations for most months of the year. These abbreviations use the first three letters of the name of the month. The months *May*, *June*, and *July* are not usually abbreviated because their names are already so short.

Month of the Year	Abbreviation
January	Jan.
February	Feb.
March	Mar.

Gracie's Planner	Things to Do
September	Plan fundraiser for club.
October	Take trip with family to see foliage.
November	Make pies for Thanksgiving.
December	Buy presents for family.
January	Sign up for piano lessons.
February	Annual checkup.
March	Start working on garden.
April	Plan neighborhood block party.
May	Buy Mom a present for Mother's Day!

Use the planner to answer the questions. Write the correct abbreviation for each month.

1. In what month will Gracie sign up for piano lessons?   Jan.
2. In what month will Gracie plan her club's fundraiser?   Sep.
3. In what month does Gracie need to buy presents for her family?   Dec.
4. In what month will Gracie start working in her garden?   Mar.
5. In what month will Gracie buy Mom a present for Mother's Day?   May

Page 124

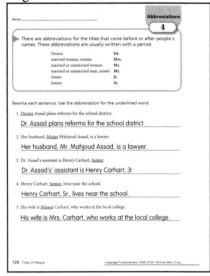

Abbreviations 4

There are abbreviations for the titles that come before or after people's names. These abbreviations are usually written with a period.

Doctor	Dr.
married woman, missus	Mrs.
married or unmarried woman	Ms.
married or unmarried man, mister	Mr.
Junior	Jr.
Senior	Sr.

Rewrite each sentence. Use the abbreviation for the underlined word.

1. Doctor Assad plans reforms for the school district.
Dr. Assad plans reforms for the school district.

2. Her husband, Mister Mahjoud Assad, is a lawyer.
Her husband, Mr. Mahjoud Assad, is a lawyer.

3. Dr. Assad's assistant is Henry Carhart, Junior.
Dr. Assad's assistant is Henry Carhart, Jr.

4. Henry Carhart, Senior, lives near the school.
Henry Carhart, Sr., lives near the school.

5. His wife is Missus Carhart, who works at the local college.
His wife is Mrs. Carhart, who works at the local college.

Page 125

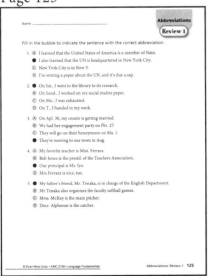

Abbreviations Review 1

Fill in the bubble to indicate the sentence with the correct abbreviation.

1. Ⓐ I learned that the United States of America is a member of Nato.
   ● I also learned that the UN is headquartered in New York City.
   Ⓒ New York City is in N.Y.
   Ⓓ I'm writing a paper about the UN, and it's due a.sap.

2. ● On Sat., I went to the library to do research.
   Ⓑ On Sund., I worked on my social studies paper.
   Ⓒ On Mo., I was exhausted.
   Ⓓ On T., I handed in my work.

3. Ⓐ On Apl. 30, my cousin is getting married.
   Ⓑ We had her engagement party on Fbr. 27.
   Ⓒ They will go on their honeymoon on Ma. 1.
   ● They're moving to our town in Aug.

4. Ⓐ My favorite teacher is Mist. Ferrara.
   Ⓑ Bob Jones is the presid. of the Teachers Association.
   ● Our principal is Ms. Iyo.
   Ⓓ Mrs Ferrara is nice, too.

5. ● My father's friend, Mr. Tenaka, is in charge of the English Department.
   Ⓑ Mr Tenaka also organizes the faculty softball games.
   Ⓒ Mrs. McKay is the main player.
   Ⓓ Docr. Alphonse is the catcher.

Page 126

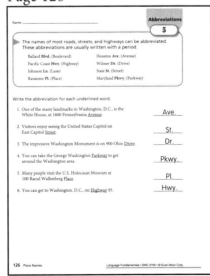

Abbreviations 5

The names of most roads, streets, and highways can be abbreviated. These abbreviations are usually written with a period.

Ballard Blvd. (Boulevard)	Houston Ave. (Avenue)
Pacific Coast Hwy. (Highway)	Wilmer Dr. (Drive)
Johnson Ln. (Lane)	State St. (Street)
Ransome Pl. (Place)	Maryland Pkwy. (Parkway)

Write the abbreviation for each underlined word.

1. One of the many landmarks in Washington, D.C., is the White House, at 1600 Pennsylvania Avenue.   Ave.

2. Visitors enjoy seeing the United States Capitol on East Capitol Street.   St.

3. The impressive Washington Monument is on 900 Ohio Drive.   Dr.

4. You can take the George Washington Parkway to get around the Washington area.   Pkwy.

5. Many people visit the U.S. Holocaust Museum at 100 Raoul Wallenberg Place.   Pl.

6. You can get to Washington, D.C., on Highway 95.   Hwy.

Page 127

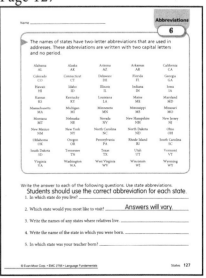

Abbreviations 6

The names of states have two-letter abbreviations that are used in addresses. These abbreviations are written with two capital letters and no period.

Alabama AL	Alaska AK	Arizona AZ	Arkansas AR	California CA
Colorado CO	Connecticut CT	Delaware DE	Florida FL	Georgia GA
Hawaii HI	Idaho ID	Illinois IL	Indiana IN	Iowa IA
Kansas KS	Kentucky KY	Louisiana LA	Maine ME	Maryland MD
Massachusetts MA	Michigan MI	Minnesota MN	Mississippi MS	Missouri MO
Montana MT	Nebraska NE	Nevada NV	New Hampshire NH	New Jersey NJ
New Mexico NM	New York NY	North Carolina NC	North Dakota ND	Ohio OH
Oklahoma OK	Oregon OR	Pennsylvania PA	Rhode Island RI	South Carolina SC
South Dakota SD	Tennessee TN	Texas TX	Utah UT	Vermont VT
Virginia VA	Washington WA	West Virginia WV	Wisconsin WI	Wyoming WY

Write the answer to each of the following questions. Use state abbreviations.
Students should use the correct abbreviation for each state.

1. In which state do you live? _____
2. Which state would you most like to visit?   Answers will vary.
3. Write the names of any states where relatives live. _____
4. Write the name of the state in which you were born. _____
5. In which state was your teacher born? _____

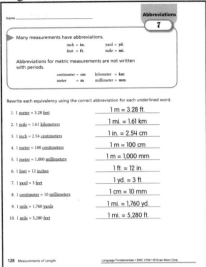

Abbreviations 7

Many measurements have abbreviations.

inch = **in.**   yard = **yd.**
foot = **ft.**   mile = **mi.**

Abbreviations for metric measurements are not written with periods.

centimeter = **cm**   kilometer = **km**
meter = **m**   millimeter = **mm**

Rewrite each equivalency using the correct abbreviation for each underlined word.

1. 1 meter = 3.28 feet — 1 m = 3.28 ft.
2. 1 mile = 1.61 kilometers — 1 mi. = 1.61 km
3. 1 inch = 2.54 centimeters — 1 in. = 2.54 cm
4. 1 meter = 100 centimeters — 1 m = 100 cm
5. 1 meter = 1,000 millimeters — 1 m = 1,000 mm
6. 1 foot = 12 inches — 1 ft. = 12 in.
7. 1 yard = 3 feet — 1 yd. = 3 ft.
8. 1 centimeter = 10 millimeters — 1 cm = 10 mm
9. 1 mile = 1,760 yards — 1 mi. = 1,760 yd.
10. 1 mile = 5,280 feet — 1 mi. = 5,280 ft.

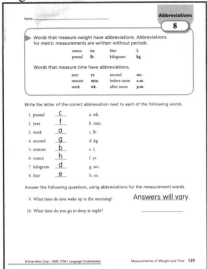

Abbreviations 8

Words that measure weight have abbreviations. Abbreviations for metric measurements are written without periods.

ounce   **oz.**   liter   **L**
pound   **lb.**   kilogram   **kg**

Words that measure time have abbreviations.

year   **yr.**   second   **sec.**
minute   **min.**   before noon   **a.m.**
week   **wk.**   after noon   **p.m.**

Write the letter of the correct abbreviation next to each of the following words.

1. pound — c   a. wk.
2. year — f   b. min.
3. week — a   c. lb.
4. second — g   d. kg
5. minute — b   e. L
6. ounce — h   f. yr.
7. kilogram — d   g. sec.
8. liter — e   h. oz.

Answer the following questions, using abbreviations for the measurement words.

9. What time do you wake up in the morning? **Answers will vary.**

10. What time do you go to sleep at night? _____

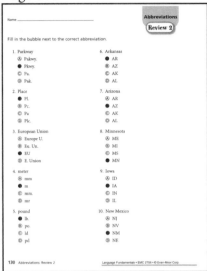

Abbreviations Review 2

Fill in the bubble next to the correct abbreviation.

1. Parkway
   Ⓐ Pakwy.
   ● Pkwy.
   Ⓒ Pa.
   Ⓓ Pak.

2. Place
   ● Pl.
   Ⓑ Pc.
   Ⓒ Pa
   Ⓓ Plc.

3. European Union
   Ⓐ Europe U.
   Ⓑ Eu. Un.
   ● EU
   Ⓓ E. Union

4. meter
   Ⓐ mm
   ● m
   Ⓒ mm.
   Ⓓ mr

5. pound
   ● lb.
   Ⓑ po.
   Ⓒ ld
   Ⓓ pd

6. Arkansas
   ● AR
   Ⓑ AZ
   Ⓒ AK
   Ⓓ AL

7. Arizona
   Ⓐ AR
   ● AZ
   Ⓒ AK
   Ⓓ AL

8. Minnesota
   Ⓐ ME
   Ⓑ MI
   Ⓒ MS
   ● MN

9. Iowa
   Ⓐ ID
   ● IA
   Ⓒ IN
   Ⓓ IL

10. New Mexico
    Ⓐ NJ
    Ⓑ NV
    ● NM
    Ⓓ NE

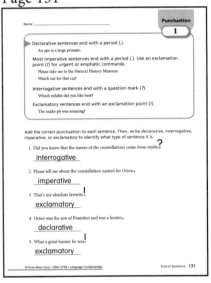

Punctuation 1

Declarative sentences end with a period (.).
An ape is a large primate.

Most imperative sentences end with a period (.). Use an exclamation point (!) for urgent or emphatic commands.
Please take me to the Natural History Museum.
Watch out for that car!

Interrogative sentences end with a question mark (?).
Which exhibit did you like best?

Exclamatory sentences end with an exclamation point (!).
The snake pit was amazing!

Add the correct punctuation to each sentence. Then, write *declarative, interrogative, imperative,* or *exclamatory* to identify what type of sentence it is.

1. Did you know that the names of the constellations come from myths?
   interrogative

2. Please tell me about the constellation named for Orion.
   imperative

3. That's my absolute favorite!
   exclamatory

4. Orion was the son of Poseidon and was a hunter.
   declarative

5. What a great hunter he was!
   exclamatory

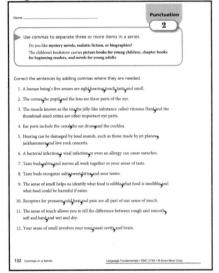

Punctuation 2

Use commas to separate three or more items in a series.
Do you like mystery novels, realistic fiction, or biographies?
The children's bookstore carries picture books for young children, chapter books for beginning readers, and novels for young adults.

Correct the sentences by adding commas where they are needed.

1. A human being's five senses are sight, hearing, touch, taste, and smell.
2. The cornea, the pupil, and the lens are three parts of the eye.
3. The muscle known as the iris, the jelly-like substance called vitreous fluid, and the thumbnail-sized retina are other important eye parts.
4. Ear parts include the canal, the ear drum, and the cochlea.
5. Hearing can be damaged by loud sounds, such as those made by jet planes, jackhammers, and live rock concerts.
6. A bacterial infection, a viral infection, or even an allergy can cause earaches.
7. Taste buds, saliva, and nerves all work together in your sense of taste.
8. Taste buds recognize salty, sweet, bitter, and sour tastes.
9. The sense of smell helps us identify what food is edible, what food is inedible, and what food could be harmful to us.
10. Receptors for pressure, cold, heat, and pain are all part of our sense of touch.
11. The sense of touch allows you to tell the difference between rough and smooth, soft and hard, and wet and dry.
12. Your sense of smell involves your nose, nasal cavity, and brain.

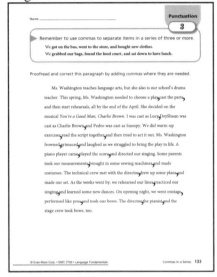

Punctuation 3

Remember to use commas to separate items in a series of three or more.
We got on the bus, went to the store, and bought new clothes.
We grabbed our bags, found the food court, and sat down to have lunch.

Proofread and correct this paragraph by adding commas where they are needed.

Ms. Washington teaches language arts, but she also is our school's drama teacher. This spring, Ms. Washington needed to choose a play, cast the parts, and then start rehearsals, all by the end of the April. She decided on the musical *You're a Good Man, Charlie Brown.* I was cast as Lucy, DeShaun was cast as Charlie Brown, and Pedro was cast as Snoopy. We did warm-up exercises, read the script together, and then tried to act it out. Ms. Washington frowned, grimaced, and laughed as we struggled to bring the play to life. A piano player came, played the score, and directed our singing. Some parents took our measurements, brought in some sewing machines, and made costumes. The technical crew met with the director, drew up some plans, and made our set. As the weeks went by, we rehearsed our lines, practiced our singing, and learned some new dances. On opening night, we went onstage, performed like pros, and took our bows. The director, the pianist, and the stage crew took bows, too.

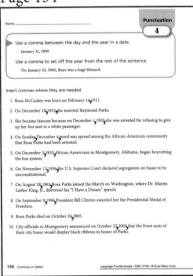

Punctuation 4

Use a comma between the day and the year in a date.
January 31, 1999

Use a comma to set off the year from the rest of the sentence.
On January 10, 1960, there was a huge blizzard.

Insert commas where they are needed.

1. Rosa McCauley was born on February 14, 1913.
2. On December 18, 1932, she married Raymond Parks.
3. She became famous because on December 1, 1955, she was arrested for refusing to give up her bus seat to a white passenger.
4. On Sunday, December 4, word had spread among the African-American community that Rosa Parks had been arrested.
5. On December 5, 1955, African Americans in Montgomery, Alabama, began boycotting the bus system.
6. On November 13, 1956, the U.S. Supreme Court declared segregation on buses to be unconstitutional.
7. On August 28, 1963, Rosa Parks joined the March on Washington, where Dr. Martin Luther King, Jr., delivered his "I Have a Dream" speech.
8. On September 9, 1996, President Bill Clinton awarded her the Presidential Medal of Freedom.
9. Rosa Parks died on October 24, 2005.
10. City officials in Montgomery announced on October 27, 2005, that the front seats of their city buses would display black ribbons in honor of Parks.

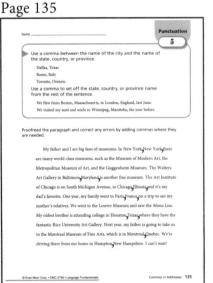

Punctuation 5

Use a comma between the name of the city and the name of the state, country, or province.
Dallas, Texas
Rome, Italy
Toronto, Ontario

Use a comma to set off the state, country, or province name from the rest of the sentence.
We flew from Boston, Massachusetts, to London, England, last June.
We visited our aunt and uncle in Winnipeg, Manitoba, the year before.

Proofread the paragraph and correct any errors by adding commas where they are needed.

My father and I are big fans of museums. In New York, New York, there are many world-class museums, such as the Museum of Modern Art, the Metropolitan Museum of Art, and the Guggenheim Museum. The Walters Art Gallery in Baltimore, Maryland, is another fine museum. The Art Institute of Chicago is on South Michigan Avenue, in Chicago, Illinois, and it's my dad's favorite. One year, my family went to Paris, France, on a trip to see my mother's relatives. We went to the Louvre Museum and saw the *Mona Lisa.* My oldest brother is attending college in Houston, Texas, where they have the fantastic Rice University Art Gallery. Next year, my father is going to take us to the Montreal Museum of Fine Arts, which is in Montreal, Quebec. We're driving there from our home in Hampton, New Hampshire. I can't wait!

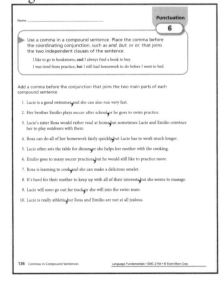

Punctuation 6

Use a comma in a compound sentence. Place the comma before the coordinating conjunction, such as *and, but,* or *or,* that joins the two independent clauses of the sentence.
I like to go to bookstores, and I always find a book to buy.
I was tired from practice, but I still had homework to do before I went to bed.

Add a comma before the conjunction that joins the two main parts of each compound sentence.

1. Lacie is a good swimmer, and she can also run very fast.
2. Her brother Emilio plays soccer after school, or he goes to swim practice.
3. Lacie's sister Rosa would rather read at home, but sometimes Lacie and Emilio convince her to play outdoors with them.
4. Rosa can do all of her homework fairly quickly, but Lacie has to work much longer.
5. Lacie often sets the table for dinner, or she helps her mother with the cooking.
6. Emilio goes to many soccer practices, but he would still like to practice more.
7. Rosa is learning to cook, and she can make a delicious omelet.
8. It's hard for their mother to keep up with all of their interests, but she seems to manage.
9. Lacie will soon go out for track, or she will join the swim team.
10. Lacie is really athletic, but Rosa and Emilio are not at all jealous.

Page 137

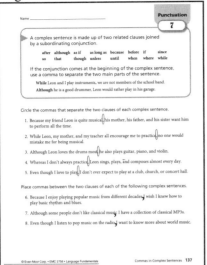

Punctuation 7

A complex sentence is made up of two related clauses joined by a subordinating conjunction.

after · although · as if · as long as · because · before · if · since
so · that · though · unless · until · when · where · while

If the conjunction comes at the beginning of the complex sentence, use a comma to separate the two main parts of the sentence.

While Leon and I play instruments, we are not members of the school band.
Although he is a good drummer, Leon would rather play in his garage.

Circle the commas that separate the two clauses of each complex sentence.

1. Because my friend Leon is quite musical, his mother, his father, and his sister want him to perform all the time.
2. While Leon, my mother, and my teacher all encourage me to practice, no one would mistake me for being musical.
3. Although Leon loves the drums most, he also plays guitar, piano, and violin.
4. Whereas I don't always practice, Leon sings, plays, and composes almost every day.
5. Even though I love to play, I don't ever expect to play at a club, church, or concert hall.

Place commas between the two clauses of each of the following complex sentences.

6. Because I enjoy playing popular music from different decades, I wish I knew how to play basic rhythm and blues.
7. Although some people don't like classical music, I have a collection of classical MP3s.
8. Even though I listen to pop music on the radio, I want to know more about world music.

Commas in Complex Sentences 137

Page 138

Punctuation Review 1

Fill in the bubble next to the sentence that uses the correct punctuation.

1. Ⓐ My favorite writer is J. K. Rowling!
   Ⓑ She was born in Great Britain in 1965,
   ● She wrote some of the best books I've ever read!
   Ⓓ Do you think she will write another series.

2. Ⓐ Rowling worked as a secretary as a waiter and as a teacher.
   Ⓑ She has lived in London in Scotland, and in Portugal.
   ● Chris Columbus Alfonso Cuarón, and Mike Newell directed movies based on her books.
   Ⓓ Rowling's children are named Jessica, David, and Mackenzie.

3. Ⓐ First I read the book next I see the movie then I reread the book.
   Ⓑ I like to get a snack, find a comfortable chair, and read all afternoon.
   ● My friend Matthew tries to read the books gives up, and waits for the movies.
   Ⓓ At the movies we buy our tickets buy popcorn and watch the screen.

4. Ⓐ I like Ron best but my brother likes Hermione the most.
   ● I think that Professor Snape is scary, and I always get nervous when he shows up.
   Ⓒ I like the actor who plays Harry but the character is different in the books.
   Ⓓ I wish that I could ride the Hogwarts Express and then I could see Hogwarts!

5. Ⓐ Although I love the *Harry Potter* series I have many other favorite books.
   Ⓑ Whereas my brother loves Tolkien I am more of a C. S. Lewis fan.
   ● While *The Lord of the Rings* books are exciting, I really enjoy the *Narnia* books.
   Ⓓ Even though I've mentioned fantasy authors I also like many authors of realistic fiction.

138 Punctuation: Review 1

Page 139

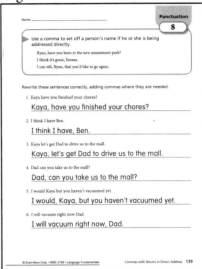

Punctuation 8

Use a comma to set off a person's name if he or she is being addressed directly.

Ryan, have you been to the new amusement park?
I think it's great, Emma.
I can tell, Ryan, that you'd like to go again.

Rewrite these sentences correctly, adding commas where they are needed.

1. Kaya have you finished your chores?
   Kaya, have you finished your chores?

2. I think I have Ben.
   I think I have, Ben.

3. Kaya let's get Dad to drive us to the mall.
   Kaya, let's get Dad to drive us to the mall.

4. Dad can you take us to the mall?
   Dad, can you take us to the mall?

5. I would Kaya but you haven't vacuumed yet.
   I would, Kaya, but you haven't vacuumed yet.

6. I will vacuum right now Dad.
   I will vacuum right now, Dad.

Commas with Nouns in Direct Address 139

Page 140

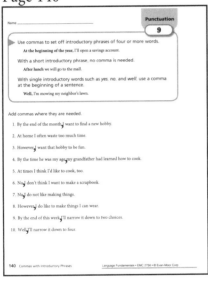

Punctuation 9

Use commas to set off introductory phrases of four or more words.

At the beginning of the year, I'll open a savings account.

With a short introductory phrase, no comma is needed.

After lunch we will go to the mall.

With single introductory words such as *yes, no,* and *well,* use a comma at the beginning of a sentence.

Well, I'm mowing my neighbor's lawn.

Add commas where they are needed.

1. By the end of the month, I want to find a new hobby.
2. At home I often waste too much time.
3. However, I want that hobby to be fun.
4. By the time he was my age, my grandfather had learned how to cook.
5. At times I think I'd like to cook, too.
6. No, I don't think I want to make a scrapbook.
7. No, I do not like making things.
8. However, I do like to make things I can wear.
9. By the end of this week, I'll narrow it down to two choices.
10. Well, I'll narrow it down to four.

140 Commas with Introductory Phrases

Page 141

Punctuation 10

In a friendly letter, use a comma after the greeting and after the closing.

Dear Alexandra,
Sincerely,

Add commas where they belong in the greetings and the closings.

Dear Patty,   Dear Auntie Reni,
Your friend,   Much love,
Dear Mary,   Your niece, Anja
Dearest Lou,   Dear Grandpa,
Your sister,   Fondly,

Read the letter from Daniel to his parents. Write the greeting and the closing. Use commas.

June 26, 2007

Dear Mom and Dad,

I'm having a great time at Grandma's. There is a pond where all the neighbors meet to go swimming. We have cookouts every weekend. I've made many new friends.

I do miss you, of course. It will be great to come back home.

Answers may vary.   Love,

Daniel

Commas in Letter Writing 141

Page 142

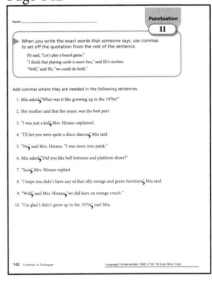

Punctuation 11

When you write the exact words that someone says, use commas to set off the quotation from the rest of the sentence.

Eli said, "Let's play a board game."
"I think that playing cards is more fun," said Eli's mother.
"Well," said Eli, "we could do both."

Add commas where they are needed in the following sentences.

1. Mia asked, "What was it like growing up in the 1970s?"
2. Her mother said that the music was the best part.
3. "I was just a kid," Mrs. Hirano explained.
4. "I'll bet you were quite a disco dancer," Mia said.
5. "No," said Mrs. Hirano, "I was more into punk."
6. Mia asked, "Did you like bell bottoms and platform shoes?"
7. "Sure," Mrs. Hirano replied.
8. "I hope you didn't have any of that silly orange and green furniture," Mia said.
9. "Well," said Mrs. Hirano, "we did have an orange couch."
10. "I'm glad I didn't grow up in the 1970s," said Mia.

142 Commas in Dialogue

Page 143

Punctuation Review 2

Fill in the bubble next to the sentence or phrase that uses the correct punctuation.

1. ● Henry, do you like poetry?
   Ⓑ I love it Tanya.
   Ⓒ Do you like song lyrics Henry?
   Ⓓ Tanya I like them if they are poetic.

2. ● Well Tanya didn't think that she could write well.
   Ⓑ As the years went by writing was always a struggle for Tanya.
   Ⓒ Yes, Tanya did like to sing.
   Ⓓ No her parents thought she should focus on school.

3. Ⓐ "Maybe we should go to a poetry reading" said Henry.
   Ⓑ "I don't think so," said, Tanya.
   Ⓒ "They'll have musicians playing along with the poetry" said, Henry.
   ● Tanya said, "That sounds interesting."

4. ● Henry said, "You should have seen Tanya at the reading!"
   Ⓑ His mother asked "Why is that?"
   Ⓒ "They asked for volunteers" said Henry.
   Ⓓ Henry explained "She read fantastic poems that I didn't even know she had written!"

5. Which greeting for a friendly letter is written correctly?
   Ⓐ Dear Dad
   Ⓑ Dear, Mom
   Ⓒ Dear Grandma:
   ● Dear Grandpa,

Punctuation: Review 2 143

Page 144

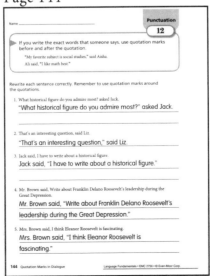

Punctuation 12

If you write the exact words that someone says, use quotation marks before and after the quotation.

"My favorite subject is social studies," said Aisha.
Ali said, "I like math best."

Rewrite each sentence correctly. Remember to use quotation marks around the quotations.

1. What historical figure do you admire most? asked Jack.
   "What historical figure do you admire most?" asked Jack.

2. That's an interesting question, said Liz.
   "That's an interesting question," said Liz.

3. Jack said, I have to write about a historical figure.
   Jack said, "I have to write about a historical figure."

4. Mr. Brown said, Write about Franklin Delano Roosevelt's leadership during the Great Depression.
   Mr. Brown said, "Write about Franklin Delano Roosevelt's leadership during the Great Depression."

5. Mrs. Brown said, I think Eleanor Roosevelt is fascinating.
   Mrs. Brown said, "I think Eleanor Roosevelt is fascinating."

144 Quotation Marks in Dialogue

Page 145

Punctuation 13

If a quotation is interrupted by words telling who is speaking, use quotation marks to set off the speaker's words.

"It's a close call," said Emma, "but I think he was out."

Add quotation marks to the sentences where needed.

1. "I'm not sure," said Leah, "but I think I'm doing this book report wrong."
2. Chen said that he would read it to see if it was okay.
3. "I'm sure you'll think it's silly," Leah said, "since I don't know what to include."
4. "This is okay," said Chen, "but I'm not sure what you think of the book."
5. "I liked it," said Leah, "but I don't love it."
6. Chen asked Leah what she liked about the book and what its weaknesses were.
7. "If that's what you think," said Chen, "then that's what you need to include."
8. "Okay, I'll rewrite the report," said Leah. "Is there anything here that I should keep in my revision?"
9. "Of course!" said Chen. "Your summary of the book is really good and so are the character descriptions."
10. "Thanks," said Leah, "I think I know how to fix this now."
11. "Would you read it again," asked Leah, "once I make the revisions?"
12. "Sure," said Chen, "I'd be happy to."

Quotation Marks in Dialogue 145

Page 146

Punctuation 14

Use quotation marks around the titles of short stories, poems, and songs.

"The Lottery" "Ballad of the Morning Streets" "Red River Valley"

Write each of the following sentences correctly. Remember to use quotation marks.

1. I read a story called The Selfish Giant.

   I read a story called "The Selfish Giant."

2. My favorite poem is Dream Variations.

   My favorite poem is "Dream Variations."

3. My mom likes to sing You've Got a Friend.

   My mom likes to sing "You've Got a Friend."

Write the titles of two songs, poems, and short stories that you know. Use quotation marks.

4. (songs) _____ Answers will vary.

5. (poems) _____

6. (short stories) _____

Page 147

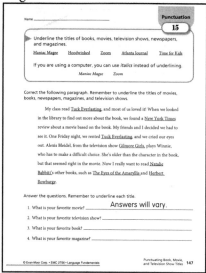

Punctuation 15

Underline the titles of books, movies, television shows, newspapers, and magazines.

Maniac Magee   Hoodwinked   Zoom   Atlanta Journal   Time for Kids

If you are using a computer, you can use *italics* instead of underlining.

Maniac Magee   *Zoom*

Correct the following paragraph. Remember to underline the titles of movies, books, newspapers, magazines, and television shows.

My class read Tuck Everlasting, and most of us loved it! When we looked in the library to find out more about the book, we found a New York Times review about a movie based on the book. My friends and I decided we had to see it. One Friday night, we rented Tuck Everlasting, and we cried our eyes out. Alexis Bleidel, from the television show Gilmore Girls, plays Winnie, who has to make a difficult choice. She's older than the character in the book, but that seemed right in the movie. Now I really want to read Natalie Babbitt's other books, such as The Eyes of the Amaryllis and Herbert Rowbarge.

Answer the questions. Remember to underline each title.

1. What is your favorite movie? _____ Answers will vary.

2. What is your favorite television show? _____

3. What is your favorite book? _____

4. What is your favorite magazine? _____

Page 148

Punctuation Review 3

Fill in the bubble next to the correct answer to each question.

1. Which sentence is punctuated correctly?
   - Ⓐ Carlos said "I want to take a trip.
   - ● Mrs. Carales asked, "Where do you want to go?"
   - Ⓒ Carlos said, I'd like to see the ocean."
   - Ⓓ "Start saving your allowance said Mrs. Carales.

2. Which sentence is punctuated correctly?
   - Ⓐ I'd like to go to the forest," said Dora, "where we could camp.
   - Ⓑ "Aside from the fact that we don't have a tent, said Mrs. Carales, that sounds great.
   - ● "If Carlos and I save our allowance," said Dora, "we could buy a tent before long."
   - Ⓓ "Don't count me in, said Carlos, since I'm saving to go to the beach.

3. Which poem title is written correctly?
   - Ⓐ The Barefoot Boy
   - Ⓑ *The Barefoot Boy*
   - Ⓒ The Barefoot Boy
   - ● "The Barefoot Boy"

4. Which book title is written correctly?
   - ● Alice in Wonderland
   - Ⓑ "Alice in Wonderland"
   - Ⓒ Alice in Wonderland
   - Ⓓ Alice in Wonderland

5. Which movie title is written correctly?
   - Ⓐ Over the Hedge
   - Ⓑ "Over the Hedge"
   - ● Over the Hedge
   - Ⓓ "Over the Hedge"

Page 149

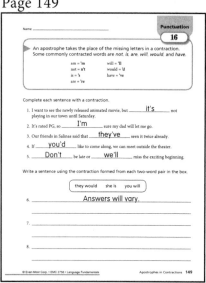

Punctuation 16

An apostrophe takes the place of the missing letters in a contraction. Some commonly contracted words are *not, is, are, will, would,* and *have.*

am = 'm	will = 'll
not = n't	would = 'd
is = 's	have = 've
are = 're	

Complete each sentence with a contraction.

1. I want to see the newly released animated movie, but _it's_ not playing in our town until Saturday.

2. It's rated PG, so _I'm_ sure my dad will let me go.

3. Our friends in Salinas said that _they've_ seen it twice already.

4. If _you'd_ like to come along, we can meet outside the theater.

5. _Don't_ be late or _we'll_ miss the exciting beginning.

Write a sentence using the contraction formed from each two-word pair in the box.

they would	she is	you will

6. _____ Answers will vary.

7. _____

8. _____

Page 150

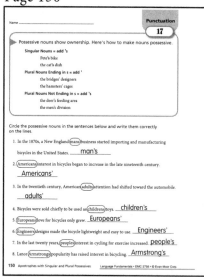

Punctuation 17

Possessive nouns show ownership. Here's how to make nouns possessive.

Singular Nouns = add 's
   Pete's bike
   the cat's dish

Plural Nouns Ending in s = add '
   the bridges' designers
   the hamsters' cages

Plural Nouns Not Ending in s = add 's
   the deer's feeding area
   the men's division

Circle the possessive nouns in the sentences below and write them correctly on the lines.

1. In the 1870s, a New England man's business started importing and manufacturing bicycles in the United States. _man's_

2. Americans interest in bicycles began to increase in the late nineteenth century. _Americans'_

3. In the twentieth century, American adults attention had shifted toward the automobile. _adults'_

4. Bicycles were sold chiefly to be used as children toys. _children's_

5. Europeans love for bicycles only grew. _Europeans'_

6. Engineers designs made the bicycle lightweight and easy to use. _Engineers'_

7. In the last twenty years, peoples interest in cycling for exercise increased. _people's_

8. Lance Armstrongs popularity has raised interest in bicycling. _Armstrong's_

Page 151

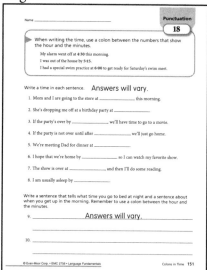

Punctuation 18

When writing the time, use a colon between the numbers that show the hour and the minutes.

My alarm went off at 4:30 this morning.
I was out of the house by 5:15.
I had a special swim practice at 6:00 to get ready for Saturday's swim meet.

Write a time in each sentence. Answers will vary.

1. Mom and I are going to the store at _____ this morning.

2. She's dropping me off at a birthday party at _____

3. If the party's over by _____ we'll have time to go to a movie.

4. If the party is not over until after _____ we'll just go home.

5. We're meeting Dad for dinner at _____

6. I hope that we're home by _____ so I can watch my favorite show.

7. The show is over at _____ and then I'll do some reading.

8. I am usually asleep by _____

Write a sentence that tells what time you go to bed at night and a sentence about when you get up in the morning. Remember to use a colon between the hour and the minutes.

9. _____ Answers will vary.

10. _____

Page 152

Punctuation 19

When writing a business letter, use a colon after the greeting.

Dear Ms. Stasio:
To Whom It May Concern:
Dear Sir or Madam:

Add a colon to each greeting that would be for a business letter.

1. Dear Aunt Elaine
2. Dear Dr. Kirk:
3. Dear President Marquez:
4. Dear Grandma
5. Dear Sir or Madam:

6. My dear friend
7. Dear Customer Service Manager:
8. Dear Principal Collins:
9. Dear Mom
10. To Whom It May Concern:

Write a greeting for each business letter described.

11. You ordered a jacket. The wrong one was sent.

    _____ Answers will vary.

12. You want to convince the mayor of your city to vote for a new park.

    _____

13. You want to write an opinion letter to the local newspaper.

    _____

14. You found a grammatical error in a magazine. You want to alert the editor of the error.

    _____

Page 153

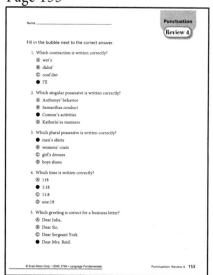

Punctuation Review 4

Fill in the bubble next to the correct answer.

1. Which contraction is written correctly?
   - Ⓐ wer'e
   - Ⓑ didnt'
   - Ⓒ coul'dnt
   - ● I'll

2. Which singular possessive is written correctly?
   - Ⓐ Anthonys' behavior
   - Ⓑ Samanthas conduct
   - ● Connor's activities
   - Ⓓ Katherin'es manners

3. Which plural possessive is written correctly?
   - ● men's shirts
   - Ⓑ womens' coats
   - Ⓒ girl's dresses
   - Ⓓ boys shoes

4. Which time is written correctly?
   - Ⓐ 118
   - ● 1:18
   - Ⓒ 11:8
   - Ⓓ one:18

5. Which greeting is correct for a business letter?
   - Ⓐ Dear Julia,
   - Ⓑ Dear Sir,
   - Ⓒ Dear Sergeant York
   - ● Dear Mrs. Reid:

Page 154

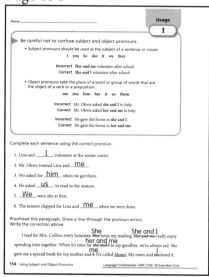

Usage 1

Be careful not to confuse subject and object pronouns.

- Subject pronouns should be used as the subject of a sentence or clause.
   I you he she it we they

   Incorrect Her and me volunteer after school.
   Correct She and I volunteer after school.

- Object pronouns take the place of a word or group of words that are the object of a verb or a preposition.
   me you him her it us them

   Incorrect Mr. Okwu asked she and I to help.
   Correct Mr. Okwu asked her and me to help.

   Incorrect He gave the forms to she and I.
   Correct He gave the forms to her and me.

Complete each sentence using the correct pronoun.

1. Lina and _I_ volunteer at the senior center.

2. Mr. Okwu trained Lina and _me_

3. We asked for _him_ when we got there.

4. He asked _us_ to read to the seniors.

5. _We_ were shy at first.

6. The seniors clapped for Lina and _me_ when we were done.

Proofread this paragraph. Draw a line through the pronoun errors. Write the correction above.

I read for Mrs. Collins every Saturday. Her loves my reading. Me and her really enjoy spending time together. When it's time for she and I to say goodbye, we're always sad. She gave me a special book for my mother and I. It's called Moms. My mom and me loved it.

Page 155

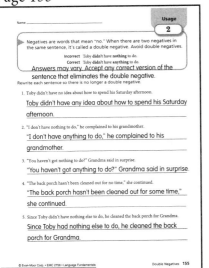

Usage 2

Negatives are words that mean "no." When there are two negatives in the same sentence, it's called a double negative. Avoid double negatives.

Incorrect Toby didn't have **nothing** to do.
Correct Toby didn't have **anything** to do.

Answers may vary. Accept any correct version of the sentence that eliminates the double negative.

Rewrite each sentence so there is no longer a double negative.

1. Toby didn't have no idea about how to spend his Saturday afternoon.

Toby didn't have any idea about how to spend his Saturday afternoon.

2. "I don't have nothing to do," he complained to his grandmother.

"I don't have anything to do," he complained to his grandmother.

3. "You haven't got nothing to do?" Grandma said in surprise.

"You haven't got anything to do?" Grandma said in surprise.

4. "The back porch hasn't been cleaned out for no time," she continued.

"The back porch hasn't been cleaned out for some time," she continued.

5. Since Toby didn't have nothing else to do, he cleaned the back porch for Grandma.

Since Toby had nothing else to do, he cleaned the back porch for Grandma.

Page 156

Usage 3

People often confuse the words *good, well, bad,* and *badly.*

- The word *good* is an adjective. It describes a noun or pronoun.
  Greg is a **good** singer.
- The word *well* is an adverb. It describes a verb and sometimes an adjective.
  Greg sings **well.**
- The word *bad* is an adjective. It describes a noun or pronoun. Do not use *bad* as an adverb.
  Miranda is a **bad** singer.
- The word *badly* is an adverb. It describes a verb or adjective.
  Miranda sings **badly.**

Complete each sentence correctly.

1. Choir practice went **well/badly** yesterday.
2. Everyone sang **well/badly**, especially the tenors.
3. However, Greg's solo was really **good/bad**
4. He performed **well/badly** during practice.

Write four sentences using the words in parentheses.

5. (good) **Answers will vary.**
6. (well) _____
7. (bad) _____
8. (badly) _____

Page 157

Usage Review 1

Fill in the bubble next to the correct answer to each question.

1. Which sentence is written correctly?
   Ⓐ Auntie Meg gave a puppy to my brother and I.
   Ⓑ Me and my brother always wanted a puppy.
   ● My brother and I promised to take good care of the puppy.
   Ⓓ The puppy chased my brother and I all over the yard.

2. Which sentence is written correctly?
   ● My dad and I play basketball after dinner.
   Ⓑ Him and me shoot baskets for about an hour.
   Ⓒ My mother joins my dad and I sometimes.
   Ⓓ Her and me like to fake out my dad.

3. Which sentence is written correctly?
   Ⓐ Cercie and Emily didn't hear no key in the door.
   ● There was no sound as the door opened.
   Ⓒ When Andy walked in the room, she didn't see no cats.
   Ⓓ Cercie and Emily didn't waste no time running to greet Andy.

4. Which sentence is written correctly?
   Ⓐ I wanted to win bad.
   Ⓑ She was well as a chess player.
   Ⓒ Today's game went good.
   ● I performed badly on the oral quiz.

5. Which sentence is written correctly?
   ● Sienna is a good writer.
   Ⓑ She writes good whenever we have to hand something in.
   Ⓒ Her writing is always as well anyone's.
   Ⓓ Sienna's has written good since she was in first grade.

Page 158

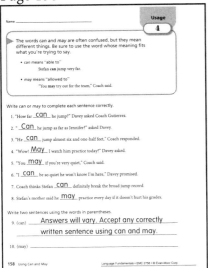

Usage 4

The words *can* and *may* are often confused, but they mean different things. Be sure to use the word whose meaning fits what you're trying to say.

- *can* means "able to"
  Stefan **can** jump very far.
- *may* means "allowed to"
  "You **may** try out for the team," Coach said.

Write *can* or *may* to complete each sentence correctly.

1. "How far **can** he jump?" Davey asked Coach Gutierrez.
2. "**Can** he jump as far as Jennifer?" asked Davey.
3. "He **can** jump almost six and one-half feet," Coach responded.
4. "Wow! **May** I watch him practice today?" Davey asked.
5. "You **may** if you're very quiet," Coach said.
6. "I **can** be so quiet he won't know I'm here," Davey promised.
7. Coach thinks Stefan **can** definitely break the broad jump record.
8. Stefan's mother said he **may** practice every day if it doesn't hurt his grades.

Write two sentences using the words in parentheses.

9. (can) **Answers will vary. Accept any correctly written sentence using can and may.**

10. (may) _____

Page 159

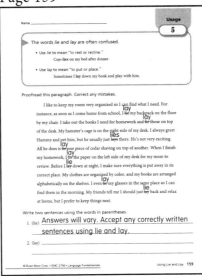

Usage 5

The words *lie* and *lay* are often confused.

- Use *lie* to mean "to rest or recline."
  Cujo **lies** on my bed after dinner.
- Use *lay* to mean "to put or place."
  Sometimes I **lay** down my book and play with him.

Proofread this paragraph. Correct any mistakes.

I like to keep my room very organized so I can find what I need. For instance, as soon as I come home from school, I ~~lay~~ (lay) my backpack on the floor by my chair. I take out the books I need for homework and ~~lie~~ those on top of the desk. My hamster's cage is on the right side of my desk. I always greet Hammy and pet him, but he usually just ~~lays~~ (lies) there. He's not very exciting. All he does is ~~lie~~ (lay) one piece of cedar shaving on top of another. When I finish my homework, I ~~lie~~ (lay) the paper on the left side of my desk for my mom to review. Before I ~~lay~~ (lie) down at night, I make sure everything is put away in its correct place. My clothes are organized by color, and my books are arranged alphabetically on the shelves. I even ~~lie~~ (lay) my glasses in the same place so I can find them in the morning. My friends tell me I should just ~~lay~~ (lie) back and relax at home, but I prefer to keep things neat.

Write two sentences using the words in parentheses.

1. (lie) **Answers will vary. Accept any correctly written sentences using lie and lay.**

2. (lay) _____

Page 160

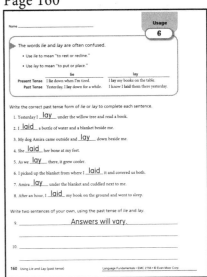

Usage 6

The words *lie* and *lay* are often confused.

- Use *lie* to mean "to rest or recline."
- Use *lay* to mean "to put or place."

	lie	lay
Present Tense	I lie down when I'm tired.	I lay my books on the table.
Past Tense	Yesterday, I lay down for a while.	I know I laid them there yesterday.

Write the correct past tense form of *lie* or *lay* to complete each sentence.

1. Yesterday I **lay** under the willow tree and read a book.
2. I **laid** a bottle of water and a blanket beside me.
3. My dog Amira came outside and **lay** down beside me.
4. She **laid** her bone at my feet.
5. As we **lay** there, it grew cooler.
6. I picked up the blanket from where I **laid** it and covered us both.
7. Amira **lay** under the blanket and cuddled next to me.
8. After an hour, I **laid** my book on the ground and went to sleep.

Write two sentences of your own, using the past tense of *lie* and *lay.*

9. **Answers will vary.**

10. _____

Page 161

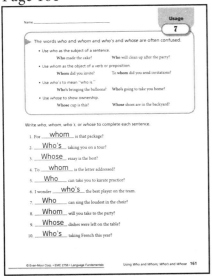

Usage 7

The words *who* and *whom* and *who's* and *whose* are often confused.

- Use *who* as the subject of a sentence.
  Who made the cake? **Who** will clean up after the party?
- Use *whom* as the object of a verb or preposition.
  Whom did you invite? To **whom** did you send invitations?
- Use *who's* to mean "who is."
  Who's bringing the balloons? **Who's** going to take you home?
- Use *whose* to show ownership.
  Whose cup is this? **Whose** shoes are in the backyard?

Write *who, whom, who's,* or *whose* to complete each sentence.

1. For **whom** is that package?
2. **Who's** taking you on a tour?
3. **Whose** essay is the best?
4. To **whom** is the letter addressed?
5. **Who** can take you to karate practice?
6. I wonder **who's** the best player on the team.
7. **Who** can sing the loudest in the choir?
8. **Whom** will you take to the party?
9. **Whose** dishes were left on the table?
10. **Who's** taking French this year?

Page 162

Usage Review 2

Fill in the bubble next to the correct answer to each question.

1. Which sentence is written correctly?
   Ⓐ Can I go horseback riding with Aunt Lourdes?
   ● You may go if you've finished your chores.
   Ⓒ Can I go swimming on Saturday?
   Ⓓ I may swim.

2. Which sentence is written correctly?
   ● "May I have the mustard, please?" asked Maeve.
   Ⓑ "Yes, you can," replied Michael.
   Ⓒ "Can I have the pickles, too?" Maeve asked again.
   Ⓓ "No, you cannot," Michael answered.

3. Which sentence is written correctly?
   Ⓐ I lay down on the floor every night when I start my yoga exercises.
   Ⓑ First I lie the mat down on the floor.
   ● Then I lie down on the mat and stretch.
   Ⓓ Sometimes my cat lays on my stomach while I try to exercise.

4. Which sentence is written correctly?
   ● Who's going to teach band this year?
   Ⓑ Whom is coming to dinner?
   Ⓒ Whose your favorite singer?
   Ⓓ To who did you write?

5. Which sentence is written correctly?
   Ⓐ I laid down after school because I was very tired.
   Ⓑ He lay his books on the table after the meeting.
   Ⓒ Because I had a headache, I carefully layed my head on the pillow.
   ● My dad laid his hand on my shoulder to stop me from running into the street.

Page 163

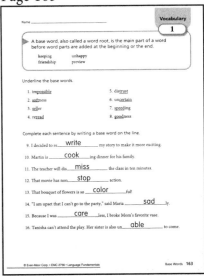

Vocabulary 1

A base word, also called a word root, is the main part of a word before word parts are added at the beginning or the end.

keeping	unhappy
friendship	preview

Underline the base words.

1. im**possible**
2. soft**ness**
3. **sell**er
4. re**read**
5. dis**trust**
6. un**certain**
7. **speed**ing
8. **good**ness

Complete each sentence by writing a base word on the line.

9. I decided to re**write** my story to make it more exciting.
10. Martin is **cook**ing dinner for his family.
11. The teacher will dis**miss** the class in ten minutes.
12. That movie has non**stop** action.
13. That bouquet of flowers is so **color**ful!
14. "I am upset that I can't go to the party," said Maria **sad**ly.
15. Because I was **care**less, I broke Mom's favorite vase.
16. Tanisha can't attend the play. Her sister is also un**able** to come.

Page 164

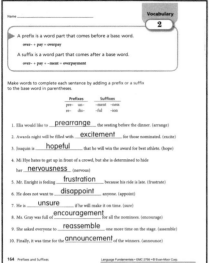

Vocabulary 2

A prefix is a word part that comes before a base word.

over- + pay = overpay

A suffix is a word part that comes after a base word.

over- + pay + –ment = overpayment

Make words to complete each sentence by adding a prefix or a suffix to the base word in parentheses.

Prefixes	Suffixes
pre– un–	–ment –ness
re– dis–	–ful –ion

1. Ella would like to **prearrange** the seating before the dinner. (arrange)
2. Awards night will be filled with **excitement** for those nominated. (excite)
3. Joaquin is **hopeful** that he will win the award for best actor. (hope)
4. Mi Hye hates to get up in front of a crowd, but she is determined to hide her **nervousness** (nervous)
5. Mr. Enright is feeling **frustration** because his ride is late. (frustrate)
6. He does not want to **disappoint** anyone. (appoint)
7. He is **unsure** if he will make it on time. (sure)
8. Ms. Gray was full of **encouragement** for all the nominees. (encourage)
9. She asked everyone to **reassemble** one more time on the stage. (assemble)
10. Finally, it was time for the **announcement** of the winners. (announce)

164 Prefixes and Suffixes

Page 165

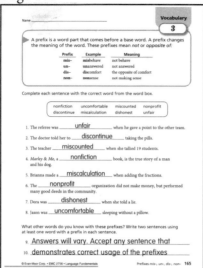

Vocabulary 3

A prefix is a word part that comes before a base word. A prefix changes the meaning of the word. These prefixes mean *not* or *opposite of:*

Prefix	Example	Meaning
mis–	misbehave	not behave
un–	unanswered	not answered
dis–	discomfort	the opposite of comfort
non–	nonsense	not making sense

Complete each sentence with the correct word from the word box.

| nonfiction | uncomfortable | miscounted | nonprofit |
| discontinue | miscalculation | dishonest | unfair |

1. The referee was **unfair** when he gave a point to the other team.
2. The doctor told her to **discontinue** taking the pills.
3. The teacher **miscounted** when she tallied 19 students.
4. *Marley & Me*, a **nonfiction** book, is the true story of a man and his dog.
5. Brianna made a **miscalculation** when adding the fractions.
6. The **nonprofit** organization did not make money, but performed many good deeds in the community.
7. Dora was **dishonest** when she told a lie.
8. Jason was **uncomfortable** sleeping without a pillow.

What other words do you know with these prefixes? Write two sentences using at least one word with a prefix in each sentence.

9. **Answers will vary. Accept any sentence that**
10. **demonstrates correct usage of the prefixes.**

Prefixes mis–, un–, dis–, non– 165

Page 166

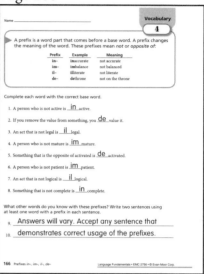

Vocabulary 4

A prefix is a word part that comes before a base word. A prefix changes the meaning of the word. These prefixes mean *not* or *opposite of:*

Prefix	Example	Meaning
in–	inaccurate	not accurate
im–	imbalance	not balanced
il–	illiterate	not literate
de–	dethrone	not on the throne

Complete each word with the correct base word.

1. A person who is not active is **in**active.
2. If you remove the value from something, you **de**value it.
3. An act that is not legal is **il**legal.
4. A person who is not mature is **im**mature.
5. Something that is the opposite of activated is **de**activated.
6. A person who is not patient is **im**patient.
7. An act that is not logical is **il**logical.
8. Something that is not complete is **in**complete.

What other words do you know with these prefixes? Write two sentences using at least one word with a prefix in each sentence.

9. **Answers will vary. Accept any sentence that**
10. **demonstrates correct usage of the prefixes.**

166 Prefixes in–, im–, il–, de–

Page 167

Vocabulary 5

A prefix is a word part that comes before a base word. Some prefixes express number.

Prefix	Meaning	Example
uni–	one	unison
bi–	two	bilingual
tri–	three	triathlete
quadr–	four	quadralateral

Write the definition of each word. **Answers may vary slightly.**

1. univision **one vision**
2. biannual **twice a year**
3. tricycle **having three wheels or cycles**
4. quadrangle **four angles**

Write the word for each definition.

5. having three colors **tricolored**
6. having one form **uniform**
7. one of four offspring born in a single birth **quadruplet**
8. having two valves **bivalve**

What other words do you know with these prefixes? Write two sentences using at least one word with a prefix in each sentence.

9. **Answers will vary. Accept any sentence that**
10. **demonstrates correct usage of the prefixes.**

Prefixes uni–, bi–, tri–, quadr– 167

Page 168

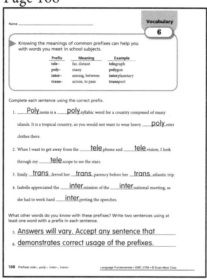

Vocabulary 6

Knowing the meanings of common prefixes can help you with words you meet in school subjects.

Prefix	Meaning	Example
tele–	far, distant	telegraph
poly–	many	polygon
inter–	among, between	interplanetary
trans–	across, to pass	transport

Complete each sentence using the correct prefix.

1. **Poly**nesia is a **poly**syllabic word for a country composed of many islands. It is a tropical country, so you would not want to wear heavy **poly**ester clothes there.
2. When I want to get away from the **tele**phone and **tele**vision, I look through my **tele**scope to see the stars.
3. Emily **trans**ferred her **trans**parency before her **trans**atlantic trip.
4. Isabelle appreciated the **inter**mission at the **inter**national meeting, as she had to work hard **inter**preting the speeches.

What other words do you know with these prefixes? Write two sentences using at least one word with a prefix in each sentence.

5. **Answers will vary. Accept any sentence that**
6. **demonstrates correct usage of the prefixes.**

168 Prefixes tele–, poly–, inter–, trans–

Page 169

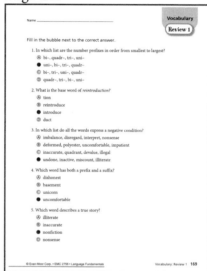

Vocabulary Review 1

Fill in the bubble next to the correct answer.

1. In which list are the number prefixes in order from smallest to largest?
   - Ⓐ bi–, quadr–, tri–, uni–
   - Ⓑ uni–, bi–, tri–, quadr–
   - Ⓒ bi–, tri–, uni–, quadr–
   - Ⓓ quadr–, tri–, bi–, uni–

2. What is the base word of *reintroduction*?
   - Ⓐ tion
   - Ⓑ reintroduce
   - Ⓒ introduce
   - Ⓓ duct

3. In which list do all the words express a negative condition?
   - Ⓐ imbalance, disregard, interpret, nonsense
   - Ⓑ deformed, polyester, uncomfortable, impatient
   - Ⓒ inaccurate, quadrant, devalue, illegal
   - Ⓓ undone, inactive, miscount, illiterate

4. Which word has both a prefix and a suffix?
   - Ⓐ dishonest
   - Ⓑ basement
   - Ⓒ unicorn
   - Ⓓ uncomfortable

5. Which word describes a true story?
   - Ⓐ illiterate
   - Ⓑ inaccurate
   - Ⓒ nonfiction
   - Ⓓ nonsense

Vocabulary: Review 1 169

Page 170

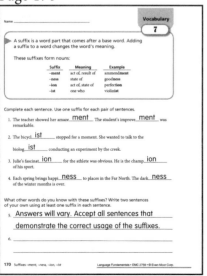

Vocabulary 7

A suffix is a word part that comes after a base word. Adding a suffix to a word changes the word's meaning.

These suffixes form nouns:

Suffix	Meaning	Example
–ment	act of, result of	amendment
–ness	state of	goodness
–ion	act of, state of	perfection
–ist	one who	violinist

Complete each sentence. Use one suffix for each pair of sentences.

1. The teacher showed her amaze**ment**. The student's improve**ment** was remarkable.
2. The bicycl**ist** stopped for a moment. She wanted to talk to the biolog**ist** conducting an experiment by the creek.
3. Julie's fascinat**ion** for the athlete was obvious. He is the champ**ion** of his sport.
4. Each spring brings happi**ness** to places in the Far North. The dark**ness** of the winter months is over.

What other words do you know with these suffixes? Write two sentences of your own using at least one suffix in each sentence.

5. **Answers will vary. Accept all sentences that**
   demonstrate the correct usage of the suffixes.
6.

170 Suffixes –ment, –ness, –ion, –ist

Page 171

Vocabulary 8

A suffix is a word part that comes after a base word. Adding a suffix to a word changes the word's meaning.

These suffixes form nouns:

Suffix	Meaning	Example
–ship	state or quality of	friendship
–ism	characteristic of	optimism
–dom	state or quality of	wisdom
–ology	study or science of	geology

Complete each noun with the correct base word for the suffix.

1. A hero shows **hero**ism.
2. Some people face hard times, but learn to grow from their **hard**ship.
3. A free nation holds **free**dom as a right.
4. The scientists at a zoo study **zo**ology.
5. A citizen of a country has **citizen**ship.
6. A country with a king is a **king**dom.
7. Something that seems real has the characteristic of **real**ism.
8. The study of the ecosystem is **ec**ology.

What other words do you know with these suffixes? Write two sentences of your own using at least one suffix in each sentence.

9. **Answers will vary. Accept all sentences that**
10. **demonstrate the correct usage of the suffixes.**

Suffixes –ship, –ism, –dom, –ology 171

Page 172

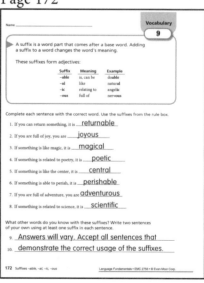

Vocabulary 9

A suffix is a word part that comes after a base word. Adding a suffix to a word changes the word's meaning.

These suffixes form adjectives:

Suffix	Meaning	Example
–able	is, can be	doable
–al	like	natural
–ic	relating to	angelic
–ous	full of	nervous

Complete each sentence with the correct word. Use the suffixes from the rule box.

1. If you can return something, it is **returnable**.
2. If you are full of joy, you are **joyous**.
3. If something is like magic, it is **magical**.
4. If something is related to poetry, it is **poetic**.
5. If something is in the center, it is **central**.
6. If something is able to perish, it is **perishable**.
7. If you are full of adventure, you are **adventurous**.
8. If something is related to science, it is **scientific**.

What other words do you know with these suffixes? Write two sentences of your own using at least one suffix in each sentence.

9. **Answers will vary. Accept all sentences that**
10. **demonstrate the correct usage of the suffixes.**

172 Suffixes –able, –al, –ic, –ous

Page 173

Name _____

Vocabulary Review 2

Fill in the bubble next to the correct answer.

1. *Encouragement* most nearly means _____
   - Ⓐ an encouraging person
   - ● the act of encouraging
   - Ⓒ able to be encouraged
   - Ⓓ full of courage

2. Something that can be agreed upon is _____
   - Ⓐ agreeist
   - Ⓑ agreeship
   - ● agreeable
   - Ⓓ agreement

3. Someone who has the characteristics of a patriot shows _____
   - Ⓐ patriotic
   - Ⓑ patriotist
   - Ⓒ patriotable
   - ● patriotism

4. *Symbolic* most nearly means _____
   - Ⓐ can be a symbol
   - Ⓑ study of symbols
   - Ⓒ state of being a symbol
   - ● like a symbol

5. The state of being protected is _____
   - Ⓐ protectist
   - Ⓑ protectous
   - ● protection
   - Ⓓ protectable

© Evan-Moor Corp. • EMC 2756 • Language Fundamentals   Vocabulary: Review 2   173

Page 174

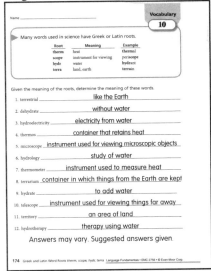

Name _____

Vocabulary 10

Many words used in science have Greek or Latin roots.

Root	Meaning	Example
therm	heat	thermal
scope	instrument for viewing	periscope
hydr	water	hydrant
terra	land, earth	terrain

Given the meaning of the roots, determine the meaning of these words.

1. terrestrial _____ like the Earth
2. dehydrate _____ without water
3. hydroelectricity _____ electricity from water
4. thermos _____ container that retains heat
5. microscope _____ instrument used for viewing microscopic objects
6. hydrology _____ study of water
7. thermometer _____ instrument used to measure heat
8. terrarium _____ container in which things from the Earth are kept
9. hydrate _____ to add water
10. telescope _____ instrument used for viewing things far away
11. territory _____ an area of land
12. hydrotherapy _____ therapy using water

Answers may vary. Suggested answers given.

174   Greek and Latin Word Roots therm, scope, hydr, terra   Language Fundamentals • EMC 2756 • © Evan-Moor Corp.

Page 175

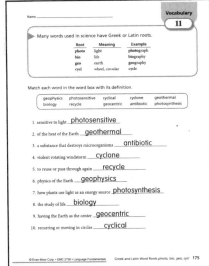

Name _____

Vocabulary 11

Many words used in science have Greek or Latin roots.

Root	Meaning	Example
photo	light	photograph
bio	life	biography
geo	earth	geography
cycl	wheel, circular	cycle

Match each word in the word box with its definition.

geophysics   photosensitive   cyclical   cyclone   geothermal
biology   recycle   geocentric   antibiotic   photosynthesis

1. sensitive to light _____ photosensitive
2. of the heat of the Earth _____ geothermal
3. a substance that destroys microorganisms _____ antibiotic
4. violent rotating windstorm _____ cyclone
5. to reuse or pass through again _____ recycle
6. physics of the Earth _____ geophysics
7. how plants use light as an energy source _____ photosynthesis
8. the study of life _____ biology
9. having the Earth as the center _____ geocentric
10. recurring or moving in circles _____ cyclical

© Evan-Moor Corp. • EMC 2756 • Language Fundamentals   Greek and Latin Word Roots photo, bio, geo, cycl   175

Page 176

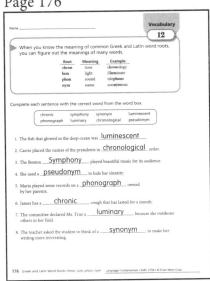

Name _____

Vocabulary 12

When you know the meaning of common Greek and Latin word roots, you can figure out the meanings of many words.

Root	Meaning	Example
chron	time	chronology
lum	light	illuminate
phon	sound	telephone
nym	name	anonymous

Complete each sentence with the correct word from the word box.

chronic   symphony   synonym   luminescent
phonograph   luminary   chronological   pseudonym

1. The fish that glowed in the deep ocean was _____ luminescent
2. Carrie placed the names of the presidents in _____ chronological order.
3. The Boston _____ Symphony played beautiful music for its audience.
4. She used a _____ pseudonym to hide her identity.
5. Maria played some records on a _____ phonograph owned by her parents.
6. James has a _____ chronic cough that has lasted for a month.
7. The committee declared Ms. True a _____ luminary because she outshone others in her field.
8. The teacher asked the student to think of a _____ synonym to make her writing more interesting.

176   Greek and Latin Word Roots chron, lum, phon, nym   Language Fundamentals • EMC 2756 • © Evan-Moor Corp.

Page 177

Name _____

Vocabulary Review 3

Fill in the bubble next to the correct answer.

1. *Thermostat* most nearly means _____
   - Ⓐ doing something quickly
   - ● a device to control the heating and air conditioning
   - Ⓒ a container used to keep drinks cold
   - Ⓓ measuring the circumference of the Earth

2. *Hydrofoil* most nearly means _____
   - Ⓐ without water
   - Ⓑ wrapping your food in aluminum foil
   - ● a boat that skims the surface of the water
   - Ⓓ a plant that requires no sunlight or food

3. *Periscope* most nearly means _____
   - ● an instrument used for viewing over or around objects
   - Ⓑ a mechanical device used for transportation
   - Ⓒ the inability to walk
   - Ⓓ a knife used to cut pears

4. *Anachronism* most nearly means _____
   - Ⓐ a painful disease affecting the joints
   - Ⓑ the ability to hear arachnids
   - Ⓒ the dark shapes you see when you close you eyes
   - ● something in the incorrect place in time

5. *Phonetic* most nearly means _____
   - Ⓐ moving at an increased and irregular pace
   - Ⓑ having the ability to construct towers
   - ● representing the sounds of speech with symbols
   - Ⓓ the ability to produce light for photographic purposes

© Evan-Moor Corp. • EMC 2756 • Language Fundamentals   Vocabulary: Review 3   177

Page 178

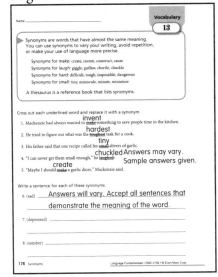

Name _____

Vocabulary 13

Synonyms are words that have almost the same meaning. You can use synonyms to vary your writing, avoid repetition, or make your use of language more precise.

Synonyms for *make*: create, invent, construct, cause
Synonyms for *laugh*: giggle, guffaw, chortle, chuckle
Synonyms for *hard*: difficult, tough, impossible, dangerous
Synonyms for *small*: tiny, miniscule, minute, miniature

A thesaurus is a reference book that lists synonyms.

Cross out each underlined word and replace it with a synonym.

1. Mackenzie had always wanted to ~~make~~ invent something to save people time in the kitchen.
2. He tried to figure out what was the ~~toughest~~ hardest task for a cook.
3. His father said that one recipe called for ~~small~~ tiny slivers of garlic.
4. "I can never get them small enough," he ~~laughed~~ chuckled. Answers may vary. Sample answers given.
5. "Maybe I should ~~make~~ create a garlic dicer," Mackenzie said.

Write a sentence for each of these synonyms.

6. (sad) _____ Answers will vary. Accept all sentences that demonstrate the meaning of the word.

7. (depressed) _____

8. (somber) _____

178   Synonyms   Language Fundamentals • EMC 2756 • © Evan-Moor Corp.

Page 179

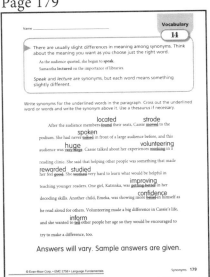

Name _____

Vocabulary 14

There are usually slight differences in meaning among synonyms. Think about the meaning you want as you choose just the right word.

As the audience quieted, she began to **speak**.
Samantha **lectured** on the importance of libraries.

Speak and *lecture* are synonyms, but each word means something slightly different.

Write synonyms for the underlined words in the paragraph. Cross out the underlined word and write the synonym above it. Use a thesaurus if necessary.

After the audience members ~~found~~ located their seats, Cassie ~~moved~~ strode to the podium. She had never ~~talked~~ spoken in front of a large audience before, and this audience was ~~very large~~ huge. Cassie talked about her experiences ~~working~~ volunteering in a reading clinic. She said that helping other people was something that made her feel ~~good~~ rewarded. She ~~worked~~ studied very hard to learn what would be helpful in teaching younger readers. One girl, Katrinka, was ~~getting better~~ improving in her decoding skills. Another child, Emeka, was showing more ~~belief~~ confidence in himself when he read aloud for others. Volunteering made a big difference in Cassie's life, and she wanted to ~~tell~~ inform other people her age so they would be encouraged to try to make a difference, too.

Answers will vary. Sample answers are given.

© Evan-Moor Corp. • EMC 2756 • Language Fundamentals   Synonyms   179

Page 180

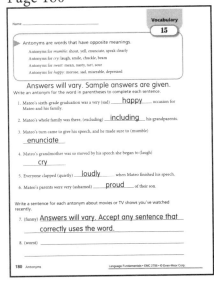

Name _____

Vocabulary 15

Antonyms are words that have opposite meanings.

Antonyms for *mumble*: shout, yell, enunciate, speak clearly
Antonyms for *cry*: laugh, smile, chuckle, beam
Antonyms for *sweet*: mean, nasty, tart, sour
Antonyms for *happy*: morose, sad, miserable, depressed

Answers will vary. Sample answers are given.

Write an antonym for the word in parentheses to complete each sentence.

1. Mateo's sixth-grade graduation was a very (sad) _____ happy occasion for Mateo and his family.
2. Mateo's whole family was there, (excluding) _____ including his grandparents.
3. Mateo's turn came to give his speech, and he made sure to (mumble) _____ enunciate
4. Mateo's grandmother was so moved by his speech she began to (laugh) _____ cry
5. Everyone clapped (quietly) _____ loudly when Mateo finished his speech.
6. Mateo's parents were very (ashamed) _____ proud of their son.

Write a sentence for each antonym about movies or TV shows you've watched recently.

7. (funny) _____ Answers will vary. Accept any sentence that correctly uses the word.

8. (worst) _____

180   Antonyms   Language Fundamentals • EMC 2756 • © Evan-Moor Corp.

Page 181

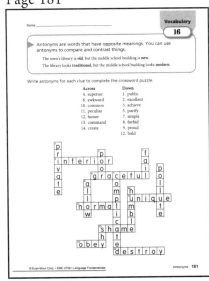

Name _____

Vocabulary 16

Antonyms are words that have opposite meanings. You can use antonyms to compare and contrast things.

The town's library is **old**, but the middle school building is **new**.
The library looks **traditional**, but the middle school building looks **modern**.

Write antonyms for each clue to complete the crossword puzzle.

Across
4. superior
6. awkward
10. common
11. peculiar
12. honor
13. command
14. create

Down
1. public
2. excellent
3. achieve
5. purify
7. forbid
8. forbid
9. proud
12. bold

© Evan-Moor Corp. • EMC 2756 • Language Fundamentals   Antonyms   181

Page 182

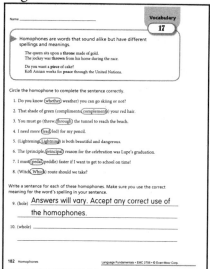

Name _____

Vocabulary 17

Homophones are words that sound alike but have different spellings and meanings.

The queen sits upon a **throne** made of gold.
The jockey was **thrown** from his horse during the race.

Do you want a **piece** of cake?
Kofi Annan works for **peace** through the United Nations.

Circle the homophone to complete the sentence correctly.

1. Do you know (whether/ weather) you can go skiing or not?
2. That shade of green (compliments/ complements) your red hair.
3. You must go (threw/ through) the tunnel to reach the beach.
4. I need more (lead/ led) for my pencil.
5. (Lightening/ Lightning) is both beautiful and dangerous.
6. The (principle/ principal) reason for the celebration was Lupe's graduation.
7. I must (pedal/ peddle) faster if I want to get to school on time!
8. (Witch/ Which) route should we take?

Write a sentence for each of these homophones. Make sure you use the correct meaning for the word's spelling in your sentence.

9. (hole) **Answers will vary. Accept any correct use of the homophones.**

10. (whole) _____

Page 183

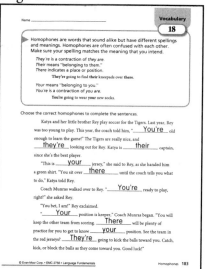

Name _____

Vocabulary 18

Homophones are words that sound alike but have different spellings and meanings. Homophones are often confused with each other. Make sure your spelling matches the meaning that you intend.

They're is a contraction of *they are.*
Their means "belonging to them."
There indicates a place or position.
They're going to find **their** kneepads over **there.**

Your means "belonging to you."
You're is a contraction of *you are.*
You're going to wear **your** new socks.

Choose the correct homophones to complete the sentences.

Katya and her little brother Rey play soccer for the Tigers. Last year, Rey was too young to play. This year, the coach told him, "___**You're**___ old enough to learn the game!" The Tigers are really nice, and ___**they're**___ looking out for Rey. Katya is ___**their**___ captain, since she's the best player.

"This is ___**your**___ jersey," she said to Rey, as she handed him a green shirt. "You sit over ___**there**___ until the coach tells you what to do," Katya told Rey.

Coach Munras walked over to Rey. "___**You're**___ ready to play, right!" she asked Rey.

"You bet, I am!" Rey exclaimed.

"___**Your**___ position is keeper," Coach Munras began. "You will keep the other team from scoring. ___**There**___ will be plenty of practice for you to get to know ___**your**___ position. See the team in the red jerseys? ___**They're**___ going to kick the balls toward you. Catch, kick, or block the balls as they come toward you. Good luck!"

Page 184

Name _____

Vocabulary Review 4

Fill in the bubble next to the correct answer.

1. Which word is a synonym for *vacant*?
   Ⓐ full
   ● unoccupied
   Ⓒ thin
   Ⓓ wealthy

2. Which two words are synonyms?
   Ⓐ create and destroy
   Ⓑ create and beginning
   ● create and make
   Ⓓ create and speak

3. Which word is an antonym for *solemn*?
   Ⓐ sober
   Ⓑ depressed
   Ⓒ giddiness
   ● silly

4. Which words are homophones?
   ● some and sum
   Ⓑ broke and joke
   Ⓒ tell and tale
   Ⓓ finished and done

5. _____ going to play hockey with their friends this afternoon.
   Ⓐ Their
   Ⓑ There
   ● They're
   Ⓓ Theyre

Page 186

Name _____

EDITING: Nouns
1

Proofread this paragraph. Use proofreading marks to correct the 10 errors.

Our class will have a ~~M~~meeting on ~~t~~uesday. We will vote on issues that
affect the ~~lifes~~ lives of sixth-grade students. Everyone in the sixth grade will cast a
secret ballot. The ballots will be collected in sealed ~~boxs~~ boxes. The principal and
our teacher will have the power to veto any motion. If a motion receives
these two ~~vetos~~ vetoes, it cannot pass. There are two political ~~partys~~ parties in our class.
One calls itself the Foxes, and the other calls itself the ~~Wolfs~~ Wolves. The ~~Foxs~~ Foxes and
the Wolves will elect representatives to sit in the class congress. All the ~~class's~~ classes
in our school are holding elections. We are learning about ~~D~~democracy.

Write the words correctly on the lines below.

1. meeting
2. Tuesday
3. lives
4. boxes
5. vetoes
6. parties
7. Wolves
8. Foxes
9. classes
10. democracy

Page 187

Name _____

EDITING: Adjectives
2

Proofread this paragraph. Use proofreading marks to correct the 10 errors.

The art museum in our city is the ~~older~~ oldest one in the state. Paintings by
Monet, Picasso, and Cassatt hang in one gallery. Monet was a ~~french~~ French painter,
Picasso a Spanish painter, and Cassatt an ~~american~~ American painter. Monet's
paintings have more ~~beautifuller~~ beautiful colors than Picasso's paintings. I like the
~~brightest~~ bright pinks and pale blues that he used to paint ~~taller~~ tall cathedrals. Monet's
paintings seem ~~softest~~ softer than Picasso's. I once saw a Picasso painting about war
in a book. The ~~picasso~~ Picasso paintings in our museum are not as scary as ~~this~~ that
painting in the book. I think that the Cassatt paintings are the ~~better~~ best ones in
the whole museum. I like the sweet scenes of mothers and children. The
expressions are very realistic.

Write the words correctly on the lines below.

1. oldest
2. French
3. American
4. beautiful
5. bright
6. tall
7. softer
8. Picasso
9. that
10. best

Page 188

Name _____

EDITING: Adjectives
3

Use proofreading marks to correct the 10 errors.

My brother and I collect vinyl records, the kind that our grandparents
played on machines called record players. I have many records, but my
brother has the ~~most~~ more than me. I collect ~~older~~ old rock-and-roll records. I have
~~the~~ a record by Elvis and one by Chubby Checker. ~~These~~ Those records are my
favorites. ~~A~~ An old song called "The Twist" is on the ~~checker~~ Checker record. Everyone
danced to that song when my grandmother was ~~the~~ a girl. She still dances! She
dances when my brother plays his records, too. My brother likes recordings
of polka music! He says that the polka is the ~~goodest~~ best dance in the world. Our
family is ~~polish~~ Polish, and we all like ~~a~~ the polka.

Find the errors. Write the words correctly on the lines below.

1. more
2. old
3. a
4. Those
5. An
6. Checker
7. a
8. best
9. Polish
10. the

Page 189

Name _____

EDITING: Pronouns
4

Proofread these paragraphs. Find the 10 errors, cross them out, and write the words correctly above them.

Last night, snow fell. My sisters and brothers and ~~me~~ I decided to put on
our snowshoes and go into the woods today. Snowshoes have been around
for a long time. In our barn, we have a really old pair. I took one old
snowshoe down from the shelf once. I thought ~~they was~~ it was a tennis racket! Our
modern snowshoes have fancier clamps, but ~~it works~~ they work the same way. I put on
my snowshoes myself, but my youngest brother needs help. He says that it
won't be long before he can do it for ~~hisself~~ himself.

In the woods, my siblings and ~~me~~ I found a wide trail. I stopped to adjust
Bobby's clamps, and I tightened ~~my~~ mine, too. The others forged ahead. Bobby
and ~~me~~ I took our time. We looked for a sign of life along the snowy trail. It
wasn't long before we found ~~them~~ it. We examined little footprints made by
a field mouse. For Bobby and ~~I~~ me, the footprints were an exciting discovery.
Suddenly, a large crow called from a tree. ~~They~~ It reminded us that many
creatures live in the winter woods.

Page 190

EDITING:
Pronouns

5

Proofread these paragraphs. Find the 10 errors, cross them out, and write the words correctly above them.

On a sunny summer day, many neighbors visit our backyard. Most yards
in the neighborhood are small, but ~~our~~ **ours** is large. My friends and ~~me~~ **I** have

room for running and shady spots for resting. Last night, my dad and mom

cooked hot dogs on the grill in the backyard. Some parents don't cook

outside, but ~~my~~ **mine** like to cook for a crowd in our backyard.

Almost all of the neighbors came over. Ms. Lee brought potato salad. I

like potato salad, and ~~her's~~ **hers** is the best I've ever tasted. Mr. Carson brought

lemonade and soda. ~~Him~~ **He** and Ms. Carson brought lawn chairs, too. ~~There~~ **Their**

lawn chairs provided all of us places to sit while we waited for a freshly

grilled hot dog.

"~~Whom~~ **Who** brought the marshmallows?" I asked after dinner. My older

sister Carol brought out a bag of marshmallows for toasting. ~~Her~~ **She** and her

friends never forget the marshmallows. ~~Them~~ **They** volunteered to toast a

marshmallow for everyone.

As the sun set, the mosquitoes came out. It was time to put on bug spray.
The adults talked and laughed while the kids kicked a soccer ball. When it

was too dark to see, the other kids and ~~me~~ **I** told stories. What a perfect

summer day!

Page 191

EDITING:
Verbs

6

Proofread these paragraphs. Use proofreading marks to correct
the 10 errors.

The last imperial ruler of Russia was Tsar Nicholas II. Nicholas inherited

the throne from his father. An assassin ~~shooted~~ **shot** Nicholas's father in the

street, making Nicholas the tsar. He never really ~~want~~ **wanted** to have that awesome

responsibility, but he ~~take~~ **took** his duties seriously. Nicholas ~~marryed~~ **married** Alexandra,

a German princess. A shy person, Alexandra ~~is~~ **was** uncomfortable with her

public position. Still, she ~~support~~ **supported** her husband.

Nicholas and Alexandra ~~have~~ **had** a family of four daughters and one son.

Their son was born with a serious illness. He ~~bleeded~~ **bled** and bruised at the

slightest bump. The bleeding was difficult to stop and the bruising ~~is~~ **was** quite

painful. Doctors ~~tryed~~ **tried** to ease the little boy's pain. Alexandra, the desperate

mother, believed that a mysterious man named Rasputin could save her little

boy. Rasputin was able to ease the boy's suffering, but there was no cure for

his disease.

Write the words correctly on the lines below.

1. ___shot___ 6. ___supported___
2. ___wanted___ 7. ___had___
3. ___took___ 8. ___bled___
4. ___married___ 9. ___was___
5. ___was___ 10. ___tried___

Page 192

EDITING:
Verbs

7

Proofread these paragraphs. Find the 10 errors, cross them out, and write the words correctly above them.

Early yesterday morning, James and Marshall ~~go~~ **went** fishing. They baited

their hooks with worms and ~~wait~~ **waited**. It was very quiet. All at once, a large fish

~~bursted~~ **burst** through the surface of the lake. The scales of the fish gleamed like

gold in the sun. The golden fish ~~dive~~ **dived/dove** deep again. The boys wondered if they

might catch that amazing fish. Marshall ~~says~~ **said** that he would cook the fish if he

~~catched~~ **caught** it. James said that he would mount the fish and hang it above the

fireplace.

The boys settled back with their fishing poles. Suddenly, the big fish

~~breaked~~ **broke** the surface of the lake again. The fish ~~fliped~~ **flipped** his golden fins. He

shook his tail. The fish, the boys thought, is having a good time. He's

showing off! Over and over the gleaming fish jumped.

By the time the fish was finished with his show, the boys ~~finded~~ **found** that they

had put down their poles. "I don't want to catch him," Marshall said to

James. "I want to see him jump every time I come to the lake."

"Me, too," said James. "I ~~had~~ **have** an idea! The next time we come here, let's

bring binoculars instead of poles and hooks."

Page 193

EDITING:
Verbs

8

Proofread these paragraphs. Use proofreading marks to correct
the 10 errors.

The first time I ~~seen~~ **saw** the room in the attic of our new house, I ~~knowed~~ **knew**

that I had to make it mine. Our old house ~~were~~ **was** very modern and ~~has~~ **had** only

one floor. It was a nice house, but I ~~am~~ **am** thrilled to be moving into our new

home.

The attic ~~be~~ **is** a little spooky now, but soon I ~~am making~~ **will make** it cozy and

cheerful. My dad and mom will help by covering the beams with something

called wallboard. Here ~~is~~ **are** some wallpaper samples. I will pick out something

pretty to cover the wallboard.

The attic room is huge! There ~~is~~ **are** two windows. Next weekend, Mom

~~helped~~ **will help** me find curtains. From one window, I can see big pine trees. The

other window is the best part of this attic room. From that window, I can

see my best friend's house!

Find the errors. Write the words correctly on the lines below.

1. ___saw___ 6. ___is___
2. ___knew___ 7. ___will make___
3. ___was___ 8. ___are___
4. ___had___ 9. ___are___
5. ___am___ 10. ___will help___

Page 194

Name _____

EDITING: Verbs 9

Proofread these paragraphs. Use proofreading marks to correct the 10 errors.

This morning, my mom and dad I are ~~pack~~ **packing** for our summer vacation. Every year, we ~~rents~~ **rent** the same cottage at the shore. My dad ~~say~~ **says** the cottage is "rustic." He means that it is old-fashioned. We ~~likes~~ **like** it that way.

On our first vacation at the cottage, I was surprised not to see a television in the living room. I ~~wonder~~ **wondered** what we would do in the evenings, but after a few days, I liked the quiet. I started reading some old kids' books that I found in a bookcase. That is when I ~~discover~~ **discovered** mystery books. Have you ever ~~heared~~ **heard** of Nancy Drew?

Today I am packing two books to read and a board game to play. Earlier today, I ~~buyed~~ **bought** stamps at the post office. Next week, I will ~~sent~~ **send** postcards to my friends. The cottage ~~do~~ **does** not have a computer connection, so I have no e-mail!

Find the errors. Write the words correctly on the lines below.

1. packing
2. rent
3. says
4. like
5. wondered
6. discovered
7. heard
8. bought
9. send
10. does

Page 195

Name _____

EDITING: Adverbs 10

Proofread these paragraphs. Find the 10 errors, cross them out, and write the words correctly above them.

Monica ~~eager~~ **eagerly** drank the cool water. Maybe running the track at noon, the hottest part of the day, had not been a good idea. Kia had been running, too, but she had run ~~slow~~ **more slowly/slower** than Monica. Now Kia breathed ~~easiest~~ **easier** than her friend did. "Monica, let's run in the morning tomorrow," Kia suggested. "We'll be able to run ~~fastest~~ **faster** and ~~longest~~ **longer** when it is cooler."

Monica hated to get up ~~more early~~ **earlier** than necessary, but she agreed to try a morning run the next day. "I'll set my alarm," Monica promised.

The next morning, Monica's alarm rang ~~loudest~~ **louder** than a fire alarm, and Monica groaned ~~more long~~ **longer** than she ever had before. The sleepy girl pushed a button on the alarm clock. She thought it was the snooze button, but she had turned off the alarm altogether. Before long, Monica was sleeping more ~~deeper~~ **deeply** than her snoring dog, Buster.

Monica slept. She woke up gradually when Buster licked her nose. The phone was ringing. "Oh, no!" she said to Buster, "Look at the time!"

"Hmm," Kia said on the phone, "maybe you'd run ~~gooder~~ **better** in the evening than you do in the morning!"

Page 196

Name _____

EDITING: Sentences 11

Proofread this paragraph. Correct the sentence fragments by adding words to make them complete or connecting them to another sentence. Then rewrite the paragraph below.

On July 20, 1969, An American spaceship landed on the moon. My uncle watched the landing on television In his college dorm. **He** Said that everyone was very excited. An astronaut **climbed** down the spaceship's ladder to step on the surface of the moon. Uncle Tito and his friends cheered. **They** Cheered again when an American flag was planted On the moon. In the photographs, **the flag** looks like it is waving in a breeze, but it is not. **There is** No wind on the moon. The flag has wires in it to make it look like it is standing out in a breeze. The flag **is** still there, but we cannot see it from Earth. I've tried. My friends and I have started an astronomy club. **We** Will read about the moon and look at it through a telescope.

On July 20, 1969, an American spaceship landed on the moon. My uncle watched the landing on television in his college dorm. He said that everyone was very excited. An astronaut climbed down the spaceship's ladder to step on the surface of the moon. Uncle Tito and his friends cheered. They cheered again when an American flag was planted on the moon. In the photographs, the flag looks like it is waving in a breeze, but it is not. There is no wind on the moon. The flag has wires in it to make it look like it is standing out in a breeze. The flag is still there, but we cannot see it from Earth. I've tried. My friends and I have started an astronomy club. We will read about the moon and look at it through a telescope.

Page 197

Name _____

EDITING: Sentences 12

Find each run-on sentence in these paragraphs and correct it. You can create two sentences or make the run-on into a compound or a complex sentence by using a conjunction.

Answers may vary. Samples given.

During her long career, Margaret Chase Smith was one of the most important figures in American politics. She was born in 1897 in Maine, **and** she would come to serve that state with distinction. In fact, she would become the first woman to serve in both houses of the United States Congress.

Before Margaret Chase became a well-known politician, she worked as a teacher, a telephone operator, a newspaper circulation manager, and an office manager at a textile mill. During that time, she helped to establish a local club for business and professional women. Later, she became the president of the state office of that club. Her experiences would serve her well.

Mrs. Smith was a committed public servant with strong principles. She stood up to the infamous Senator McCarthy **because** she strongly objected to his scare tactics. In 1964, she became the first woman to be placed in nomination for the presidency of the United States by a major political party. Although she never became president, her country has not forgotten her contributions to its government.

She was instrumental in helping women achieve permanent status in the military, **and** she traveled to 23 countries during the cold war to improve relations. She held a perfect attendance record in Congress for many years **and** spent very little money on campaigns. Some people told her she could never hope to achieve many of these goals. In response to those attitudes, Margaret Chase Smith said, "When people keep telling you that you can't do a thing, you kind of like to try it."

EDITING: Sentences 13

Name _____

Read these paragraphs and then rewrite them below to make them read more smoothly. Combine sentences to avoid choppiness and unnecessary repetition. Use compound sentences, complex sentences, and other sentence-combining techniques.

Answers may vary. Paragraphs below are suggested.

I have been reading about bees. The honeybee is native to Europe. It is native to Africa, too. It is not native to America. Human travelers brought honeybees to America. They brought bees to America because the bees help with plant pollination. They brought bees to America because honeybees produce honey.

Honey is a sweetener that we can use in tea. We can use it in special desserts. In ancient times, honey was used as a salve for wounds. It was used as a salve for wounds because bacteria cannot live in honey. Bacteria cannot pass through a layer of honey. Honey is used in medicines even today. It is used in medicines since it can cover up bitter tastes.

I have been reading about bees. The honeybee is native to Europe and Africa, but not to America. Human travelers brought honeybees to America because the bees help with plant pollination and produce honey.

Honey is a sweetener that we can use in tea and special desserts. In ancient times, honey was used as a salve for wounds because bacteria cannot live in or pass through a layer of honey. Since it can cover up bitter tastes, honey is used in medicines even today.

Language Fundamentals • EMC 2756 • © Evan-Moor Corp.

EDITING: Capitalization 14

Name _____

Proofread these paragraphs. Use proofreading marks to correct the 10 errors. Hint: One five-word proper noun counts as one error.

Have you ever been to pittsburgh? Pittsburgh is in pennsylvania. My friend katelyn lives there, and I visit her every november. Last saturday, her parents took us into the city to see the awesome dinosaur skeletons at the carnegie museum of natural history. The huge skeletons tower over the museum visitors. I wanted to study the skeletons, but katelyn's little brother was scared, so we moved on.

Next we went to see the exhibit of minerals and gems. We saw everything from coal to emeralds. The guide had a special machine that clicked and crackled as it measured the amount of radioactivity in the different minerals. the machine is called a Geiger counter because it was invented by a german professor named geiger. I think it would be fun to have a Geiger counter. I would use it to look for special minerals in my backyard.

Find the errors. Write the words correctly on the lines below.

1. Pittsburgh
2. Pennsylvania
3. Katelyn
4. November
5. Saturday
6. Carnegie Museum of Natural History
7. Katelyn's
8. The
9. German
10. Geiger

© Evan-Moor Corp. • EMC 2756 • Language Fundamentals

EDITING: Capitalization 15

Name _____

Proofread these paragraphs. Use proofreading marks to correct the 10 errors. Hint: Multiple-word proper nouns count as one error.

My cat's name is Tiger Lily. She is both independent and affectionate. I adopted tiger lily from garver animal friends, a shelter on ferry road. It was a cold friday afternoon in early february when my mom and I went to the shelter. Ms. cindric, one of the volunteers at the shelter, told us that a little cat had been found in a recent snowstorm. The cat had not had enough to eat and was very cold.

I called to my mom, "can we keep her?"

"Of course, we can," Mom answered. "we can give her the love and care she needs."

At first, Tiger Lily was very shy, and she hid from us. However, it did not take long for her to learn that the sound of a can opener meant gourmet kitty, her favorite brand of cat food. By presidents' day, Tiger Lily had become a healthy and happy cat. She knows that we love her and will never let her be cold and hungry again.

Find the errors. Write the words correctly on the lines below.

1. Tiger Lily
2. Garver Animal Friends
3. Ferry Road
4. Friday
5. February
6. Cindric
7. Can
8. We
9. Gourmet Kitty
10. Presidents' Day

Language Fundamentals • EMC 2756 • © Evan-Moor Corp.

EDITING: Sentences 16

Name _____

Proofread these paragraphs. Use proofreading marks to correct the 10 errors. Hint: Multiple-word proper nouns count as one error.

In the year 1914, a war began in europe. That war would become known first as the Great War, then as the World War, and finally as world war I. War was declared on Serbia by austria on July 28 at 11 o'clock. That was the time when Archduke franz Ferdinand died after being shot as he rode through the streets of sarajevo. The war that began with a shot fired in a small city in serbia would soon engulf much of the world. The united states entered the war in 1917. Many people died. The world would never be the same.

Every year, we honor the veterans of all wars on November 11, veterans day. This holiday was originally called armistice day. The agreement that ended the great war was signed in 1918 on the eleventh day of the eleventh month. At 11 o'clock that day, the guns fell silent.

Find the errors. Write the words correctly on the lines below.

1. Europe
2. World War
3. Austria
4. Franz
5. Sarajevo
6. Serbia
7. United States
8. Veterans Day
9. Armistice Day
10. Great War

© Evan-Moor Corp. • EMC 2756 • Language Fundamentals

Page 202

EDITING: Sentences

17

Proofread these paragraphs. Use proofreading marks to correct the 10 errors. Hint: Multiple-word proper nouns count as one error.

Nathaniel Hawthorne wrote one of my favorite books. Published in 1853, the book is called tanglewood tales. In that Book, Hawthorne wrote stories based on famous greek myths. He wrote them so that the boys and girls of his century would enjoy them. Today, hawthorne's writing style seems a little old-fashioned, but that is one of the reasons I like it. My favorite story in the book is "the minotaur."

I want to read the house of the seven gables, a novel Hawthorne wrote about a real house in salem, Massachusetts. I visited that amazing house last year. It is a bit spooky. It even has a secret passageway! after I visited the house, I started to read the novel, but it was a little too hard for me then. On monday, I'll ask mr. brown, our school librarian, if he thinks I could read it now.

Find the errors. Write the words correctly on the lines below.

1. Tanglewood Tales
2. book
3. Greek
4. Hawthorne's
5. "The Minotaur"
6. The House of the Seven Gables
7. Salem
8. After
9. Monday
10. Mr. Brown

Page 203

EDITING: Punctuation

18

Proofread this letter. Use proofreading marks to correct the 10 errors.

January 5, 2008

Dear Aunt Lee:

What a surprise it was to receive that package from you. Dad and I could not imagine what it might be. Because the box was so heavy, we thought that it might be full of big books. Of course, we both love books, but we love cookies and cakes, too. How did you know we would not have time to bake for ourselves?

You know that my favorite cookies are the ones with green icing. Thank you, Aunt Lee, for including those. My dads favorite cookies are the ones that look like pinwheels. We are looking forward to trying the new kinds of cookies in the box.

We are grateful for that fruitcake, too. The pieces of candied fruit in the cake look like little jewels. Dad and I think the fruitcake might be too pretty to eat. Did you use Great-grandpa's recipe? I'm guessing that you did!

Love,

Terry

Page 204

EDITING: Punctuation

19

Proofread these paragraphs. Use proofreading marks to correct the 10 errors.

I have a piano lesson on Saturday at 10:30 in the morning. I'm a new student. I have learned three scales so far. I can play a C-major scale, a G-major scale, and a D-major scale. I can only play the scales with my right hand, but next week my piano teacher will teach me how to play the scales with my left hand. The pieces I am learning to play are easy and a little silly. I have learned "Teddy's Picnic," "Dance Tune," and "Sunny Day." My teacher says that it won't be long before I can learn more interesting music. I want to play the great pieces of Bach, Beethoven, Brahms, and the Beatles.

Musical talent runs in our family. Mom plays the cello in an orchestra, and dad plays the trumpet in a Dixieland band. Because she is still very small, my little sister plays a tiny violin. Did you know that violins come in different sizes for kids? When she first started taking violin lessons, my little sister practiced on a violin made from a cardboard box. It had just one string! My little sister is glad that I am taking piano lessons. "We can play duets," she says.

Page 205

EDITING: Punctuation

20

Proofread this business letter. Use proofreading marks to correct the 10 errors.

Mr. Paul Pecan, President
Bake-Oh Company
30 Drury Lane
Middleville, ME 00001

Dec. 21, 2006

Dear Mr. Pecan:

For many years, I have been a fan of your company's products. My favorite is the Morning Madness Muffin. I often pack one of these nutritious muffins in my backpack. Because your product is full of fruit, fiber, and nuts, it gives me the energy that I need to walk to school.

I am writing to ask if you might consider giving a tour of your factory. I am the president of the Good Food for Good Fun Club at Middleville Middle School, and I have been telling the club members about your fabulous products. All of the members have agreed that they would be interested in seeing how the Morning Madness Muffin is made.

Thank you for considering my request.

Sincerely,

P. J. Wetzel

237

Page 206

EDITING: Punctuation
21

Proofread these paragraphs. Use proofreading marks to correct the 10 errors.

Since the beginning of this school year, I have been reviewing books for the Sixth Grade Gazette. It's now time for me to offer my recommendations for fun summer reading. What should you read first?

If you have not read Blue Willow, start there. The book was written by Doris Gates. The main character, Janey, is the daughter of migrant workers. Although I had learned about migrant workers in school, I did not know about what it might be like to grow up in a migrant family until I read this book. Blue Willow is at the very top of my list. I'll read it for a second time this summer.

Short stories can be fun to read, too. On a hot day, read Jack London's story "To Build a Fire." Once you read that story about a man being lost in the Arctic ice and snow, you will never complain about the summer heat again!

Page 207

EDITING: Punctuation
22

Proofread this paragraph. Use proofreading marks to correct the 10 errors.

What are you doing on this rainy Saturday? I'm going to watch an old movie on television. It's called Plan Nine from Outer Space. I like science fiction movies. Before the movie comes on, I'll watch an old science fiction television show called Lost in Space. I've seen a few episodes, and they were pretty silly. One episode was called Invasion from the Fifth Dimension. Do you want to come over to watch TV with me? You can have some of my mom's famous pizza! Send me an e-mail or an instant message. I'll be writing e-mails until Lost in Space comes on.

Rewrite the paragraph on the lines below. Remember to include all of the correct punctuation.

What are you doing on this rainy Saturday? I'm going to watch an old movie on television. It's called Planet Nine from Outer Space. I like science fiction movies. Before the movie comes on, I'll watch an old science fiction television show called Lost in Space. I've seen a few episodes, and they were pretty silly. One episode was called "Invasion from the Fifth Dimension." Do you want to come over to watch TV with me? You can have some of my mom's famous pizza! Send me an e-mail or an instant message. I'll be writing e-mails until Lost in Space comes on.

Page 208

EDITING: Punctuation
23

Proofread these paragraphs. Use proofreading marks to correct the 10 errors.

"Are you coming to the talent show tonight, Mr. Robson?" Cindy asked.

"I will," she continued, "be reading a poem I wrote."

"Thank you, Cindy, for reminding me. I'll be there!"

Cindy was glad that her language arts teacher would be coming to hear her read poetry tonight. Before taking Mr. Robson's class, Cindy didn't even know that she liked poetry. Now she was writing her own poetry and reading it out loud!

That evening, the auditorium was crowded. Cindy's parents and her sister were there. At first, Cindy was very nervous, but then she saw her parents' smiling faces. Mr. Robson was there, too, and he gave a thumbs-up sign and grinned. Cindy began reading her poem "My Cat Mimi" with confidence.

Page 209

EDITING: Punctuation
24

Proofread these paragraphs. Use proofreading marks to correct the 10 errors.

I like it when my dad drives me to school in his really old car. He keeps the radio tuned to a station that only plays old songs, and he sings along. He knows almost all the words. When he doesn't know a word, he just makes something up. It's always something funny that doesn't make any sense at all.

When my big brother drives me to school, it's not as much fun. He listens to the radio, too, but I don't like the music he listens to very much. He never sings along. He just keeps time by tapping his fingers on the steering wheel. Maybe he's nervous because he just earned his license.

When Mom drives me to school, she turns the radio off. She wants to talk. "What will you do in school today?" she asks. I don't always want to talk, but sometimes it's nice.

Rewrite the first paragraph with the correct punctuation.

I like it when my dad drives me to school in his really old car. He keeps the radio tuned to a station that only plays old songs, and he sings along. He knows almost all the words. When he doesn't know a word, he just makes something up. It's always something funny that doesn't make any sense at all.

Page 210

Proofread these paragraphs. Find the 10 errors, cross them out, and write the words correctly above them.

Last winter, my neighbors lost their home to a fire. Life has been pretty rough for them the past few months. Today, people in the community have joined together to help rebuild their house. I'm one of several kids who decided to help.

"~~Can~~ **May** I carry that for you?" I asked one of the workers.

"Yes, you may," she replied. "Thank you. Now I can help with the framing."

I decided I could help most by doing little things for the workers. Pretty soon, I hardly had time to ~~set~~ **sit** down!

"~~Lie~~ **Lay** that bag of sand by the wheelbarrow, please!"

I ~~layed~~ **laid** the sand by the wheelbarrow and ran back to the workers.

"What's next?"

"Find out ~~whose~~ **who's** pouring the concrete," requested Rick.

"And ~~who's~~ **whose** hammer is this?" asked Gina.

"And to ~~who~~ **whom** does this hard hat belong?" Will called.

I don't think I ~~never~~ **ever** ran around so much in one day! When I went in my room that night, I ~~laid~~ **lay** down and went to sleep right away. I knew I needed to work just as hard for a whole week. However, I was happy to help make our neighbors' lives ~~more good~~ **better** than before.

Page 211

Proofread these paragraphs. Find the 10 errors, cross them out, and write the words correctly above them.

Our class put on a play for the whole school yesterday. It went pretty ~~good~~ **well**. My friends and ~~me~~ **I** had a lot of fun!

All the actors remembered their lines, and the audience ~~set~~ **sat** still in their seats for the whole hour. I didn't have ~~no~~ **any** lines to memorize because I worked backstage. I like being behind the scenes better than being on stage. Being in front of all those people would be too nerve-racking!

I was the prop master. My job was to make sure all the props were where they needed to be and were returned to the right places. During a play, things can get pretty hectic! At one point, we lost some props!

Before the show, I ~~layed~~ **laid** the swords by the prop table. Kerry and Catalina picked them up for their scene. They said they ~~lay~~ **laid** them in the same place after the scene, but no one could find them. ~~Whom~~ **Who** could have moved them?

It turned out that Kevin thought he needed them for the next scene, but he wasn't supposed to be onstage until the next act! He had stayed up all night rehearsing his lines and was confused. Thankfully, we found them in time and didn't have ~~no~~ **any** more problems.

Kevin ~~laid~~ **lay** down for a nap this afternoon, so he is ready to go for our next performance. Our director and ~~him~~ **he** had a talk about getting enough sleep before a performance!

Page 212

Proofread these paragraphs. Find the 10 errors, cross them out, and write the words correctly above them.

My soccer coach retired this year. He was my coach for several years, so I wanted to do something special for him. My mom makes the ~~better~~ **best** chocolate chip cookies in the world, so I decided to ask her to help me bake some for him. It was an interesting experience because I had never baked before!

"Mom, ~~may~~ **can** you help me bake some cookies?" I asked.

"What? You, bake? For ~~who~~ **whom**?" she asked, shocked.

"I want to make them for Coach Brewer's retirement party."

Mom taught me the basics of baking. I think I did pretty ~~good~~ **well**! I insisted on doing most of it myself. Mom showed me how to measure the ingredients, told me what the abbreviations meant, and reminded me to keep an eye on the cookies in the oven. My only big mistake was when I ~~lay~~ **laid** the butter on the table and our cat ate it. That went ~~bad~~ **badly**.

I thought the cookies were really ~~well~~ **good**. I hope Coach likes them. I don't have ~~no~~ **any** other presents!

"~~Who's~~ **Whose** cookies are these?" Coach asked, with a cookie in his mouth.

"They're mine," I answered. "I baked them."

"You're kidding!" he exclaimed. "I might have to retire again next year just to get some more of these cookies!"

My favorite picture from the party is of Coach and ~~I~~ **me** with cookie crumbs all over our faces!